Practical
E/M

Documentation and Coding Solutions for Quality Patient Care

Stephen R. Levinson, MD

AMERICAN
MEDICAL
ASSOCIATION

Second
Edition

Practical E/M
Documentation and Coding Solutions for Quality Patient Care

American Medical Association
Executive Vice President, Chief Executive Officer: Michael D. Maves, MD, MBA
Chief Operating Officer: Bernard L. Hengesbaugh
Vice President and General Manager, Publishing: Frank J. Krause
Publisher, Physician Practice Solutions: Jay T. Ahlman
Vice President, Business Operations: Vanessa Hayden
Senior Acquisitions Editor: Elise Schumacher
Director, Production and Manufacturing: Jean Roberts
Director of Marketing, Business Marketing and Communication: Pam Palmersheim
Manager, Marketing and Strategic Planning: Erin Kalitowski
Director of Sales, Business Products: J. D. Kinney
Developmental Editor: Elizabeth Kennedy
Production Manager: Rosalyn Carlton
Senior Print Production Specialist: Ronnie Summers
Marketing Manager: Leigh Adams

Additional copies of this book may be ordered by calling 800 621-8335 or from the secure AMA web site at www.amabookstore.com. Refer to product number OP504008.

Library of Congress Cataloging-in-Publication Data

Practical E/M : documentation and coding solutions for quality patient care / Stephen R. Levinson. -- 2nd ed.
 p. ; cm.
 Includes bibliographical references.
 Summary: "A learning tool and guide to correctly completing E/M documentation and coding in a
  timley fashion"--Provided by publisher.
 ISBN 978-1-60359-010-5
 1. Medicine--Terminology--Code numbers. 2. Health insurance claims--Code numbers. I. American
Medical Association. II. Title.
 [DNLM: 1. Relative Value Scales--United States. 2. Insurance, Health, Reimbursement--United States.
3. Medical Records--United States. W 74
AA1 L665p 2008]
R728.L485 2008
610.1'4--dc22

                        2008036370

ISBN 978-1-60359-010-5
AC30:08-P-072:12/08

CONTENTS

During the 3 years since the publication of the first edition of *Practical E/M: Documentation and Coding Solutions for Quality Patient Care*, the imperatives for understanding and incorporating a high-quality history and physical (H&P) in the medical record continue to escalate. The importance of performing and documenting effective evaluation and management (E/M) services is emphasized by recent initiatives for implementation of quality measures, more sophisticated reporting of hospital inpatient E/M services, adoption of electronic health records, and continued economic constriction (relative to practice costs) in the Medicare and insurer payment systems.

As physicians and administrators confront the challenges created by these and other changes in the health care environment, they consistently discover that meaningful solutions depend upon effective, compliant, and efficient medical record documentation. Meeting this goal begins with documentation of a meaningful H&P, which helps physicians ensure that their patients receive levels of clinical care that are appropriately matched to the severity of their illnesses (ie, matched to the nature of the presenting problems), a central concept of *Practical E/M*.

Although this book directly addresses requirements for compliant documentation and coding, the primary message that has reverberated for physicians, coders, and information management specialists is that physicians' focus must be on *quality patient care*. Practical E/M methodology supports and promotes quality care while providing usable and efficient tools to integrate compliant documentation and coding into the care process.

FEATURES OF THE SECOND EDITION

In addition to a number of clarifications throughout the book, this new edition adds several new sections to existing chapters, three new chapters with detailed information about a wide range of E/M services beyond outpatient care, and a CD-ROM containing an extensive variety of sample forms for physicians and coders.

For many years, I had attempted, without success, to uncover the origin of the E/M coding system. In 2006, while glancing at my daughter's medical library, I fortuitously discovered the book that unquestionably provided the source material for creating the E/M system and the *Documentation Guidelines for Evaluation and Management Services*. That revelation, which is discussed in detail in Chapter 1, is among the important new materials in this edition. It forges a seamless linkage between E/M compliance and physicians' fundamental principles guiding quality medical care. Understanding this connection allows medical audiences to immediately appreciate the quality care benefits of incorporating the methodology and compliance-based tools presented in this book into their medical record and their medical care.

The Second Edition responds to requests for greater depth and breadth of intelligent medical record (IMR) tools. These are addressed in three new chapters (19–21) that together comprise a new Part 4 of *Practical E/M*, along with a CD-ROM that is an integral part of the book.

The three new chapters explore most of the additional E/M services. Chapter 19 examines the benefits of applying Practical E/M principles and IMR tools for the other services that are based on the three key components and the nature of the presenting problem (NPP). These include inpatient services, emergency department services, hospital observation care, nursing facility services, and home care services. Chapter 20 discusses E/M services that may be defined by the nature of the patients' presentation but are not based on the three key components. This chapter includes a detailed examination of preventive care services and critical care services, both of which particularly benefit from the use of appropriately designed medical record tools that incorporate compliance rules into their design. Chapter 21 introduces tools to assist physicians with compliant documentation of patient care that involves other caregivers. This includes examples of compliant forms that can assist physicians in teaching hospitals to submit claims for care based on the combination of their own documentation and that of their residents. It also presents compliant forms for documenting "incident to" services for physicians working with a nurse practitioner or physician's assistant.

The accompanying CD has four sections of sample forms that readers can print to accompany their reading and use as model suggestions for their own practices. Part 1 of the CD provides sample IMR forms for most of the common E/M types of service, including outpatient, inpatient, nursing facility, and emergency department care. While these sample forms all include the general multisystem examination, Part 2 of the CD provides sample forms that incorporate each of the 11 single-organ-system examinations into the most common outpatient and inpatient types of care. The third section presents forms for the services discussed in Chapters 20 and 21: preventive care, critical care, and documentation of "physician presence." Part 4 offers a set of outpatient and inpatient Practical E/M audit forms that allow coders and health information management professionals to provide the types of educational and physician informative audits described in Chapters 24 and 25. These audit forms are fully compliant, based entirely on the E/M principles in the *Current Procedural Terminology (CPT®)* codebook and the 1995 and 1997 *Documentation Guidelines.* They include consideration of medical necessity (the nature of the presenting problem) and they eliminate reliance on noncompliant audit shortcuts often encountered to determine levels of medical decision making.

This edition incorporates additional details that have resulted from my experiences in developing electronic health record solutions for medical practices. While this topic has been explored in depth in a second publication,[1] some of the newer electronic documentation tools are now discussed in Chapter 23, which gives an overview of the relationship between quality E/M documentation and physicians' success with electronic health records (EHRs). Other E/M compliance issues have been exacerbated by the use of certain EHR data entry tools that have been identified by the Department of Health and Human Services (HHS) and the Office of the National Coordinator for Health Information Technology (ONCHIT) as creating potentially fraudulent documentation.[2] The most dramatic of these concerns, which is reviewed in Chapter 13, relates to distortion of the way physicians record and even obtain the history of present illness.

Finally, multiple chapters have added information and refinements that reflect my experiences in providing training in Practical E/M principles and providing responses to questions raised by physicians, administrators, coders, and information management specialists. All of the Second Edition's new and modified materials are intended to maintain and reinforce *Practical E/M*'s focus on quality E/M care and its central relevance in our evolving medical landscape.

---

[1]Levinson SR. *Practical EHR: Electronic Record Solutions for Compliance and Quality Care.* Chicago, IL: American Medical Association; 2008

[2]Office of the National Coordinator for Health Information Technology. Recommended Requirements for Enhancing Data Quality in Electronic Health Record Systems. Final report. May 2007. www.rti.org/pubs/enhancing_data_quality_in_ehrs.pdf

Practical E/M: Documentation and Coding Solutions for Quality Patient Care is the summation of everything I, and others, have learned on a journey that began with the simple expedient of devising a method that would permit physicians to complete evaluation and management (E/M) coding and documentation correctly and in a timely fashion, without interfering with patient care. Amazingly, this journey has led to the totally unexpected discovery that the same insights and tools that make this system functional and easy to use also legitimately improve office efficiency, augment productivity, enhance the quality of medical care provided, and even increase our satisfaction from practicing medicine.

Practical E/M was written for physicians by a practicing physician who has used and taught the practical side of the E/M coding system from its inception. It has now been more than 16 years since the introduction of the E/M coding system, and many physicians still believe that it imposes a barrier to their patient care efforts. In contrast to this perception, Practical E/M principles demonstrate not only that it is possible for the E/M system, when used optimally, to coexist with high-quality patient care, but that it will actually assist physicians in providing optimal care.

I immersed myself in the E/M system in October 1991, three months before its initial publication in the 1992 edition of the American Medical Association's (AMA) *Current Procedural Terminology* (CPT®) codebook. My involvement was the result of invitations from both the Connecticut State Medical Society and the American Academy of Otolaryngology–Head & Neck Surgery to become one of 50 physicians trained as "physician trainers" for the E/M coding system (along with Medicare coding and audit personnel).

During this training program, we were taught that physicians should first perform and document their care, then calculate the appropriate E/M code to report that care. Throughout this book we call this paradigm the traditional "document first, then code" approach, which the majority of physicians still follow.

At the end of the 7-hour introduction and training session, which was conducted by representatives of the AMA and the Health Care Financing Administration (now known as the Centers for Medicare and Medicaid Services [CMS]), I imagined how difficult it would be for me and my associates to use this system in our own practice while caring for multiple patients per hour. I then offered the following impressions to the instructors and the rest of the group:

> I appreciate the reasons for introducing the E/M system and how it is supposed to function. I am certain that for auditors it will be valuable, accurate, and easy to use. However, for a physician practicing medicine in the real world, it just won't work. It is not possible, after spending 15, 30, or 60 minutes evaluating and communicating with each patient, to have to subsequently scan through fifty pages of instructions and vignettes plus pages of mathematical calculations to figure out the correct code that describes the level of care you have performed.

The only response from our instructors was, "No one has ever made that comment before." From our current perspective, 17 years in the future, it is apparent that my observation was completely on target.

This observation was also my impetus to begin analyzing how we could make the E/M system function successfully for physicians practicing medicine in the real world.

I have been training physicians in the successful use of E/M since 1992. The Practical E/M approach evolved by introducing and continually refining useful tools and concepts to make the system work for physicians in the patient care environment.

Just as physicians can no longer provide state-of-the-art medical care without sophisticated laboratory and imaging tests, they also require a more elegant system for obtaining and documenting the most valuable diagnostic tool in the medical armamentarium, the medical history and physical (H&P). Practical E/M is an approach to providing care that fulfills the requirements for compliant E/M coding while helping physicians focus on patients and high-quality medical care. It builds upon the CPT system's principle of "nature of the presenting problem" (NPP) and its relationship to the level of care and documentation indicated for each patient's medical problems.

This system provides physicians with two critical resources that work together to transform the E/M coding system from a perceived impediment to a real asset. First, it presents *Practical E/M methodology*, a concept for implementing the E/M system reasonably and seamlessly in the real world of medical practice. Second, it introduces *intelligent medical records (IMRs)*, a structured medical record, built on CPT coding guidelines and the *Documentation Guidelines for Evaluation and Management Services*, that ensures documentation and coding compliance, increases medical care efficiency, and incorporates physician preferences to achieve flexibility and ease of use.

Practical E/M methodology targets four major goals for physicians who adopt this approach:

- Quality of patient care should be equal or increased.
- Efficiency (time spent) should be equal or improved.
- Documentation and coding should comply with the requirements of the E/M coding system and be "audit proof."
- Productivity should equal or exceed current levels, ie, compliant E/M code levels should actually increase (unless a physician is currently overcoding significantly).

Physicians who incorporate Practical E/M methodology and commit to using this system of coding and documentation commonly report three important additional benefits:

- A reduction in the amount of after-hours time required to complete patient charts, which translates into more personal and family time
- Reduced concern about the potential for financially damaging audits
- Increased enjoyment of the patient care process

The book is divided into five parts. Part 1 introduces terminology and criteria that may be used to assess the effectiveness of medical records. It also analyzes the factors that influence the evolution of medical record documentation from the standards taught in medical school through residency training and into medical practice. Part 2 discusses Practical E/M methodology and the rationale and design features of the various sections of the IMR, and Part 3 describes how physicians apply these concepts and tools while providing care. The new Part 4 represents the application of Practical E/M principles and IMR forms for a wide variety of services beyond the three common outpatient services that are the focus of Part 3. Part 5 examines several issues related to the medical record, compliance, and quality care: the use of modifiers, Practical E/M audits, and electronic health records. This final section concludes with considerations for the present and future role of Practical E/M in the rapidly changing health care environment.

In the back of the book are six appendices that provide helpful tools and information. These include:

- Examples of different types of NPP with appropriate level of care and extent of documentation (Appendix A)
- Sample consultation templates (Appendix B)
- Strategies for dealing with external E/M audits (Appendix C)
- Two sample IMR forms to help guide you through the discussions in the book (Appendix D)
- Caveats for using all medical records (Appendix E)
- Appearance options for a completed H&P record, comparing usability of IMR forms with traditional dictated records (Appendix F)

SUGGESTIONS FOR USING THIS BOOK

The most effective way to use this book is to keep a photocopy of the two sample IMR forms printed in Appendix D (for initial and established outpatient visits), or printouts from the accompanying CD-ROM of forms matched to your own specialty, at hand for reference as you read through Part 2 and Part 3 of *Practical E/M*. It will be helpful to refer to these sample forms as chapters in the book describe each component of the form in detail. Similarly, when reading Part 4, it will be helpful to print reference copies of forms from Part 3 of the CD for each of the various types of service discussed in this section. Similarly, forms printed from Part 4 of the CD are critical elements of Chapter 25, which discusses internal E/M audits.

Before incorporating the IMR in your practice, both physicians and administrators are strongly advised to read Appendix E, which outlines the importance of adhering to Practical E/M principles when using IMRs (or any other type of medical record), to avoid possible difficulties with compliance, quality care, medical liability, or other negative consequences.

Part 3 of the book examines the design and use of each section and subsection of the medical record, discussing principles that are relevant to all medical records, including electronic health records. However, these chapters examine Practical E/M principles and IMR tools expressly as they apply to paper medical records, where the design and application are relatively uniform. After readers are comfortable with these concepts, Chapter 23 addresses some of the most critical requirements and options for achieving the goals of Practical E/M and the efficiencies of IMRs in the developing environment of electronic health records.

This book is designed as a comprehensive reference on the principles of Practical E/M. It also describes the compliance and efficiency concepts intrinsic to IMR design and the protocols for using the IMR properly during patient care.

For clinicians who prefer to read an abridged version of how to use Practical E/M correctly, the divider pages for each of the five parts of the book describe a selected list of chapters, and portions of chapters, that provide an effective overview of how to use this system. Readers who elect this approach can return to the other areas of the book later, for a more comprehensive understanding of the development and design of this system.

This text brings together a number of "adventures" that have kept me mentally busy and challenged during the 38 years since I entered medical school. Obviously the medical record occupies my central focus here, but the concept of "Practical E/M" draws on many other medically relevant experiences. This starts with a longstanding concern for the quality of medical education, including what we teach medical students and residents, what we don't teach them, and how we teach it. It continues with a pervasive concern for quality medical care, striving to ensure care for patients delivered at the same high standard physicians demand when they find themselves on the opposite side of the white coat (as patients). Stirred into the mix is the fact that physicians all have to work within medicine's current economically restricted environment, with its consequential pressure for ever-increasing speed of care and enhanced productivity. Added to this are the realities of practicing within the constraints of Medicare compliance and with the obstacles of private insurer rules and regulations, which are both disparate and concealed. Blending all these thoughts into a coherent presentation proved more daunting than anticipated, but it also offered the opportunity for me to analyze concepts proven to work in practice, and to discover the reasons why they work.

I want to extend thanks to the American Medical Association, which requested I write this book and also contributed significantly to its review. I also thank my editors, Elise Schumacher, Elizabeth Kennedy, and Lisa Chin-Johnson, whose efforts ensure that the language and explanations are realistic and understandable by physicians and administrators alike.

The concepts in this book have evolved through years of feedback from patients and the constructive input of the dedicated staff in my own medical office. Special thanks go to some of those who were my colleagues for more than 10 (and as many as 26) years: Dr Alan Gill, Linda Schulman, Candace Callan, Susan Bongiorni, and Cecile Rodia.

I also want to share recognition for a group of expert coding and information management specialists who, since the publication of the first edition of *Practical E/M*, have freely shared their compliance experiences and expertise, helping me to confirm, clarify, and refine the concepts for the Second Edition. My thanks and appreciation to Robin Linker, Deborah Grider, Susan Garrison, Susan Thurston, Bill Dacey, Kenneth Wolfgang, Lydia Johnson, and Angela Dinh. Additionally, my thanks to the readers of the First Edition who have taken their time to ask penetrating questions and offer valuable suggestions to help make this new edition as effective as possible.

Neither this book, nor the concepts that drive it, would have been possible without my wife, Barbara. Her incisive insights have been even more important than her much-needed tolerance of my preoccupation with health care issues. As a non–medical professional, she offers critical insights from an objective perspective of someone who is not "in the trenches" every day. In 1995, our dialogue about the complexities of the recently published *Documentation Guidelines for Evaluation and Management Services* led to the genesis of the core concept of intelligent medical records—you don't have to memorize all the rules if you design your medical record with a structure that incorporates all the rules and satisfies their requirements as a consequence of good medical care.

Finally, this book is dedicated to my two medical daughters, Randi (graduating this year) and Kimberly (now a second year ob-gyn resident). In addition to contributing essential real-time insights on how the history and physical (H&P) and the medical record are treated in our current medical education system, they offered honest criticism and encouragement in helping edit this work to make it as meaningful and reader-friendly as possible. Most importantly, their personal passion for providing the best care to patients, and for striving to make our health care system work better for everyone, draws my highest respect and admiration, and it makes this effort worthwhile.

Stephen R. Levinson, MD, completed his undergraduate and medical education at Johns Hopkins University in 1971, followed by specialty training in head and neck surgery at UCLA, which he completed in 1976. He was a member of a private group medical practice in Connecticut for 26 years.

Dr Levinson has participated on numerous committees at the county, state, and national medical society levels. These efforts have included working with the Medicare carrier in Connecticut, Clinical Indicators and Referral Guideline development for the Otolaryogology–Head and Neck Surgery Academy, and committees delving into issues related to insurer compliance and reimbursement conflicts.

In 2001, Dr Levinson became one of the named plaintiffs in several of the national class action lawsuits against health insurers for their noncompliant reimbursement practices. From 2002 until 2004, he worked with the physicians' attorneys in this litigation effort as an expert on coding and compliance issues.

His involvement in evaluation and management (E/M) coding and documentation began in 1991, when two different medical societies asked that he become one of a small number of physicians to be trained by the American Medical Association (AMA) and the Health Care Financing Administration (now the Centers for Medicare and Medicaid Services) as an E/M coding educator. Since then, he has presented multiple courses on the E/M coding system, contributed to the development of coding and auditing software, and designed "intelligent medical record" (IMR) chart tools for E/M compliance in the written format.

Dr Levinson began evaluating the compliance, usability, and quality care features of electronic health records (EHRs) in 1995. In 2004, he began actively developing the concepts that would bring Practical E/M principles and tools into the electronic record environment. The advantages of this approach have been compiled in the book *Practical EHR: Electronic Record Solutions for Compliance and Quality Care*, which the AMA published in June 2008.

Dr Levinson consults on these topics and a variety of issues related to physician practice, patient care, and the health of the health care system through his company ASA, LLC (203 371-4797). His websites are www.PracticalEM.com and www. IntelligentMedical Records.com. Readers can also contact him at asallc@aol.com with questions and to obtain customized IMR forms.

Introduction

As clinicians, *quality of care* is our central theme. It is the reason we chose medicine as a career, and it should be a driving principle for the way we practice and for our growth as physicians. It would be possible to write a book far larger than this one with the sole purpose of attempting to define all of the parameters of "quality of care." In the interest of brevity, I propose a basic assumption that the provision of quality of care calls for physicians to (1) make the optimal effort to determine correct diagnoses in the most timely manner possible and (2) institute the optimal therapies to address patient problems, with a minimum number of complications. Quality of care also involves identifying patients' risk factors, providing preventive counseling and interventions, and maintaining a good physician-patient relationship. Finally, consideration of cost-effectiveness has become an additional and important component of quality care in today's health care environment.

Practical evaluation and management (E/M) methodology applies concepts and tools that unite the goal of quality patient care with the demands of a complex health care system, while maintaining compliance with the E/M coding system as presented in the Current Procedural Terminology (CPT®) codebook and the *Documentation Guidelines for Evaluation and Management Services*. Practical E/M methodology builds on the relationship, emphasized in the CPT codebook, between the severity of a patient's illness and the indicated complexity of medical care. The implementation of Practical E/M methodology is facilitated by the creation and use of an intelligent medical record (IMR).

Several features contribute to creating "intelligence" in a medical record. First, the structure of an IMR must incorporate all of the E/M coding rules and documentation requirements into a useful and usable structure. This removes the need for physicians or their staff to memorize the myriad of complex coding rules. The IMR design also assists physicians in obtaining relevant medical information and guides them in matching the scope of medical care to each patient's individual needs. Therefore, not only does an IMR ensure correct coding and documentation, but it also becomes an integral part of the patient care process.

The IMR design enables patients and office staff to enter health information into the medical record, thereby reducing the time physicians require for accomplishing standardized tasks. This feature expands the amount of medical information available to clinicians and increases the amount of time they have to devote to medical problems, decisions, and patient communication. The result is both a more thorough history and physical (H&P) and a highly effective integration of patient care, practice management, economics, and compliance.

IMR in Different Formats

Given the proliferation of acronyms related to medical records, it is important to distinguish the Practical E/M concept and IMR design from the electronic medical record (EMR), electronic health record (EHR), personal health record (PHR), and so on.

continued

The IMR features are independent of the format of the medical record. They can be applied, with appropriate modifications, to written records, dictated records, and EHRs. As explained in Chapter 22 of this book, the IMR approach was originally developed in the pure paper environment, where data is entered by writing and stored in paper charts. It subsequently expanded to include a hybrid format, which permits dictation, where appropriate, for some of the data entry. Most recently, these concepts have been successfully integrated into the electronic format by employing another hybrid approach, which is described in Chapter 23.

TRADITIONAL E/M TRAINING

The conventional approach to training physicians in the E/M coding system instructs them to finish their medical encounter and then secondarily attempt to calculate the proper E/M code. In reality, we all know this approach usually doesn't work. Physicians have neither the time nor the inclination to perform mathematical calculations or to review vignettes in the CPT codebook after each patient visit. Furthermore, this approach to E/M coding has failed to yield consistently accurate coding and documentation. Also, it typically ignores the E/M component of medical necessity, or at best advises using it as a "checking point." While traditional training in E/M coding always offers physicians an extensive list of coding rules to follow, it provides little in the way of practical tools. Physicians generally do not feel that this traditional coding technique helps them with patient care, and most remain uncomfortable with their coding and documentation skills.

Audit Results for Traditional E/M Coding Technique

My own experience auditing E/M charts, as well as personal discussions with consultants, Medicare auditors, and private insurance auditors, reveals that on average only 15% to 25% of E/M codes are submitted correctly. That is, 75% to 85% of the submitted codes are either overcoded or undercoded when measured against the actual medical record documentation and against medical necessity. Furthermore, the E/M codes physicians submit usually do not correlate well with the severity of the patients' illness(es).

PRACTICAL E/M PRINCIPLES

The chapters in Part 2 and Part 3 of this book are devoted to the details of creating IMR tools and implementing the Practical E/M methodology. This approach is built on the following five medical record principles that differ fundamentally from the traditional E/M coding and documentation method traditionally taught to physicians.

Principle 1: Quality Care Must be the Principal Measure for Medical Records

Practical E/M mandates that quality of care issues are of paramount importance to the design and use of medical records. Documenting the medical record should complement and augment the patient care process.

Principle 2: The Process Must Work for Clinicians

Each clinician's medical record must assist him or her in providing optimal care to patients. It must not delay, impede, or interfere with care. The coding process should require only a minimal effort that is additional to providing medical care. The Practical E/M approach seamlessly integrates coding and documentation into the patient care process as efficiently as possible. The IMR can also be customized to meet the individual physician's needs and preferences.

Principle 3: The "Nature of Presenting Problem" Indicates the Level of Care and Coding Warranted by the Patient's Illness

Very few coding texts or courses pay significant attention to the role of the nature of presenting problem (NPP) in coding and documentation. In contrast, Practical E/M adheres to the concepts presented in the CPT codebook in Appendix C, "Clinical Examples," which emphasizes NPP as an integral component of coding and documentation and recognizes it as the indicator for selecting the appropriate level of medical care warranted by the severity of the patient's illness(es).[1]

Nature of Presenting Problem and Medical Necessity

The CPT codebook introduces NPP as one of the seven components for determining levels of E/M services. While the CPT codebook labels NPP as a "contributory factor," its relationship to code selection is an essential element in the CPT codebook's detailed description of most E/M services.

The presenting problem is defined as "a disease, condition, illness, injury, symptom, sign, finding, complaint, or other reason for encounter, with or without a diagnosis being established at the time of the encounter."[1] The CPT codebook presents five types, or levels, of severity of NPP. These describe the natural course, severity, risk, and/or long-term sequelae of patients' health problems. As shown in Appendix C of the CPT codebook,[1] presenting problems with higher-severity NPPs warrant higher levels of E/M care. This concept correlates with the mandate from the Centers for Medicare and Medicaid Services (CMS) for "medical necessity" as a requirement for reimbursement of services.

The CMS defines medical necessity as "services or supplies that: are proper and needed for the diagnosis or treatment of your medical condition, are provided for the diagnosis, direct care, and treatment of your medical condition, meet the standards of good medical practice in the local area, and aren't mainly for the convenience of you or your doctor."[2] Medicare medical directors and auditors commonly apply this principle when reviewing E/M services, by determining that increasing levels of care are "proper and needed" with increasing severity of illness.

Principle 4: Coding and Documentation Are Integrated Into the Process of Providing Care

Practical E/M coordinates documentation and coding as part of the care process, rather than requiring a mathematical analysis at the end of each patient visit.

Principle 5: Use Tools, Not Rules

To date, the general approach to teaching physicians E/M coding and the *Documentation Guidelines for Evaluation and Management Services* has been to provide a vast set of specialized rules, and then to require physicians to interpret and follow these rules while caring for their patients. Practical E/M replaces this with the IMR, which provides integral tools that guide compliant documentation and coding during care.

The Practical E/M Approach and E/M Audits

There is a marked contrast between the audit results of physicians using the Practical E/M approach to E/M coding and those of physicians who use the traditional approach of calculating E/M codes. In my experience during the last 13 years working with physicians who use an IMR and apply Practical E/M coding principles, I am unaware of any instances in which the physician's records failed to pass an insurance audit. The most frequent comment offered by auditors whom I have asked to analyze an IMR is, "I wish all doctors would use these records."

PRACTICAL E/M APPLIES THE PRINCIPLE OF "COMPLIANCE AS A SOLUTION"

In 2002, Dr Edward Miller, dean of Johns Hopkins Medical School and CEO of the Johns Hopkins Hospital, wrote an editorial titled "Compliance and Creativity," in which he described the hospital's experience in dealing with a significant error that occurred during a research protocol.[3] He meticulously described the institution's process in addressing this issue and ensuring that their own protocols were in compliance with scientific and administrative protocols. Dr Miller described how the hospital had used the experience as an opportunity to improve and enhance all of its research. He concluded the editorial with his impression that "the solution to the 'problem' of compliance is to see compliance as a solution."

Seven years after I compiled the first version of an IMR, Dr Miller's conclusion summarized for me the reason for the effectiveness of the IMR: it starts with a template structure and documentation prompts, which are both 100% compliant with the E/M coding system and *Documentation Guidelines for Evaluation and Management Services*.[4] It then enables physicians to customize their own office forms within that framework to meet their own specialty needs, personal medical preferences, and practice style.

Practical E/M applies the principle of "compliance as a solution" to the challenge of addressing the complexities of E/M coding and documentation while providing quality patient care.

References

1. American Medical Association. *Current Procedural Terminology CPT® 2008*. Chicago, IL: American Medical Association; 2007.

2. Centers for Medicare and Medicaid Services. www.cms.hhs.gov. Accessed June 19, 2008.

3. Miller ED. Compliance and creativity. Hopkins Medical News, winter 2002. www.hopkinsmedicine.org/hmn/W02/postop.html. Accessed June 19, 2008.

4. Health Care Financing Administration. *Documentation Guidelines for Evaluation and Management Services*. Chicago, IL: American Medical Association; 1997.

E/M Excellence and Quality Health Care

Selected reading for an abridged overview of Practical E/M and the effective use of Intelligent Medical Records (IMR):

Quality of Care and the Role of the Medical Record

Physicians face the constant challenge of maintaining high-quality patient care while simultaneously addressing the demands of our current complex medical environment. These demands include maximizing efficiency, complying with multiple government regulations (such as the Health Insurance Portability and Accountability Act of 1996 [HIPAA]), and coping with progressive economic constriction imposed by Medicare, Medicaid, and insurance companies.

Currently, various public and private agencies are seeking to promote quality medical care and patient safety by developing standards for preventive care and protocols for the treatment of several prevalent chronic diseases (eg, diabetes, hypertension, asthma, coronary artery disease, and congestive heart failure). The intelligent medical record (IMR) complements this quality initiative by providing physicians with tools to improve their diagnostic acumen and foster their awareness of related and developing medical concerns.

An IMR should enhance physicians' ability to perform (and document) the tasks that are crucial in the provision of quality medical care as they are described in the introduction of this book, including:

- obtaining thorough and appropriate information about our patients' health,
- performing an appropriate examination and identifying all significant abnormalities,
- making a reasonable differential diagnosis,
- selecting appropriate tests to confirm the correct diagnosis,
- initiating appropriate treatments and referrals,
- developing and maintaining a positive relationship with patients, and
- helping patients maintain a healthy lifestyle and practice appropriate preventive care.

QUALITY OF CARE: THE HISTORY AND PHYSICAL AND THE MEDICAL RECORD

How important is the medical record in facilitating quality patient care? The introduction to physical diagnosis in the second year of medical school generally begins with a statement such as, "A good history and physical is our most reliable diagnostic tool." This is arguably still an accurate statement, even in the era of sophisticated laboratory tests, magnetic resonance imaging, angiography, and other powerful new diagnostic tools. As physicians have been taught, the information obtained in the history and physical (H&P) is crucial for the development of an effective differential diagnosis. Only after generating a working differential diagnosis should physicians select the appropriate tests to confirm or deny their impressions and more precisely define the severity of a patient's illness.

Emphasizing the importance of this H&P process, one of the best clinicians at my medical school once declared that "obtaining a good medical history from your patient will give you the correct diagnosis 95% of the time, before you even pick up your stethoscope to examine the patient." Many of my colleagues heard similar statements during their medical school training. In the hands of great clinicians, this statement is often true. Refining the evaluation and management (E/M) medical record into a sophisticated diagnostic asset, such as the IMR, can help all physicians be more successful in attaining this standard of quality care.

When E/M coding debuted in 1992, it was introduced as a method of assessing (and calculating a code for) the amount of work done during a conventional patient visit using a conventional medical record form, which at that time usually started with a blank sheet of paper. The idea of designing a medical record to actually assist physicians with documenting and coding their H&Ps emerged after the introduction of the *Documentation Guidelines for Evaluation and Management Services*[1] in 1995, and it has continued to evolve since that time. The initial concept was simply to build the coding and documentation rules into the medical record, replacing the blank sheet of paper with a template capable of satisfying the new requirements of the *Documentation Guidelines,* without interfering with patient care.

Testing the first set of forms I drafted led to the exciting discovery that they provided information about patients in my practice that I would not have obtained with the conventional medical record forms. In addition to causing me to wonder how much important information I might have missed before, this insight also triggered a drive to discover how much more productive the medical record could become in facilitating my quality of care. What had begun as an effort to fulfill the obligations of compliance had evolved into a more important discovery—that an intelligently constructed medical record can be a potent engine that increases efficiency and enhances the quality of medical care.

The Insight Moment

Within only a few weeks of implementing a compliant E/M medical record form, I saw an established patient returning to schedule delicate sinus surgery. The patient looked well and voiced no immediate concerns when I greeted her. The established patient form prompted me to ask her whether there had been any change in her overall medical status since her last visit 4 weeks ago. Specifically, I asked whether, for example, she had seen another physician for any reason, been admitted to a hospital, had any change in medications, or developed any new health issues. The patient looked somewhat surprised, paused for a moment, and then with an insightful look on her face advised me, "Oh yes, 2 weeks ago I had an angioplasty, and now I'm on Coumadin®."

I was surprised, frightened, and relieved, all at the same time. In this era of specialized care, the patient had neglected to advise her cardiologist of the pending sinus surgery and had neglected to advise the otolaryngologist of the recent cardiac issue. Given this appropriate information, it was easy to provide quality medical care. All I had to do was obtain a medical assessment from her cardiologist, ensure that I could eliminate the blood thinner before surgery, and then schedule the indicated operation.

Thanks to the *Documentation Guidelines* "rules" for eliciting a comprehensive history on an established patient, a number of significant potential problems had been avoided. If I had scheduled the operation without obtaining this information, hopefully the anesthesiologist would have discovered the angioplasty and the Coumadin on the morning of surgery. The result would have been the loss of scheduled operating room

continued

time, embarrassment on my part, significant inconvenience for the patient, and unavoidable damage to the physician-patient relationship. Had the anesthesiologist also missed this information, the result could have been catastrophic.

Instead, as a result of asking the right question, I was pleased, my patient was impressed that I had discovered this information and directed proper care, and we had a smooth and successful outcome to the medical issue. After I discussed this case with my associates, we developed an ongoing dialogue of "can you top this," swapping stories about how following the compliance rules uncovered valuable medical information we might not have obtained before.

Connecting Compliance and the IMR to Quality Patient Care

It was surprising to discover that using medical record forms constructed on a foundation of E/M compliance principles not only matches physicians' optimal patient care workflow but also actually promotes medical care quality. This knowledge next led me to question how there could be such an excellent fit between E/M compliance and good patient care. It did not appear to be the result of coincidence. Since my E/M training in 1991, I had asked numerous knowledgeable individuals whether they knew how the E/M concept had been created. No one could provide an answer. While most physicians seem to believe that this coding system was developed only as an administrative payment tool, its ability to replicate and promote optimal clinical care practices suggested something far more sophisticated.

Discovering the E/M "Rosetta Stone"

Seven months after the release of the first edition of *Practical E/M*, I stumbled upon the source material for the E/M documentation and coding system, even though I didn't realize it at first. While walking past the medical bookshelves in the apartment of one of my medical daughters, my eye was caught by a large black book with bright gold lettering on the jacket: *Bates' Guide to Physical Examination and History Taking, Eighth Edition.* Unfamiliar with the volume, whose first edition had been published several years after I graduated from medical school, I asked my daughter what role the book played in her medical education. She informed me this was the reference text used to teach the course for the introduction to clinical medicine. I quickly scanned the index, looking for some reference to "E/M Coding" or "Documentation Guidelines"; none existed, so I replaced the book on the shelf and basically forgot about it.

Six weeks later, while developing a comprehensive E/M solutions workshop for the American Academy of Professional Coders (AAPC), I decided that it could be illuminating to compare the CPT guidelines for E/M coding with the quality care principles being taught in the *Bates' Guide.* I proceeded to open copies of the CPT E/M section, the *Documentation Guidelines,* and the *Bates' Guide* and review them side-by-side-by-side. The results were amazing and conclusive.

Comparing the *Current Procedural Terminology* (CPT®) codebook's E/M section and the *Documentation Guidelines* with the *Bates' Guide* text of clinical practice immediately reveals that this reference book is unquestionably the source of the E/M coding system. The descriptions of medical history and physical examination match concept for concept, paragraph for paragraph, and often almost word for word among the three documents. This includes not only the broad concepts, but also the details such as the various organ systems listed in the review of systems and physical examination and the specific definitions for chief complaint and history of present illness. It also includes a similar overview of formulating and documenting clinical assessments and treatment plans. Most impressively, the *Bates' Guide* also presents the concept of the "nature of the patient's problem."[2] This component of patient assessment parallels the CPT codebook's similarly named E/M component "nature of the presenting problem," which plays a pivotal role for Practical E/M in helping physicians understand how an effective E/M system promotes excellence in patient care.

In summary, the E/M coding system is actually a codification of the medical diagnostic process that all physicians learn in their training as being the most effective method for providing high-quality patient care. Making physicians aware of this relationship allows them to view compliance-based records from a fresh perspective: rather than being an added chore at the conclusion of patient care, carefully designed IMR tools can help physicians comfortably and compliantly provide optimal care within a time frame that meets the limitations of the current health care environment.

CRITERIA FOR MEASURING MEDICAL RECORDS

We consider eight criteria when evaluating the effectiveness of medical record designs in fulfilling physicians' needs for their medical practices. Five are considered to be primary measures of the ability of medical records to meet the needs of physicians at the point of care. The other three measures are considered to be additional benefits but are of lesser importance. The primary criteria I consider here are (1) compliance, (2) efficiency, (3) user-friendliness, (4) the ability to facilitate quality of care, and (5) data integrity.

Compliance

Compliance is achieved when coding and documentation practices follow the rules for medical records that are described in the CPT codebook and the *Documentation Guidelines*. Audits that discover noncompliant coding can result in severe financial penalties, including penalties for fraud (sometimes identified by government reviewers as "false claims").

Physicians gain a number of benefits from employing medical records that ensure E/M coding compliance. Foremost among these is that it allows submission of claims for more complex levels of care when appropriate, and the physician can be free of concern about audits and potential financial penalties. An additional advantage of having records that accurately document care according to the severity of each patient's illness is that they provide an added degree of protection in the event of a medicolegal review. Defense attorneys and physicians who have testified in legal cases on behalf of physicians generally agree that detailed medical records are often a physician's best defense in a medicolegal case.

Efficiency

Efficiency requires that the medical record expedites the documentation process while also facilitating the patient encounter, promoting quality care, and ensuring E/M compliance. The IMR accomplishes this by identifying the most effective interface (graphic or narrative) and data entry person for each section of the medical record, as well as enabling each physician to select the format of data entry (writing vs dictation vs keyboard and mouse) best suited to his or her needs.

User-Friendliness, or Usability

Medical records become *user-friendly* when their structure and data entry options offer sufficient flexibility to meet the needs of each specialty and each physician. Their features must be adaptable to both a physician's style of patient care and his or her preferred means of documentation. In other words, the physician should not have to adapt his or her style of patient care to meet the requirements of the medical record; rather, the design of the record should meet the physician's medical requirements.

Quality of Care

While the quality of medical care provided is largely the result of each physician's skills and efforts, it can also be enhanced by employing a medical record that:

- maximizes the physician's ability to obtain a complete and pertinent medical history in *all* cases,
- directs a more extensive examination when appropriate, and
- guides in-depth documentation of all actively considered diagnoses and treatment options in complex cases.

Data Integrity

The medical record should facilitate physicians' ability to provide an accurate and easily understood recording of their clinical findings, their diagnostic impressions, and the diagnostic procedures and treatment options considered and selected. It should readily allow someone reading a patient's chart to understand not only what the physician did during an encounter, but also the reasons for the conclusions reached and recommendations made. While the integrity of this information is important when another physician or a reviewer analyzes the record, it is critical for continuity of care and ongoing patient reassessment that the same physician can clearly understand these details during a patient's subsequent visits.

Secondary Goals

Additional desirable goals that contribute to the value of a medical record include (1) increased productivity for those physicians who do not overcode, (2) more free time for those physicians who currently do not complete their documentation at the point of care, and (3) reduced physician stress plus increased physician enjoyment and satisfaction from the practice of medicine.

There are three reasons that Practical E/M methodology helps to increase productivity. First, the IMR design enables physicians to obtain and document medical information more efficiently. Next, physicians are able to efficiently and compliantly document higher E/M code levels for those patients whose medical problems warrant more complex levels of care. Finally, obtaining and documenting a comprehensive history for every patient visit heightens physicians' awareness of a greater number of significant medical problems. Those visits during which the in-depth history reveals an increased number and/or severity of identified medical issues may result in a more severe nature of presenting problem and more complex levels of care, which in turn warrant submitting codes for higher levels of E/M service. Also, in some cases, these patients may require supplemental visits to receive the care indicated for these additional problems. Of course, this improved productivity is a natural consequence of the benefits for the patient of the physician being able to identify, and treat, underlying medical problems.

The current demands on their time leave some physicians unable to complete their documentation during each patient's visit. Consequently, many physicians find themselves staying late or taking records home to complete during the evening. This practice increases the challenge of accurate documentation, because it is extremely difficult to remember all the details of a 10 AM visit at 10 PM. It also introduces the further danger that inadvertently omitted information might have a negative impact on future patient care or prove crucial in the unwelcome event of a medical liability case. Finally, this practice can negatively impact physicians' quality of life and their attitude toward their medical practices.

To address this issue, the efficiency features of the IMR (ie, graphic interfaces and nonphysician data entry) greatly reduce the time and effort physicians require to fulfill E/M documentation requirements, thereby enabling them to complete the medical record at the point of care. The printed text and documentation prompts also create a system of checks and balances that protect against the omission of pertinent medical information.

The opportunity for experiencing less stress is a natural consequence of fulfilling compliance demands. For most physicians, the greatest personal rewards and enjoyment in medicine come from providing the best possible care that they can, including thorough evaluation, accurate diagnosis, optimal treatment, and increased time to communicate with our patients.

"Study" Shows IMR Prevents Marriage Counseling

When I recently asked a young physician (in practice 2 years) how he liked using an "intelligent medical record," he flashed a wide smile while reporting that he previously had to spend 2 hours at home each night completing his writing and dictation. Now he has 2 more hours each night to spend with his wife and young children. This certainly has increased his enjoyment, not only of medical practice but of his personal life as well.

SUMMARY

This chapter defines a set of criteria that can be used to measure the effectiveness of medical records in helping clinicians meet the requirements of coding and documentation while facilitating patient care. The primary criteria are quality care, E/M compliance, efficiency, user friendliness, and data integrity. Secondary goals include increasing productivity, eliminating the use of after-hours time for the completion of documentation, and enhancing physicians' satisfaction with the practice of medicine.

Early in their training, all physicians are taught that their medical record documentation should be an accurate reflection of the quality of care they provide. Although not commonly discussed, the "flip side" of this observation is equally true—the quality of care that physicians provide is most often a reflection of the quality of their medical record. Limitations in the H&P documentation capabilities of either paper or electronic records will tend to restrict the extent of care physicians perform. On the other hand, enhancing the quality of physicians' medical record tools generally facilitates more comprehensive levels of care (when medically indicated), resulting in more accurate diagnoses and improved treatment planning, in addition to audit protection and improved protection in the event of a liability claim.

The Practical E/M journey began with an effort to discover how to achieve coding and documentation compliance without interfering with patient care. It led to the discovery that fulfilling compliance requirements is a first step in designing an IMR.

The IMR should function as a powerful ally in obtaining and documenting a history that tells the patient's medical story, guiding and recording an examination that paints a clear picture of the patient's normal and abnormal findings, and drawing a blueprint for evaluation, treatment, and future management.

References

1. Health Care Financing Administration. *Documentation Guidelines for Evaluation and Management Services.* Chicago, IL: American Medical Association; 1995.
2. Bickley LS, Szilagyi PG. *Bates' Guide to Physical Examination and History Taking.* 8th ed. Philadelphia, PA: Lippincott Williams & Wilkins; 2003.

Evolution of the E/M Coding System

The American Medical Association (AMA) published the first edition of the Current Procedural Terminology (CPT®) codebook in 1966, coincident with the implementation of the US Medicare system. From its inception through 1991, Medicare's payment system was formulated on the basis of "customary, prevailing, and reasonable charges" (CPR), which corresponded to the "usual, customary, and reasonable" (UCR) system applied by many private health insurance companies.[1]

At that time, the CPT Editorial Panel determined the differing intensities of cognitive medical care solely on the basis of the amount of time the physician spent with a patient during each visit. Four levels of new patient visits were established, designated as brief, limited, moderate, and extensive.

The entire CPR-based payment system came under Medicare's scrutiny in the late 1980s because of dramatic variation in physician charges (and therefore payments) for performing the same services. The Health Care Financing Administration (HCFA; now the Centers for Medicare and Medicaid Services [CMS]) identified this issue by comparing charges submitted by different physicians for identical CPT codes. They observed significant disparities not only among individual physicians, but also across different regions of the United States. They also found that these disparities were most dramatic in the codes for cognitive services. As a result, Medicare determined to find a different basis for their payment system, and they ultimately replaced the CPR-based payment system with the evaluation and management (E/M) coding system on January 1, 1992.[1]

DEVELOPMENT OF THE E/M CODING SYSTEM

The search for a new reimbursement system that would prove workable and fair for both physicians and Medicare led to the development of the Resource Based Relative Value System (RBRVS), which Congress authorized in the 1989 Omnibus Budget Reconciliation Act, for implementation in 1992. The RBRVS was based on a series of studies conducted between 1979 and 1992 by principal investigators William Hsiao, PhD, and Peter Braun, MD, at Harvard University. Their investigations developed value comparisons among CPT coding procedures, which were based on the sum of the work value, the practice expense value, and the professional liability insurance value of each individual service. The result was a relative value scale for CPT coding procedures across all specialties. After extensive review of the initial RBRVS report, the AMA House of Delegates unanimously adopted a resolution to support the Harvard RBRVS study and data as "an acceptable basis for a Medicare indemnity payment system."[1] An important element of this support was to advocate for identical payment for identical services across all specialties.

The E/M coding system first appeared in the 1992 edition of the CPT codebook, and it was adopted by Medicare and private insurers alike. Since then, new categories of services have been added, such as hospital observation care and neonatal intensive care. However, the major features of the coding system have remained relatively constant since its inception.

First Policy Era: E/M Coding and Qualitative Documentation (1991–1994)

During the last 4 months of 1991, the AMA and HCFA conducted a series of seminars to teach the individuals who would train physicians in the new E/M coding system. Medicare medical directors and staff attended, as well as approximately 50 physicians who were nominated by various state medical societies and medical specialty societies.

These seminars explained the new system and taught physicians a method for approaching E/M coding. This method, which is still generally taught to physicians today, instructs physicians to identify the correct type of service, perform and document their medical care, and then select an appropriate E/M code on the basis of three "key components":

- the extent of the medical history obtained,
- the extent of the examination performed, and
- the complexity of medical decision making (MDM).

After assessing the level of complexity of each of these components, physicians are instructed to match these with descriptions in the CPT codebook for each level of care to identify the proper code level.

Assessment of Original Key Component Descriptions

As described in the CPT codebook, the descriptions of extent of history, extent of examination, and complexity of decision making are all *qualitative*, not quantitative. As a result, it was not possible for physicians, auditors, and trainers to have a common understanding of the amount of documentation necessary to satisfy the subjective requirements presented in the E/M coding section. For example, the description of a "detailed" history states that it consists of:

Chief complaint, *extended* history of present illness; *problem-pertinent* system review extended to include a review of a *limited number* of additional systems; *pertinent* past, family, and/or social history directly related to the patient's problems.[2] (Note: words have been italicized for emphasis)

However, none of these italicized qualitative descriptors is defined. Neither auditors nor physicians could objectively determine how much history needed to be documented to be extended, or how many additional systems qualified as a "limited number."

Beginning in January 1992, the regional Medicare carriers planned a three-step process to train physicians prior to full implementation of the E/M coding system. This blueprint allowed 3 months for the Medicare carriers' trainers to conduct multiple instructional seminars for physicians. After this training period, the second phase consisted of random "friendly audits" of medical record charts by the carriers. These reviews analyzed the records for compliant E/M coding but did not result in any downcoding or financial penalties for incorrect coding. Their purpose was to assess whether physicians had been able to learn and apply the new system in order to document and code correctly. The third phase, scheduled to begin in July 1992, was supposed to include full implementation of the E/M coding system for payments, plus formal audits that would result in correction of improper coding and the return of any improper payments.

The third phase never happened. According to information I received from a carrier medical director, this was because the informal audits demonstrated that physicians' coding had too high a failure rate. Formally, the carriers indicated an incorrect coding rate of approximately 33%. Informally, however, the audit personnel and directors discussed that the failure rate was much higher. At that time, Medicare apparently felt it could not impose strict audits on physicians who had not been able to master the system. In response, the carriers resumed training sessions and continued conducting informal audits for another 6 months but still failed to find any significant improvement in physicians' coding accuracy. Formal audits never occurred during this first policy era, from 1992 through 1994. Without the stimulus of audits or oversight, physicians rapidly lost interest in learning the E/M system. In general, they simply continued with the medical record systems they had always used in their practices.

The Genesis of Practical E/M During the First Policy Era

As noted in the preface to this book, at the end of my own train-the-trainer session, I observed that the E/M system as taught was not practical for physicians to use in medical practice. My observation was based less on the qualitative nature of the descriptors than on the amount of time and effort required at the end of each visit to review the chart, review the CPT codebook, and attempt to calculate a code.

I voluntarily attended multiple training sessions conducted by our state Medicare carrier and found that their teaching was consistent with the protocol I had been taught. I also asked the state's Medicare medical director whether I could review some of their chart audits. I found that the carrier's auditing had been quite liberal, but in spite of this, physician coding did not match their medical record documentation. In other words, the audit results confirmed my assessment that the protocol taught for coding was too time consuming and/or too challenging for physicians to employ while they were providing patient care.

I also realized that, even with my own extensive training and knowledge of the E/M system, I could not easily memorize and apply all the required coding rules while actively taking care of patients. As a result, I began developing tools to assist physicians with the coding calculations. The concept of "tools, not rules" began as a series of color-coded tables for each type of E/M service physicians commonly perform in the office or hospital. These tables correlated compliant coding with levels of care for the three key components. It is noteworthy that these tables also included information about the "nature of the presenting problem" (NPP), which had not been emphasized at all during my E/M training. Today, NPP remains a crucial focus of Practical E/M methodology in bridging the concepts of compliance and quality of care.

Finally, in 2008, it is thought provoking to look back and consider that no effort was ever made by Medicare to have the physician trainers teach E/M principles to medical students and residents. To the best of my knowledge, no medical students (and very few residents) have been taught the principles of E/M coding and the *Documentation Guidelines for Evaluation and Management Services*, even though this is the standard by which Medicare and all insurers evaluate their cognitive care and documentation. (Early during their medical school training, when my two children asked their physical diagnosis instructors when they would be taught E/M coding, they were told, "We don't teach that.")

Second Policy Era: E/M Coding and Partial Quantitative Documentation (1995–1997)

Medicare apparently attributed the inability of physicians to correctly calculate and submit E/M codes to the *qualitative* aspect of the descriptors. Their response to this shortcoming of the system appeared in 1995, when HCFA produced the first version of the *Documentation Guidelines for Evaluation and Management Services*,[3] commonly referred to simply as the *Documentation Guidelines*. The AMA's CPT Editorial Panel worked with HCFA to ensure clinical relevance and accuracy of this document with the E/M system.

This 16-page manual elaborated on the general principles of medical record documentation. It also introduced *quantitative* measures for each of the elements of the medical history plus guidelines and examples of the three components of MDM. In addition, it also defined the circumstances under which *time* becomes a "key or controlling factor to qualify for a particular level of E/M services."[3] This 1995 edition also introduced several guidelines regarding the physical examination component. These included (1) relating the extent of examination to be performed and documented to a physician's "clinical judgment and the nature of the presenting problem(s),"[3] (2) requiring documentation of both specific abnormal and relevant normal findings in affected organ systems plus specific abnormal findings in unaffected areas, and (3) offering a guideline for the number of organ systems (eight to 12) that must be documented to achieve a comprehensive examination for a general multisystem examination. On the other hand, this initial set of guidelines excluded an analysis of, or changes to, the *qualitative* descriptions in the CPT coding system for documentation of an *expanded problem-focused* examination, a *detailed* examination, or a *complete examination of a single organ system*.

Subsequent to the publication of the *Documentation Guidelines*, Medicare carriers once again provided training sessions in E/M coding, incorporating the new materials related to the *Documentation Guidelines*. Once again the carriers performed informal audits for several months, once again the medical record documentation that Medicare reviewed failed to support the E/M code levels submitted, and once again Medicare did not institute binding audits, downcoding, or financial penalties for E/M services performed by practicing physicians.

One very meaningful audit did occur during this period. In teaching hospital circles, this audit may have been the proverbial "shot heard 'round the world." The results of this audit appeared in *The New York Times* on December 13, 1995. On page 18, the *Times* reported that the "University of Pennsylvania's Health System has agreed to pay thirty million dollars to settle government complaints that it filed improper Medicare bills for doctors' services. . . . This substantial settlement followed a Government audit of one hundred patients treated in 1993."[4] This investigation introduced new realities to the coding and documentation landscape:

- Medicare was serious about oversight audits for documentation and coding. This introduced the term *compliance* to the medical record arena.
- Medicare had the authority to *extrapolate* the results of audits conducted on a limited number of medical charts, resulting in financial penalties being assessed for all the care for which Medicare had paid the physicians over a significant related time period.
- The audit addressed two major issues. One related to attending physicians' charges for care involving resident physicians. The other concerned the submission of inaccurate E/M codes that requested payment for levels of care that were significantly higher than the extent of care actually documented in the medical records.
- While the terms of this settlement provided for payment of a negotiated amount of restitution, which was presumably lower than the calculated amount of overpayments, they also included a requirement that the physicians implement an internal compliance program. This program had to be designed to correct the existing documentation and coding problems. It also had to provide ongoing

monitoring of the physicians, to ensure that similar errors would not occur in the future.

The results of the University of Pennsylvania Health System review led to the Office of Inspector General's Physicians at Teaching Hospitals (PATH) audits at 49 teaching institutions. While these audits impacted physicians practicing at teaching hospitals to a substantial degree, there was still no significant concern or impetus among most physicians in private practice to incorporate the updated principles of E/M coding and the *Documentation Guidelines* into their medical care and their medical records.

Third Policy Era: E/M Coding and Expanded Quantitative Documentation (1997–Present)

In 1997, Medicare introduced their next version of the *Documentation Guidelines*, which built on the criteria of the 1995 edition. This 1997 edition included an additional option for documentation of an *extended* history of present illness: review of the status of three or more chronic conditions. However, the major feature of this update was the addition of quantitative measures for the physical examination. Specifically, it introduced a general multisystem examination and 11 single-organ-system examinations. It also presented criteria that defined the extent of these examinations that must be performed and documented in order to meet CPT coding system standards for a problem-focused, expanded problem-focused, detailed, or comprehensive physical examination.[5]

With the publication of the 1997 edition of the *Documentation Guidelines*, HCFA also announced that it would officially begin holding physicians responsible for compliance with the E/M documentation and coding guidelines. HCFA further advised that Medicare would begin conducting meaningful audits, which would result in financial penalties for noncompliant coding practices.

There was an immediate negative response from the physician community to the new *Documentation Guidelines*. Many physicians voiced objection to "bean counting" of the medical record. This criticism was particularly directed at the new physical examination standards, most likely related to the amount of care and documentation required. Because of the widespread concern, the AMA called a special meeting to present and review the 1997 *Documentation Guidelines*. Two physicians plus members of the executive staff from each state medical society attended the so-called fly-in meeting on April 27, 1998, along with representatives from the AMA and Medicare.

At this meeting, the AMA leadership read a letter from the administrator of HCFA. This stated that physicians would be allowed to use either the 1995 or the 1997 *Documentation Guidelines* for the physical examination. This ruling allowed physicians a choice of following the qualitative (and less precise) CPT examination descriptors that had been in place since 1992 (labeled the 1995 *Documentation Guidelines*) or using one of the new quantitative (more precise) 1997 examination templates. This choice is still available to all physicians today. Although the physical examination issue had been addressed, many physicians at the fly-in meeting continued to voice concern about coding and the *Documentation Guidelines*.

Assessment of Physician Community Concerns at the Fly-in

During the fly-in meeting on April 27, 1998 those of us in attendance, who were comfortable with coding were at first puzzled that the permission to use 1995 examination guidelines did not resolve physician concerns, because the 1997 physical

---

continued

examination templates had been the original focus of the criticism. As the discussion continued, we concluded that most of the real distress was actually over HCFA's commitment to requiring physician compliance with E/M coding and the *Documentation Guidelines*. In other words, many in attendance observed that physicians had not learned, and were not following, the precepts of E/M coding, nor did they want any responsibility for doing so in the future. In response to these comments, HCFA and AMA representatives advised that there was not going to be a return to pre-1992 coding policies.

Another discussion at the April 27, 1998, meeting centered on the possible modification of the complex calculations required for MDM. The proposed change, called the "new framework," was presented, discussed, and then forwarded to HCFA for evaluation. The new framework added emphasis on the patient's severity of illness, but it also significantly reduced consideration of the three elements of MDM. HCFA ultimately rejected the new framework, in all likelihood because this approach automatically attributed a high level of complexity for MDM in sicker patients, even when a chart lacked significant documentation of MDM.

Medicare Assurances Regarding E/M Auditing Methodology

At one of the April 27, 1998, meeting's breakout sessions, HCFA provided an important assurance regarding Medicare's E/M auditing. Physicians attending this session raised concern about an unpublished MDM calculating tool (the so-called Marshfield Clinic Tool) that some auditors were reportedly using to review physician E/M charts. Physicians in the session voiced extreme concern that Medicare auditors would be applying an audit tool that was different from E/M and *Documentation Guidelines* and that was not available to physicians. Dr Aaron Primack, HCFA's national medical director, assured the group that HCFA would never apply auditing tools that differed from the standards provided to physicians. In my experience, however, this issue of non-compliant auditing formulae continues to reappear from multiple sources, including a number of Medicare Carriers. This circumstance is disruptive to physicians because their use gives results inconsistent with CPT guidelines and promotes non-compliant coding and auditing practices. It therefore erodes the credibility of CMS and the other sources that resort to these approaches.

From 1997 forward, the AMA and HCFA explored further modifications to the *Documentation Guidelines* requirements and even considered the possibility of changing the E/M system to a "vignette"-based approach. Ultimately, however, none of these proposed changes provided reliability in achieving a set of guidelines that would be consistent, workable, and acceptable to physicians.

As a result, our current compliance model for E/M services consists of the qualitative requirements defined in the CPT codebook's E/M coding section, the CPT codebook's appendix of "Clinical Examples," and the quantitative refinements presented in both editions of the *Documentation Guidelines*.

AUDITS AND E/M CODING

Audits have played a significant role in the evolution of the E/M coding system. Since the initial implementation of the E/M coding system in 1992, Medicare audits have demonstrated that physician coding frequently does not align with the medical record documentation or with the level of medical necessity.

However, E/M auditing has also proven itself to be a means of measuring the integrity of the system itself. Assessing the results of E/M audits allows us to judge whether clinicians are able to apply the coding guidelines appropriately and consistently. When Medicare delayed implementation of chart review from 1992 until 1995, it was probably due in large part to the fact that audits had demonstrated that the E/M system lacked sufficient quantitative measures to ensure consistency in both coding and auditing. This led to the development of the *Documentation Guidelines* to provide the means for conducting more objective analyses.

As with umpires in baseball, it is critical that Medicare and insurer audits and auditors be impartial and reliable. This is mandatory to ensure fairness and integrity throughout the system, for physicians and patients as well as for Medicare and insurers. However, as discussed earlier, some auditors have resorted to nonsanctioned and unpublished auditing shortcut tools, particularly in assessing MDM. For example, they may employ the so-called Marshfield Clinic Tool for MDM, even though this aberrant formula can result in either overcoding or undercoding when compared with CPT-compliant E/M auditing. These noncompliant audit results occur because this auditing technique introduces a distinction between new medical problems and existing problems. It values all new problems in a way that enables designation of moderate or high complexity MDM, even for a simple new problem such as a viral respiratory infection. It similarly de-values established problems by tending to designate them as straightforward or low complexity MDM, even for a severe illness such as lymphoma.

The Marshfield Tool and Improper Coding by Physicians

Some medical practices have identified the Marshfield guidelines on certain Medicare carrier websites and applied this noncompliant tool to justify claims for level 4 or level 5 services for every patient visit, regardless of the severity of the patient's problem. This tool inappropriately attributes any single *new* problem as being the equivalent of *multiple* diagnoses. With the simple addition of laboratory tests or a prescription medication, this tool therefore allows a physician to claim "moderate-complexity" MDM for any such patient. Since the tool as published also fails to consider medical necessity, physicians are therefore misled into believing such high-level claims are allowed for even minor problems, such as an ankle sprain or insect bite. The tool also fails to give consideration to "number of treatment options," further distorting CPT guidelines and interfering with physicians' ability to document and code correctly.

The greatest problem with the use of such nonsanctioned rules is that they are inconsistent with the CPT codebook and the *Documentation Guidelines*. They therefore use a noncompliant approach to evaluate the care physicians are providing and documenting. The medical director of HCFA appropriately disavowed the use of these "rules" and any other nonpublished auditing tools at the 1998 meeting. This is a critical issue for the present and for the future. As with the umpires in baseball, the auditors must follow only the same sanctioned rules that are provided to physicians to ensure a viable E/M system.

SUMMARY

The E/M coding system has evolved from using largely qualitative descriptions of coding and documentation when it was introduced in 1992. In 1995 and 1997, the *Documentation Guidelines* introduced quantitative measures to assist physicians and add necessary reliability to audits. Subsequently, possible alternatives to this system have been considered but have not met the criteria for adoption.

It is critical for the integrity of the E/M coding system that the principles and rules published in the CPT codebook and the *Documentation Guidelines* be applied consistently by physicians and reviewers alike, without the introduction of noncompliant external auditing approaches.

References

1.   Gallagher P, ed. *Medicare RBRVS: The Physicians' Guide.* Chicago, IL: American Medical Association; 2004.

2.   American Medical Association. *Current Procedural Terminology CPT® 2008.* Chicago, IL: American Medical Association; 2007.

3.   Health Care Financing Administration. *Documentation Guidelines for Evaluation and Management Services.* Chicago, IL: American Medical Association; 1995.

4.   Johnston D. University agrees to pay in settlement on Medicare. *New York Times.* December 13, 1995:A18.

5.   Health Care Financing Administration. *Documentation Guidelines for Evaluation and Management Services.* Chicago, IL: American Medical Association; 1997.

Medical Training and the Medical Record

Most physicians receive their introduction to using medical records during the second year of medical school. The process is usually presented in a course called "Introduction to Physical Diagnosis." This course teaches medical students that the medical record is not only a means of recording the patient's history, examination, and differential diagnosis but also an important framework for the interaction between physicians and patients.

Instructors generally place a strong emphasis on the importance of obtaining a comprehensive medical history. In pursuit of this goal, medical students strive to learn how to achieve a critical balance between obtaining an open-ended history by asking general questions that allow the patient to offer information without significant prompting, and a structured history by asking more narrowly focused questions that call for directed responses.

Physicians are also taught that the ability to obtain an insightful medical history is usually the most important factor in determining a patient's probable diagnosis(es). This enables the physician to use the physical examination and appropriately targeted medical testing to confirm or deny the selected diagnosis. By applying this history-centered paradigm, the provision of health care becomes more efficient, directed, and cost-effective. Also, patients derive a strong sense of physician caring from the degree of interest involved in obtaining a thorough history.

Playing Sherlock Holmes

Often, medical schools wisely select one or more of their "best" clinicians to instruct students in the art of obtaining a good history and physical (H&P). The two interrelated skills that generally set these physicians apart include (1) understanding how to obtain an efficient history that narrows down the possible diagnoses for the patient's problems, and (2) relating well to patients.

As students, many of us were privileged to be taught by such exemplary physicians, who inevitably stressed that a quality medical history is the most effective and reliable diagnostic tool in our medical armamentarium. I still vividly remember the introduction to clinical diagnosis lecture by Dr Phillip Tumulty, who admonished our student group that "with a good medical history, a physician can make the correct diagnosis 95% of the time before he or she even picks up a stethoscope."

At the time, Dr Tumulty's statement described a degree of medical ability and insight that seemed to this inexperienced student nearly impossible to achieve. However, it set an admirable goal for the future. Striving to attain such skills requires learning what I like to call "magic questions," special inquiries that elicit patient responses to specifically rule in, or rule out, a selected important diagnosis. This sense of "playing Sherlock Holmes" leads to accurate diagnoses and also offers the physician intellectual challenge and satisfaction.

THE MEDICAL RECORD IN MEDICAL SCHOOL

It is important to consider how medical schools currently teach the H&P and how they prepare their students to meet the standards for the medical records introduced in 1992 by evaluation and management (E/M) coding. My surveys of attendees at E/M coding sessions during the last several years indicate that there appear to be no physicians receiving training in E/M coding and the *Documentation Guidelines for Evaluation and Management Services*[1] during their medical school education. Rather, they are being taught a variety of techniques that include either (1) a so-called comprehensive H&P, which consists of a medical history (including chief compliant [CC], history of present illness [HP1], review of systems [ROS], and past, family, and social history [PFSH]), physical examination, impressions, and recommendations; or (2) a "SOAP" note that includes **S**ubjective findings (ie, history), **O**bjective findings (ie, examination), **A**ssessment, and a **P**lan for evaluation and/or treatment.

The SOAP note is commonly taught as a means of providing a comprehensive H&P; eg, the subjective component is presented as including the CC, HPI, ROS, and PFSH. However, as it is commonly used in practice, the SOAP approach is the furthest from achieving E/M coding compliance, because physicians' documentation for each of its four components commonly concentrates exclusively on the patient's presenting complaint. For example, the subjective component may incorporate only a CC and HPI, with no consideration of PFSH or ROS. Similarly, the objective component may describe only the affected body area, and the assessment will likely focus on a single, most-probable diagnosis. In E/M terms, this narrow approach qualifies as only "problem-focused" care, which is appropriate for only level 1 or level 2 coding.

The Downside of a Problem-Focused History

As will be discussed in Chapter 4, eliminating the ROS will downcode any initial visit to a maximum of level 1 (eg, 99201) and will downcode any established visit (that considers history in the coding assessment) to a maximum of level 2 (ie, 99212). More important, when a record eliminates PFSH and/or ROS, the absence of potentially crucial medical information from the resulting evaluation significantly challenges our primary mandate of quality first.

Both the SOAP note and the comprehensive H&P completely disregard multiple medical record components that are required by the Current Procedural Terminology (CPT®) coding system for E/M coding. These missing factors include complexity of data reviewed, risk of the presenting problem(s), risk of diagnostic procedures, risk of management options, and, perhaps most important, the nature of presenting problem (NPP). Medical students do not ordinarily receive training or instruction in how to incorporate these concepts into their medical record documentation. Even more disconcertingly, they receive little or no education concerning how their medical records relate to coding, reimbursement, and compliance; yet these are crucial concepts that directly affect the ability of physicians to achieve success in the practice of medicine. We cannot realistically expect physicians to be compliant in their coding and documentation, while still performing thorough medical evaluations, when they have not received adequate training in the terminology and requirements for creating medical records that fulfill E/M coding standards.

E/M Compliance and Academic Practice

As shown by the Physicians at Teaching Hospitals (PATH) audits discussed in Chapter 2, the importance of coding and compliance concepts impacts physicians in academic practice just as significantly as those in private practice.

Not only have medical schools failed to incorporate the skills of E/M documentation and coding into their curricula, they have also generally not equipped their students with anything more sophisticated than a pen and a blank sheet of paper as their sole means of collecting and documenting patients' health care information. The medical student can obtain and document the comprehensive H&P he or she was taught with this primitive technology, but it requires an inordinate amount of time (as much as 60 minutes per patient). Although some of this time may be attributed to the student's lack of experience, the majority of the time spent is simply a function of the amount of time and effort this inefficient system requires just to write down the headings and the normal history responses and examination findings.

While this education approach provides students with the opportunity to learn how to interact with a patient while obtaining medical information, it does not prepare them realistically for the actual practice of medical care. This interaction would actually be enhanced with the aid of intelligent medical record (IMR) tools, which enhance documentation efficiency and can increase the time medical students have available to interact with the patient by decreasing the time required to interact with the paper. Furthermore, the students would have more time to spend on the critical learning aspects of an individualized medical history, rather than eliciting straightforward background information. In addition, training students with an IMR should enrich their educational experience by allowing them to learn about, and practice with, the kinds of medical record tools they should ultimately use to help them in medical practice.

Real-Time Report from Medical School Today

One of my daughters, when she had completed her third year of medical school, reported that some of her clinical rotations have provided her with preprinted forms that were helpful for documenting the H&P. However, the downside of using these forms was that they were not designed to be compliant with the CPT E/M coding system. Further, there was no accompanying discussion of how the medical record relates to E/M coding when the physicians distributed these forms to the students. This leaves her knowing that forms can save time, but it still does not teach her how forms should be optimally designed, how to complete the record to be compliant with E/M documentation requirements, or the importance of the medical record in the coding process.

She observed that "most medical students simply don't know about compliance." She reported "the shortening of their histories and physicals from 60 minutes to 15 minutes (to complete their quantity of work) is done by trial and error, eliminating meaningful portions of the medical record they were taught, without any regard for compliance."

My other daughter advises that her medical school actually forbids the students from using more than a pen and blank paper. She believes the reasoning is that they want the students to "memorize" the components of the H&P and utilize this as a basis for being actively involved mentally in the process of obtaining the medical history. She also observes several problems with this approach:

■ The students need to learn a process they can use under the time demands of residency training and current medical practice, without cutting out critical information.

continued

■ With the pen and blank paper technique, information often gets missed. She observes that "either the information is collected, and the student forgets to or doesn't have time to document it, or the information never gets asked because the student is trying to think about and remember so many things at once that she has no systematic and fail-safe way to document all this information as she obtains it."

I believe that medical students are quite capable of memorizing a list of questions. The critical learning experience does not result from verbally asking straightforward preliminary medical history questions (which IMR obtains through direct input by the patient into the medical record in response to yes-or-no questions). Rather, it derives from learning how to use that information, once obtained, as a basis for the more sophisticated questions that lead to correct diagnoses (the documentation of which the physician enters as narrative free-text into the IMR).

Near the end of their four years of medical school, students are now confronted with a contradictory message about the appropriate levels of care they should provide, even for complex patients. Although they have been taught that comprehensive care is the best model for providing care, particularly for patients with severe or complex medical problems, they receive a different message when taking the clinical skills component of the United States Medical Licensing Exam. During this all-day test, the students must evaluate a series of actor-patients, each of whom presents with a significant medical problem. The students are required to evaluate and examine each patient and then document their care and an extensive differential diagnosis and management plan in no more than 25 minutes for each patient. This assignment also prohibits use of structured medical record forms, limiting the students to use of "a clipboard, blank paper for taking notes, and a pen."[1] Although effective IMR forms would allow students to complete this task in the time allotted, it is not possible to accomplish this amount of care and documentation with only pen and blank paper. To accommodate this restriction, the examination instructs students to limit the extent of the care they provide "by asking this patient *relevant* questions and performing a *focused* physical examination."[1]

The unfortunate message that these instructions convey to students is that performing a problem-focused history and a problem-focused examination is appropriate patient care, even for patients with high-severity illness (eg, carcinoma). This impression contradicts the lessons the students learned about quality care in medical school, the care and documentation requirements for achieving E/M compliance, and the standard of clinical care established by physicians and their specialty societies in the E/M section and clinical examples section of the CPT codebook. These sources all specify that patients with high-severity illness (ie, moderate-to-high or high NPP) warrant a *comprehensive* medical history and a *comprehensive* physical examination in addition to moderate- or high-complexity medical decision making (MDM).

Consequences of Contradictory Messages About Appropriate Levels of Care

During a consultation with a large multispecialty group, the group's compliance director asked me to work with one internist whose documentation of care consistently fell far below the level 3 and level 4 services he submitted for payment. Audit of his medical records demonstrated that he provided only problem-focused care during every medical encounter (similar to the type of care and documentation required to pass the national licensing examination). Following my review of the CPT codebook and demonstration of how IMR forms promoting a comprehensive medical history and appropriate levels of exam and MDM would help him to achieve appropriately higher

continued

levels of care in the same or less time than he was now spending with patients, he remarked, "I assumed that was just for medical school, not to be used in the real world."

Following their early exposure to comprehensive levels of history and examination, students receive little reinforcement for continuing to provide such effective (and compliant) care. In addition to the contradictory message from the licensing examination, they rarely observe more comprehensive levels of care being provided by their medical role models, because their professors and outside attending physicians face severe economically-based time constraints when providing patient care and also lack effective documentation tools.

THE MEDICAL RECORD IN RESIDENCY

How do physicians survive the time demands of residency training? Given an overwhelming burden of learning, plus patient care responsibilities, they seek shortcuts to complete their patient care responsibilities in a workable time frame. One response is to progressively reduce the amount of writing (and time) required for documenting the medical record, for both inpatients and outpatients.

Lacking concise IMR style chart tools to help them document the same comprehensive information in a reduced time frame, residents commonly resort to reducing the amount of information they obtain and document. For example, the documented description of the ROS may be limited to a statement such as "noncontributory" or "all negative." In other cases, documentation of the ROS may be altogether absent from the medical record. The greater concern is whether such documentation actually reflects that the series of specific questions normally involved in a detailed ROS actually was reduced to the resident asking the single question "Do you have any other symptoms?"

Similarly, the documented description of findings in the physical examination may include details for any abnormal findings, but then lump the description of the remainder of the examination into a statement such as "remainder of exam normal." Once again the greater concern must be about the possibility that the physical examination was actually narrowed down to only a "problem-focused" assessment of the region of the body related directly to the patient's presenting problem, as documented in the record.

Reducing the extent of medical history, physical examination, and decision making performed and/or documented has a significant potential to negatively impact the quality of patient care. It may result in incomplete or incorrect medical assessment and treatment. In addition, information omitted from the written medical record, because it did not seem relevant to a particular resident, could turn out to be important, either at a later time or in the eyes of another (and perhaps more experienced) physician.

Such expediencies may allow the resident physicians to save time. However, in addition to possibly compromising quality of care, they also sacrifice their opportunities to learn and understand compliance. As a result, during their training, residents fail to gain an appreciation for the relationship between the severity of patient illness, the amount of care that is medically indicated, their written documentation of patient encounters, and E/M coding.

Consequences of Shortening the H&P

Clearly the time and work demands on residents using only blank paper technology provide the training ground for the shortcuts that so many physicians bring with them to medical practice, commonly resulting in problem-focused care, problem-focused documentation, and noncompliant E/M coding.

The *Documentation Guidelines* declare that, when documented in the medical record, nonspecific global statements such as "ROS noncontributory" or "remainder of exam normal" are insufficient to document the performance of a significant amount of care. Because there is no specific medical content, such documentation is treated as if no significant care had been performed. This position also reflects a quality-of-care perspective, because such general statements do not report any questions that were actually asked or any patient responses; physicians cannot use this imprecise information to make critical medical judgments.

THE MEDICAL RECORD IN PRACTICE

For physicians completing residency and entering medical practice, time pressures are amplified rather than reduced. The current economic environment, fueled by a low conversion factor for the Resource Based Relative Value System (RBRVS), results in reimbursements by both Medicare and private insurers that are often lower than physicians' costs. This commonly translates to further time pressure and searches for efficiency. Some of this pressure results in "shortcuts" that may impair quality, cost-effectiveness, and/or efficiency in the long run.

One of the additional negative consequences of the increased time pressure that first confronts physicians during their residency and becomes exacerbated when they first enter practice is the tendency to narrow down the medical record documentation of their differential diagnoses to only a single, most probable disease process. This phenomenon is also commonly accompanied by winnowing down the list of potential treatment options to only a single treatment, which is the one that will be initiated at the time of the visit. This narrow focus may prolong the number of visits required to identify the correct diagnosis, overlook contributory illnesses, and delay the introduction of effective treatments.

The good news for E/M services is that since the publication of the 1997 edition of the *Documentation Guidelines*,[2] many physicians have sought to increase efficiency and compliance through the introduction of graphic interfaces for parts of their medical records. In many cases, the same physicians have also designed these portions of their records to permit their staff or their patients to become data entry personnel, as advocated by Practical E/M. However, care must be taken to be certain that the design of these templates does not conflict with CPT coding guidelines or interfere with patient care. Therefore, one of Practical E/M's primary goals is to ensure that these approaches are in fact compliant, and that they contribute to physicians' efficiency and the provision of quality medical care.

What if "I Just Didn't Have Time to Document It"?

Medical records with abbreviated documentation, as discussed in the previous two sections of this chapter, result in significant downcoding when subjected to E/M coding audits. Experienced auditors who perform these reviews hear a very common response from the physicians: "I did the work, I just didn't document it." Contrary to such claims, my experience from reviewing large numbers of medical records shows that when elements of the *history* and *examination* are not documented, it is most likely that they were, in fact, not performed. Furthermore, per the *Documentation Guidelines* and also per the Medicare Carriers Manual, reviewers are required to interpret lack of documentation as nonperformance of the care.[3]

My auditing experience also suggests that the claim that the work was actually done may, in some cases, be valid for the section of the record where the physician is

continued

considering multiple possible diagnoses and treatment options, but then documenting only one of each. My response to this rationale is that formal documentation will actually enhance quality care by encouraging appropriate evaluation of the alternative diagnoses and treatments as well.

IMPORTANCE OF THE PHYSICIAN'S MEDICAL RECORD

An effective medical record assists physicians by facilitating a comprehensive history (arguably our most reliable diagnostic tool), guiding the level of examination we perform, so that it is appropriate for the severity of each patient's disease processes, and prompting us to consider all appropriate differential diagnoses and treatment options. It therefore has the benefit of improving efficiency without sacrificing quality.

A medical record with IMR features is also extremely helpful when a patient sees an associate in your practice or a colleague in another practice. Not only can the second physician understand the elements of the patient's illness and the course of the disease, but he or she can also gain insight into the reasons for the care provided.

Thorough MDM documentation that includes a blueprint for subsequent visits also assists physicians with ongoing patient care. Specifically, at the beginning of any visit, a review of the patient's chart helps the physician to immediately recall his or her previous impressions, diagnostic tests, and treatment plans. He or she may also have documented anticipated actions based on test results and treatment responses. Renewing these notes allows the physician to quickly and efficiently "pick up where he left off," ensuring a smooth flow of care and reassuring patients of the depth of their physician's involvement with their health needs.

Legitimate Audit Protection

In my own practice, use of an IMR for documentation and coding enabled me to feel 100% secure in the event that an audit might occur. (I call this benefit "sleepability.") Because of the quality and appropriateness of our documentation and coding, my practice was able to successfully appeal any and all instances of automated E/M downcoding by managed care insurers. In the spring of 2000, a local managed care insurer hired an out-of-state auditing firm to demonstrate its ability to recapture income from physicians by auditing my medical records. Their representatives came to our office and took copies of 15 visits they had preselected for audit.

This company spent 16 weeks auditing the charts. Although they never sent me a written audit of each chart (as I believe they should have), their summary letter stated that all of the charts had passed their audit, but that I had "undercoded" three charts at level 3 when the three key components indicated that I could have submitted these visits for level 4 care.

My review of those visits showed that in fact the key components did support level 4 services, but the NPP only warranted level 3 care (ie, the patient's illness was not of moderate to high severity). I wrote back to the reviewers and pointed out the use of NPP to set the maximum level of appropriate care. I also asked them to discuss their considerations of medical necessity and how they incorporate this into their E/M audits. Not unexpectedly, they never responded to my inquiry.

The medical record is most commonly our best defense in situations where the quality and/or comprehensiveness of our care might come into question. This might include compliance audits by Medicare, insurers, or even the Health and Human Services Office of Inspector General, as occurred in the so-called PATH audits of academic medical centers.

The financial impact of such audits can be multiplied extensively by two factors:

■ The financial outcome of auditing a limited number of charts may be extrapolated to the total amount of care delivered over a prolonged period.

■ Medicare auditors have the authority to assess penalties for fraud (which can be up to $11,000 per visit) if the level of E/M codes submitted is consistently far higher than that justified by the supporting documentation and/or the level of care warranted by the NPP (ie, "medical necessity").

The other negative event for which a high-quality medical record can provide benefit is in medicolegal litigation. A well-documented record is the best evidence that a physician has provided appropriate care. It also helps the physician recall the events over the course of a patient's treatment, and it assists both the physician's attorney and the expert witnesses in defending the physician. A poorly documented record will often compel a defense attorney to recommend settlement, even in a case in which the physician and attorney both believe that no wrongdoing has occurred. In contrast, a well-documented medical record will often stop a plaintiff's attorney from filing a complaint. In all cases, audits or litigation, a well-documented medical record is the physician's strongest defense.

CONSIDERATIONS FOR TRAINING PHYSICIANS IN COMPLIANT E/M CODING

Medicare, other government agencies, insurers, and policymakers have significantly increased their focus on patient safety, quality care, and compliance. This increased level of scrutiny lends increased urgency to the questions of how physicians can be expected to document and code their medical records in compliance with the standards by which they are measured, when their education and training have not adequately stressed those standards or provided them with sufficient instruction and tools to meet these requirements. In fact, the medical records of physicians who have recently completed residency fail audit at least as often as those of physicians who have been in practice for a long time.

Since the E/M documentation system is a codification of the optimal care process physicians are taught, it should be apparent that the ideal time to begin training physicians about compliant documentation and coding is at the same time they begin learning how to perform an H&P. Teaching an integrated approach to care, documentation, coding, and compliance will allow physicians to attain the goals for patient care that are illustrated by the instructions in the Clinical Examples appendix (Appendix C) in the CPT codebook.[3]

By the time physicians complete their training and enter practice, their medical care and documentation habits have already been formed and modified (by time pressures) over a period of between 6 and 9 years. Unlearning and relearning is a far more complex task for physicians than being taught the E/M coding and documentation system correctly, from the outset, when they are introduced to clinical medicine as medical students.

Has the Time Arrived?

It is my conviction that the time has now come to make the commitment to training medical students and residents for compliant E/M coding and documentation. There are no obvious drawbacks to beginning this training in medical school, and it will be relatively straightforward to build this methodology on to current instruction for teaching a comprehensive H&P. The conceptual additions would include:

continued

■ Linking the medical record to coding, and perhaps discussing reimbursement as well. This correlates with the existing interest in including training in practice management as a component of medical education.

■ Teaching (and providing documentation tools for) the additional E/M concepts of NPP, complexity of data reviewed, and the three categories of "risk."

■ Introducing coding and documentation tools to students' medical records. The blank piece of paper and the pen are outmoded technology that promote incomplete and non-compliant care and documentation; they must be replaced with compliant chart forms that incorporate tools for efficient documentation.

Integrating Practical E/M concepts and IMR tools into graduate and postgraduate medical training would offer a significant number of educational benefits for future physicians. The increased documentation efficiency will generate time savings, which medical students and residents can invest in furthering their education in more productive ways than doing administrative paperwork. For example, the time saved offers physicians in training increased opportunity to read reference books and journals in order to learn more about their patients' illnesses, breakthrough treatments, and current medical research, as well as providing them with more time to interact with their patients.

SUMMARY

Medical schools still train students how to perform the H&P, and how to document the medical record, using approaches that predate the introduction of E/M coding and the *Documentation Guidelines*. This results in a conflict between the ideals of the diagnostic H&P, taught in the second year of medical school, and the reality of caring for patients in the later clinical years of medical school, residency, and medical practice. The comprehensive care paradigm physicians are taught provides both high-quality care and a foundation for the principles of the E/M coding system. However, current teaching approaches fail to relate these critically important medical care principles to requirements for documentation and coding compliance. In addition, in the absence of medical record tools to facilitate compliance and efficiency, this high-quality care approach requires more time to perform and document than is reasonably available to medical students, residents, or practicing physicians. This conflict between quality and time constraints commonly results in physician frustration and often leads to undesirable consequences for both care and documentation.

Time constraints plus economic demands of medical practice require physicians to perform and document patient care in no more than 10 to 20 minutes per encounter. Without tools, this reality unfortunately leads many physicians to delete significant portions of their care, their documentation, or both. Frequently this results in their providing and documenting problem-focused care, which negatively impacts quality of care. In addition, these medical records generally have poor results when audited.

It is logical and reasonable for physicians to learn about the E/M system during their medical school and residency training. This should include (1) an education in compliance and the role of the medical record in practice management, (2) emphasis on the interface between quality care and documentation and coding, and (3) the use of IMR tools that will enable the efficiency and quality care called for in medical practice. Medical institutions ought to educate and monitor students and residents for E/M compliance and quality throughout their training. The added benefit of this evolution in teaching medical records is that the time saved by using these methods can translate into more valuable creative time, which can be applied to learning about our profession and our patients.

References

1. United States Medical Licensing Examination Web site. Step 2 Clinical Skills (CS) Content Description and General Information. http://download.usmle. org/2008/2008csmanual.pdf. Accessed July 14, 2008.

2. Health Care Financing Administration. *Documentation Guidelines for Evaluation and Management Services.* Chicago, IL: American Medical Association; 1997.

3. CMS Carriers Manual, Section 7103.1(I). http://www.cms.hhs.gov. Accessed July 5, 2005.

4. American Medical Association. *Current Procedural Terminology CPT® 2008.* Chicago, IL: American Medical Association; 2007.

E/M Care in Medical Practice

During their years of training in medical school and residency, few, if any, physicians receive significant instruction in E/M principles and/or exposure to medical record tools designed to efficiently facilitate comprehensive care and compliance. In fact, most have never encountered the *Documentation Guidelines*, and the overwhelming majority have not read the Evaluation and Management section of the Current Procedural Terminology (CPT®) codebook; very few are aware of Appendix C in the codebook and its role in assessing medical necessity. It is therefore not surprising that when these newly trained physicians enter medical practice, review of their medical records commonly reveals a preponderance of charts that document problem-focused care, even for patients with complex or severe medical illnesses.

When a patient has a severe or complicated illness, but the medical record documentation supports only a low level of care (ie, low-level E/M code), it is an indication of insufficient amounts of medical history, a limited physical examination, and/or incomplete medical decision making (MDM). This type of incompatibility raises significant concern, because such low levels of documentation are frequently indicative of compromised quality of care.

This chapter will examine the reasons why the coding and documentation tasks have proven so problematic for clinicians, and have led some to argue that they hinder their ability to provide care. We must also consider how we can overcome these obstacles to assist physicians in creating and using compliant medical records that will facilitate high-quality medical care.

CHALLENGES IN IMPLEMENTING COMPLIANT E/M RECORDS IN PRACTICE

Conventional training in E/M coding has emphasized the three key components (history, examination, and MDM), minimized discussion of the nature of the presenting problem (NPP), and instructed physicians to first provide and document their medical care and then calculate an E/M code at the end of the visit. In practice, however, trying to calculate an E/M code at the end of a visit is simply too time consuming and distracting a task for physicians to complete comfortably while they are providing care to patients. The code calculations vary depending upon the type of service provided, and they require consideration of the levels of care documented for multiple sections of the medical record, including:

- Chief complaint
- History of present illness
- Past medical history
- Family history

■ Social history

■ Review of systems

■ Physical examination

— By 1995 *Documentation Guidelines*

— By 1997 *Documentation Guidelines*

■ Amount of data reviewed

■ Complexity of data reviewed

■ Number of impressions

■ Number of treatment options

■ Amount of data ordered

■ Complexity of data ordered

■ Risk of presenting problem(s)

■ Risk of diagnostic procedures ordered

■ Risk of management options selected

■ Nature of presenting problem(s)

■ Counseling

■ Coordination of care

■ Time

Because of the complexity of calculations and analysis of coding examples required, the reality is that most physicians simply do not attempt the overwhelming computational task of calculating a code at the point of service. Instead, they simply make a "best guess" when submitting their E/M codes; the consequences of this approach are shown by the results of the Office of Inspector General audit.

The objective of Practical E/M is to establish a methodology that is capable of surmounting this challenge by making coding and documentation a natural and integral component of providing patients' medical care. To accomplish this goal, it is necessary to use both an innovative approach and supportive compliance tools.

COMPLIANCE CONSEQUENCES OF THE CHALLENGES FACED IN IMPLEMENTING EFFECTIVE E/M RECORDS IN PRACTICE

The conventional methodology physicians are taught as a means of achieving proper E/M coding and documentation has resulted in a significant number of their charts having insufficient documentation to justify the E/M codes they submit for the care they provide. In 1997, the Health and Human Services Office of Inspector General conducted a Medicare audit of physician E/M coding that assessed the accuracy of this coding approach. The audit demonstrated that 55% of charts had insufficient documentation to support the E/M code submitted. It also showed that another 21% of charts were coded incorrectly for the documentation. Thus, in total, 76% of charts had a mismatch between coding and documentation.[1]

Therefore, only 24% of the charts reviewed were coded at a level consistent with documentation of the services provided. This is only slightly better than the 20% matching that we would expect by random chance. In addition, this audit revealed that another 12% of those "acceptable" charts, in which the documentation did support the submitted E/M code, actually lacked sufficient medical necessity to warrant the level of code submitted. More recent Medicare audits continue to show similar rates of noncompliant coding and documentation.

> **Selective Audits of High-Level E/M Services**
>
> Auditing outcomes appear to be even worse when applied selectively to claims submitted with either level 4 or level 5 E/M codes. In 1998, a third-party administrative company asked me to evaluate a series of medical records, which consisted exclusively of claims submitted with level 4 and level 5 services. Using software programmed with all the rules governing E/M coding and *Documentation Guidelines for Evaluation and Management Services,*[2] an audit of 210 charts produced a 99% audit failure rate. Only two charts actually had documentation sufficient to support the submitted code. Also disturbing was the finding that two-thirds of the downcoded charts had documentation that supported only level 1 or level 2 care.

ECONOMIC CONSEQUENCES OF NONCOMPLIANT CODING AND DOCUMENTATION

From an economic perspective for medical practices, one cannot overemphasize the importance of appropriate and compliant E/M coding and documentation. Potential financial catastrophe can result from either overcoding or undercoding.

Overcoding is identified in conventional E/M audits in one of two circumstances:

1. Documentation in the medical record for the three key components is not sufficient to support the submitted E/M code (a finding that is also reasonably identified as "undocumenting", the terminology preferred by *Practical E/M* to describe this situation).

2. The NPP is not of sufficient severity to warrant the level of care indicated by the submitted E/M code.

The negative financial consequences of overcoding begin with audits that reclaim "overpayments." A more severe economic penalty may occur if a Medicare audit imposes additional penalties for "fraud" in cases where the reviewer determines that the physician has a consistent pattern of excessive overcoding; this can occur regardless of whether the overcoding was intentional or unintentional. There is the additional danger that Medicare or private insurers may extrapolate a finite financial penalty from a limited audit and apply it to the entire population of E/M claims that have been filed over a prolonged time period. All of these penalties have the potential to be financially devastating to a medical practice.

Undercoding generally occurs among physicians who fear financial penalties from potential audits and simply have no confidence in the accuracy of their documentation and coding. These physicians therefore code all E/M services at low levels out of fear of being audited or investigated for fraud, even when they have performed and documented more comprehensive levels of care, and the NPP is of moderate to high severity. The negative financial consequence of undercoding is that it results in insufficient reimbursement for the services physicians have appropriately rendered and documented.

While the most frequent type of undercoding occurs when a physician submits an E/M code at a level lower than indicated by the documentation in the medical record, a common variation occurs when both the coding and the documentation are at lower levels than would be appropriate for the severity of the patients' illnesses. This is most easily appreciated in the following example:

> A physician evaluates a patient who has a severe medical problem, and the NPP would warrant level 5 care on the basis of CPT descriptors for NPP and the Clinical Examples in Appendix C. The physician documents level 3 care in the patient's medical record and also submits a level 3 E/M code.

This record would pass a *conventional* E/M audit that only compared the code submitted with the amount of care documented. However, a *Practical E/M* audit, conducted by a physician's own office (discussed in Chapter 25), would classify this example as a case of both undercoding and underdocumentation (or, in some cases, provision of less care than warranted by the NPP). In other words, this patient's condition warranted level 5 care, but the selected code was only at level 3 (undercoding), and the amount of care documented (and/or provided) was only appropriate for level 3 (underdocumentation for the level of care warranted by the NPP). Not only would this type of undercoding result in negative economic consequences for the physician, but the reduced level of documentation (and possibly reduced level of care) could also have negative consequences for the patient.

Analysis of Financial Impact of Undercoding

When evaluated with the Medicare fee schedule, undercoding outpatient initial visits by one code level costs the physician between $30 and $40 per visit. Undercoding outpatient established visits by one code level costs the physician between $15 and $37 per visit. Undercoding outpatient consultation visits by one code level costs the physician between $30 and $50 per visit. Applying these values, if a physician were to care for 5000 office patients per year, undercoding by one level per visit would translate to a loss of between $150,000 and $200,000 per year of gross income.

This is income that would otherwise be earned by implementing an approach that, for each visit, first identifies the appropriate level of care (and code) based on the NPP, and then ensures that the medical care provided and the documentation recorded both support the E/M code selected.

There are similar negative financial consequences for undercoding all the other E/M services, such as inpatient and emergency department services.

The goals of implementing the techniques of Practical E/M are to enable physicians to select *all* of their E/M codes appropriately, according to the NPP(s) for each patient encounter, and to ensure that they generate medical records that demonstrate they have provided the levels of care indicated by these codes.

ANALYZING CONVENTIONAL E/M AUDITS

We can learn important lessons from studying how auditors evaluate medical records for E/M coding. We will define these as "conventional" audits. The objective of conventional audits is simply to determine whether the amount of documentation in the medical record is sufficient to support the submitted E/M code.

As daunting as the coding challenge is for physicians, in most instances performing these conventional audits is actually a straightforward and efficient task for auditors. Using auditing prompts derived directly from CPT coding principles and the *Documentation Guidelines*, an auditor examines each section of the medical record to determine whether the documentation is sufficient to support the level of care required by the code the physician submitted. If each section has sufficient documentation, the chart passes audit. If the documentation is not sufficient, the auditor will determine the level of care that has actually been documented and indicate the revised E/M code level supported by that care.

It is instructive to appreciate how readily an auditor can evaluate a medical record and determine whether the documentation supports the submitted E/M code. An experienced auditor generally can make a reasonable assessment whether a given medical record's documentation is likely to support, or fail to support, the submit-

TABLE 4.1

Auditors' Chart Analysis Approach for an Initial Visit

Section of Medical Record	Vulnerable Areas and Maximum Code Levels (Initial Outpatient Visit Only)
1. History	1. Review of systems (ROS)
	— Absence of documented ROS limits the final E/M code to level 1 (ie, 99201)
	— Documented review of one system limits the final E/M code to level 2 (ie, 99202)
	— Documented review of 2–9 systems limits the final E/M code to level 3 (ie, 99203)
	2. Past (medical), family, and social history (PFSH)
	— Absence of documented PFSH limits the final E/M code to level 2 (ie, 99202)
	— Documented review of only 1 or 2 elements of PFSH limits the final E/M code to level 3 (ie, 99203)
	3. History of present illness (HPI)
	— Documented review of only 1–3 elements of HPI limits the final E/M code to level 2 (ie, 99202)
	— Documentation that fails to include a "chronological description of the development of the patient's present illness"[3] may limit the final E/M code to level 2 (ie, 99202) or result in a determination that a valid HPI has not been performed
2. Examination	4. Physical examination for 1997 *Documentation Guidelines* (1995 guidelines are subjective)
	— Documented examination of 1–5 defined elements limits the final E/M code to level 1 (ie, 99201)
	— Documented examination of 6–11 defined elements (except 6–8 elements for ophthalmology and psychiatry) limits the final E/M code to level 2 (ie, 99202)
	— Documented examination that has at least 12 defined elements but is less than comprehensive limits the final E/M code to level 3 (ie, 99203)
	5. Number of diagnoses or treatment options
3. Medical Decision Making	— In many cases documented MDM of only one diagnosis and one treatment option may limit the final E/M code to level 2 (ie, 99202)

ted E/M code shortly after starting a review. The auditor first screens the record to determine whether the physician has selected the correct type of service (for outpatient services, this includes checking for initial visit vs consultation vs established visit). Following this, the auditor looks at the most common "vulnerable areas" of the medical record, where physicians' documentation commonly falls short of the requirements for the submitted code level.

Table 4.1 summarizes the selected "vulnerable areas" and an auditor's analysis of outpatient initial visit services. The maximum code levels applicable for the various levels of care are derived directly from CPT coding principles and the *Documentation Guidelines*. It is important to be aware that Table 4.1 applies only to initial outpatient services. Each type of service requires different correlations between the amounts of documentation and the code levels supported.

> **The Ease of E/M Auditing**
>
> As reported in the preface to this book, my E/M training in 1991 led me to conclude, "For auditors, it will be effective, accurate, and easy." I reached this conclusion because the approach we were taught for auditing seemed practical: start with the submitted E/M code and then evaluate the adequacy of documentation to determine whether it was sufficient to justify that code.
>
> My other conclusion, which has also proven to be correct, was that the inverse approach as taught to physicians (ie, start with the documentation and then attempt to derive an E/M code) involves too many rules, too many calculations, and too much effort to achieve accurate coding by physicians who are trying to provide quality care to patients in a busy medical practice.

The "auditing prompts" shown in Table 4.1 facilitate the auditors' task. Similarly, Practical E/M methodology uses "documentation prompts" in the intelligent medical record (IMR) to guide physicians in performing and documenting the services they provide in a manner that is sufficient to support the medically indicated level of care. As discussed previously, this level of care should reflect the severity of each patient's illnesses (as represented by the NPP).

SUMMARY

The limitations of the conventional approach to E/M coding and documentation are underscored by the results of E/M chart audits, which demonstrate a high frequency of inconsistency among codes submitted, the levels of care documented in the medical record, and/or the level of care warranted by the severity of the patient's medical problems. Overcoding (or underdocumenting) exposes physicians to significant potential financial peril in the event of audits, and undercoding guarantees significant loss of income that should have been earned.

Auditors use a different method for evaluating documentation and coding than the one currently taught to physicians. They begin a review with a specific level of care, based on the E/M code the physician has submitted. They then review the medical record to determine whether the documentation demonstrates that this *level of care* has been performed. Their approach demonstrates two advantages that can be adapted to help physicians achieve compliance. First, auditors start their review with a known level of care, specifically the one submitted as an E/M code by the physician. Second, they work with compliant *auditing prompts*, which assist them in determining how much care must be documented to meet the requirements of the E/M code. Practical E/M applies these two auditing concepts to creating tools that help clinicians achieve compliant coding and documentation.

References

1.   Martin S. OIG: $20 billion in improper payments. *American Medical News.* May 11, 1998.

2.   Health Care Financing Administration. *Documentation Guidelines for Evaluation and Management Services.* Chicago, IL: American Medical Association; 1997.

3.   American Medical Association. *Current Procedural Terminology CPT® 2008, Professional Edition.* Chicago, IL: American Medical Association; 2007.

PART 2

Practical E/M Approach to Patient Care

Selected reading for an abridged overview of Practical E/M and the effective use of intelligent medical records (IMR):

Features of the E/M Coding System and the *Documentation Guidelines*

FUNDAMENTALS OF E/M CODING

Since 1992, the first section of the Current Procedural Terminology (CPT®) codebook has been devoted to "Evaluation and Management (E/M) Services." The beginning of this portion of the CPT codebook presents specific "Guidelines," which "define items that are necessary to appropriately interpret and report the procedures and services contained in [this] section."[1] It presents eight pages of the terminology used in E/M coding and documentation as well as detailed instructions for selecting the type of service and the levels of complexity for each category of medical care. The remainder of the E/M section includes 27 pages that present descriptions (which CPT labels "descriptors") of each type of service and each code level within that type of service. Finally, for further clarification, each edition of the CPT codebook has also included an appendix devoted to "clinical examples" of E/M services. All of this information is essential to understanding E/M compliance, and it provides the starting point for the Practical E/M approach to coding and documentation presented in this book.

Although minor refinements have occurred during the last 14 years, the overview provided in the "Evaluation and Management Services Guidelines" has not changed meaningfully since it first appeared in the CPT codebook in 1992. This section of the CPT codebook explains how E/M services are broken down into categories, defines commonly used E/M terminology, refers to the clinical examples presented in Appendix C, and provides "instructions for selecting a level of E/M service."[1]

Many of the E/M terms listed in the E/M guidelines are defined in *qualitative* (or subjective) rather than *quantitative* (or objective) descriptions. For example, the history of present illness (HPI) is characterized as "a chronological description of the development of the patient's present illness from the first sign and/or symptom to the present"[1] that includes review of as many as eight specific characteristics of the patient's symptoms. When the section discusses how to determine the extent of history obtained, it refers to either a "brief history of present illness" or an "extended history of present illness" without specifying how many of these characteristics must be recorded in order to classify the documentation as either a brief history or an extended history. The need to more specifically *quantify* these terms subsequently led to the development of the *Documentation Guidelines for Evaluation and Management Services.*[2]

Classification of E/M Services

At the start of the E/M chapter in the CPT codebook, the subsection "Classification of Evaluation and Management Services" explains that the coding portion of the chapter is divided into categories and subcategories of E/M services, each of which represents a different type of service. Table 1 in the Evaluation and Management Services Guidelines in *CPT® 2008* lists 41 categories and subcategories of E/M services and the code range for each.[1] Up to five levels of care are defined for each subcategory. These levels are based on the amount of care provided as defined by the three key components (medical history, examination, and medical decision making [MDM]) and the nature of presenting problem (NPP) usually associated with that level of care.

Definitions of Commonly Used Terms

The subsection entitled "Definitions of Commonly Used Terms" presents the vocabulary of E/M coding. Some of the terminology parallels traditional medical school teaching of the medical history and physical. Other descriptions, however, introduce nontraditional concepts and definitions that clinicians must understand, and be able to apply, to utilize the E/M system correctly.

Traditional Terms

It is useful to review first the terminology that mirrors the traditional approach to physical diagnosis, which is taught to physicians during their medical education. All these definitions are listed in *CPT® 2008*.[1]

- **Chief complaint (CC)** is a brief statement, generally in the patient's own words, conveying the primary reason (or reasons) for the patient's visit to the physician. This may be documented in the medical record as a symptom, a sign (such as fever or rash), or even a diagnosis.

Analysis

For cases in which the patient provides a diagnosis as the reason for the visit, it is usually relevant for the physician to ask the patient (and document) how he or she came to that diagnosis. That is, was this reported diagnosis made by another physician (and on what basis was it made), by an acquaintance, or by the patient himself or herself?

- **History of present illness (HPI)** is a chronological description of the course of the patient's presenting illness, from its initial onset to the time of the visit. This includes assessment (and documentation) of one or more of eight specific elements that are reported by the patient in relation to the presenting problem(s): (1) duration, (2) location, (3) quality, (4) severity, (5) timing, (6) context, (7) modifying factors, and (8) associated signs and symptoms.

Beneficial Features of the Eight HPI Elements

Medical records that fail to address the eight specific elements commonly convey nothing more than a chronology of physician visits, proposed diagnoses, and treatments. While this information is certainly relevant to the course of the patient's illness, such histories lack much of the pertinent information helpful to guide an accurate diagnosis and subsequent treatment.

An example of this chronological type of history might read, "The patient saw Dr X 6 weeks ago and was diagnosed with sinusitis. He was treated with medication A but did not improve. Dr X then changed treatment to medication B, and the patient improved only slightly. He then went to Dr Y, who prescribed medications C and D, but the patient still does not feel well."

---

continued

Although we know Dr X's diagnosis and a list of the patient's various treatments, we know nothing about the patient's symptoms, their duration, timing, progression, location, or severity. Consequently, this type of history provides no basis for judging the reasonableness of Dr X's diagnosis, which may or may not be valid. It also offers insufficient information for the physicians to formulate a reasonable differential diagnosis that considers potential contributory and/or alternative disease processes.

Because a history such as this one, based solely on a chronology of medical care, documents so few of the eight elements of HPI, it usually fails to meet CPT coding or audit criteria for higher levels of care. More important, this type of history is ineffective for optimal medical diagnosis and fails to meet the "quality care" criterion we should apply in obtaining and recording a medical history.

As a side note on the medical education aspect of the history and physical, one of my daughters informs me that while her medical school training includes many of these eight elements as part of the HPI, it does not advise that they are "crucial" elements of the medical record, nor does it relate them to E/M documentation and coding compliance. She feels that "as a result, some of these details can easily become lost to the students' medical history process."

On the other hand, a HPI description that includes only these elements but lacks a description of the chronological development of these features presents only an "extended" chief complaint, with no true medical history at all.

- **Past (medical) history** reviews the patient's significant past medical experiences, such as major illnesses and injuries, operations, hospitalizations, allergies (including allergy to medications), and current medications (including over-the-counter preparations, vitamins, herbal treatments, and supplements). When appropriate to the patient's age or health status, this section may also include information about immunization status and dietary habits.

- **Family history** is an inquiry into medical events in the patient's closely related family, including parents, siblings, and offspring. This may include current health status, cause of death, hereditary illness, and/or other specific disease processes (particularly those related to the patient's own medical problems as identified in the HPI, past medical history, and review of systems [ROS]).

- **Social history** is a set of questions appropriate to the patient's current age and life status. For adults, this may include the patient's use of tobacco, alcohol, and drugs. It may also investigate occupational history, marital history, sexual history, and/or educational history. When the patient is a child, the social history may include questions related to issues such as family setting, school status, behavior problems, and exposure to secondhand smoke.

- **Review of systems (ROS)** documents the patient's responses to a series of questions about possible medical symptoms and/or signs he or she might currently have or might previously have experienced. As described in the CPT codebook, the ROS provides baseline data about other aspects of the patient's health in addition to the concerns reported in the HPI. This more complete picture of the patient's health status may also assist the physician in correctly identifying the patient's primary presenting illness. The CPT coding system identifies 14 organ systems as elements of the review of systems. These include the following:
  - Constitutional (eg, fever, weight loss)
  - Eyes
  - Ears, nose, mouth, and throat
  - Cardiovascular
  - Respiratory
  - Gastrointestinal

- Genitourinary
- Musculoskeletal
- Integumentary
- Neurological
- Psychiatric
- Endocrine
- Hematologic/lymphatic
- Allergic/immunologic

Nontraditional Terms and/or Definitions

Other CPT coding system terminology introduces E/M concepts and/or definitions that are not presented during the traditional approach to physical diagnosis taught in medical school.

- **New and established patients** are defined with precise criteria related to both the time between visits and the relationship between the examining physician and other physicians who have seen the patient previously. Specifically, the CPT coding system provides that "a new patient is one who has not received any professional services from the physician or another physician of the same specialty who belongs to the same group practice, within the past three years."[1] Conversely, an established patient is defined as someone who has received such services within the previous 3 years. Of note, the CPT coding system further specifies that when one physician is covering for another who is not in the same group, the covering physician still must classify the encounter as it would have been classified by the patient's own physician.

- **Counseling** is defined as a discussion of medical care with the patient and/or family. The physician provides information related to the current and future care of the patient, which may include (but is not limited to) diagnoses, treatments, prognosis, risks, and management options.

- **Nature of presenting problem (NPP)** refers to the reason for the medical encounter, regardless of whether a diagnosis is established at the conclusion of the encounter. The CPT coding system describes five levels of severity for NPP: minimal, minor or self-limited, low, moderate, and high. The descriptions of the degree of severity are based on the natural history of a given medical problem if left untreated, plus its relative risks of morbidity, mortality, and/or significant functional impairment.

- **Levels of E/M services** are the coding categories physicians use to report the amount of E/M care they provide. Most types of service have either three or five defined levels of care, and the characteristics of the levels differ for each different type of service. There are 41 defined types of service, and the care and documentation requirements to report a level 3, for example, vary for each type of service. This lack of uniformity among requirements creates a frequently overwhelming challenge for physicians when they are instructed to apply the large number of rules needed to accurately identify E/M code levels for each different type of service.

The CPT codebook descriptions of the levels of care for a given type of service depend on seven possible components of the medical care. We concentrate on the four components that the CPT coding system considers for every E/M encounter. These include the medical history, the physical examination, MDM, and NPP. While the E/M section of the CPT codebook labels the first three factors as "key components" and the fourth as a "contributory factor," the text description indicates that all four are involved with every patient encounter (for most types of service); most important, every type of service that considers the three key components also includes consideration of the NPP. Two additional contributory factors, counseling and coordination of care, are listed in the CPT codebook, which states "it is not required that these services be provided at every patient encounter."[1] The seventh component in E/M care is *time*. The CPT codebook indicates that the amount of time required for patient care is not used in defining the level of E/M services. Rather, typical amounts of time are included only "to assist physicians in selecting the most appropriate level of E/M services."[1]

Assessment of the NPP

The exclusion of NPP from classification as one of the "key components" has frequently led (or, rather, has misled) physicians, coders, auditors, and consultants to consider only the history, physical examination, and MDM in selecting E/M codes. However, a critical insight to coordinating coding and documentation with medical necessity and appropriate quality care is to treat the NPP as a *mandatory* fourth factor in every type of service that incorporates the three key components. In fact, Practical E/M methodology establishes the NPP as the second factor to be considered (after the medical history) during these patient encounters, since it is essential for aligning the level of care warranted with the severity of each patient's medical problem(s).

Instructions for Selecting a Level of E/M Service

This set of instructions describes the traditional method that the CPT Editorial Panel recommends that physicians use to determine appropriate codes for each E/M service provided to patients. This process begins by identifying the type of service appropriate for each encounter. Currently there are 40 different types of service, plus a nonspecific category labeled "other E/M service." Each of these categories is described and defined in the E/M section of the CPT codebook.[1]

The focus for most of the discussion that follows in this chapter is on office outpatient visits, as they are the most commonly used services, and because they feature the greatest opportunity for staff and patients to participate in the care process. These visits encompass three of the CPT coding system's type of service categories: new outpatient visit, established outpatient visit, and office consultation.

After identifying the type of service, physicians are advised to review the "descriptors" provided in the CPT codebook for each level of care for the identified type of service. Next, a comprehensive list of instructions is provided for determining the extent of medical history obtained, the extent of examination performed, and the complexity of MDM involved in each specific patient encounter. Determining the complexity of MDM requires using an additional set of internal computations that involve the relationships among multiple subfactors. This assessment of the three key components is followed by instructions for mathematical calculations that must be used to correctly identify the level of care provided (ie, the E/M code) for the specific type of service.[1]

This section of instructions on selecting the level of an E/M service concludes with a caveat about the role of *time* in determining the level of care provided for a given type of service. It specifies that time may be considered the controlling factor for determining the level of E/M care (only) "when counseling and/or coordination of care dominates (more than 50%) the physician/patient and/or family encounter."[1] The CPT coding system instructions make the additional distinction that, for the purposes of choosing a code, the total time of an encounter is restricted to the "face-to-face" time spent during outpatient services, but involves the total time related to patient care for inpatient visits.

Consideration of Instructions for Code Selection

The approach of the E/M instruction section of the CPT codebook describes physicians first providing and documenting their medical care, and then subsequently calculating an E/M code that accurately reports the level of care delivered. In these instructions, there is no further consideration of NPP as a determinative factor in selecting the appropriate CPT code. However, we can gain significant additional insight into an alternative CPT approach to the coding process from Appendix C, Clinical Examples, in the CPT codebook.

The Clinical Examples Appendix and Selecting a Level of E/M Service

The E/M Services Guidelines advise that "clinical examples of the codes for E/M services are provided to assist physicians in understanding the meaning of the descriptors and selecting the correct code."[1] In *CPT® 2008*, the Clinical Examples section appears in Appendix C. This section suggests an effective alternative approach to E/M coding and documentation. It begins with the statement that the "clinical examples, when used with the E/M descriptors contained in the full text of *CPT*, provide a comprehensive and powerful tool for physicians to report the services provided to their patients."[1] The examples in the body of the appendix are clinical vignettes, composed of medical information that briefly (in about 30 words) summarizes only a few elements of each patient's medical history and/or diagnosis. Analyzing the content of the examples leads to the conclusion that each clinical summary clearly presents the nature of the patient's presenting problem(s). Therefore, the clinical examples in this appendix confirm that the CPT coding system associates the NPP for each patient encounter with an appropriate level of E/M care.

Relating the Clinical Examples to the NPP

The clinical examples presented in Appendix C of the CPT codebook offer only a brief summary of the pertinent clinical aspects of a patient's history of the presenting problem. As an illustration, a vignette listed as an example of E/M code 99203 states "initial office visit for a 50-year-old female with dyspepsia and nausea."[1] Clearly, this brief summary does not include significant medical history and has no information about the physical examination or MDM. Rather, this is a synopsis of the features of the history that enable a physician to surmise the potential severity of the patient's problems (ie, the NPP). In most cases, this information is reasonably available at the conclusion of the medical history, which is precisely the point of care where Practical E/M advises physicians to make an initial assessment of the severity of the NPP and link it to the appropriate level of care warranted by the patient's medical illness(es).

Completing the puzzle is the fact that the CPT codebook description of code 99203 indicates that "usually, the presenting problem(s) are of *moderate* severity."[1] Therefore, the examples provided for CPT code 99203 represent clinical situations that medical specialty societies have designated as having moderate NPP. Similar relationships can be derived for all the different types of service and levels of care illustrated by the clinical examples in Appendix C.

The introduction to Appendix C concludes with the important insight that "simply because the patient's complaints, symptoms, or diagnoses match those of a particular clinical example, does not automatically assign that patient encounter to that particular level of service. The three key components (history, examination, and medical decision making) must be met and documented in the medical record to report a particular level of service."[1]

In summary, the Clinical Examples appendix illustrates the integral relationship of the NPP with the level of care that should be performed, documented, and coded. Practical E/M methodology adopts this integrated approach, recommending that physicians apply their clinical judgment to assess the level of severity of the NPP after obtaining the patient's history. The CPT guidelines match the level of NPP chosen for each visit with an appropriate level of care for each of the three key components. Practical E/M advises physicians to use this technique (with the guidance of intelligent medical record tools) to ensure that their care, documentation, and coding are all consistent with the level of care warranted by the severity of the patient's illnesses.

FUNDAMENTALS OF THE *DOCUMENTATION GUIDELINES*

The 1995 and 1997 editions of the *Documentation Guidelines for Evaluation and Management Services* introduced objective (numerical) values for many of the CPT coding system's subjective E/M descriptors. Table 5.1 summarizes how the two editions of the *Documentation Guidelines* refine these descriptors and provide numerical values for most of the qualitative (non-numerical) aspects of the three key components of E/M coding. Those values that were not quantified are indicated by an asterisk (*) in the table.

T A B L E 5.1

Documentation Guidelines Quantification of E/M Coding Descriptors

E/M Category	Qualitative CPT Description	*Documentation Guidelines* Values
History of present illness (HPI)	Brief HPI	A chronological description with 1 to 3 of the 8 elements of the HPI
	Extended HPI	• A chronological description with at least 4 elements of the HPI • Status of at least 3 chronic or inactive conditions
Past/family/social history (PFSH)	Pertinent PFSH	At least 1 specific item from any of these 3 history areas (ie, PH, FH, or SH)
	Complete PFSH Initial visit	• At least 1 specific item from all 3 history areas for initial visit • At least 1 specific item from at least 2 history areas for emergency department encounters
	Complete PFSH Established vist	• May review and update previous PFSH information. Documented by noting date of previous PFSH and either describing any changes since that date, or noting there have been no changes since that date • At least 1 item from 2 history areas
	Complete PFSH Established visit in hospital or nursing facility	No PFSH information required
Review of systems (ROS)	Problem pertinent	Positive and pertinent negative responses for the 1 system related to the patient's HPI
	Extended ROS	Positive and pertinent negative responses for 2 to 9 of the 14 systems
	Complete ROS	Must review at least 10 of the 14 systems. Must document all systems with positive and pertinent negative responses (then it is permissible to document that all other systems [ie, those without pertinent responses] are negative)

continued

TABLE 5.1

Documentation Guidelines Quantification of E/M Coding Descriptors, cont'd.

E/M Category	Qualitative CPT Description	*Documentation Guidelines* Values
Review of systems (ROS) *(continued)*	Complete ROS Established visit	May review and update previous ROS information. Documented by noting date of previous ROS and either describing any changes since that date, or noting there has been no change since that date
Physical examination	Problem focused	1–5 elements of the examination template
	Extended problem focused	At least 6 elements of the examination template
	Detailed	• General examination template: performance and documentation of at least 2 elements for at least 6 organ systems or at least 12 elements in total • Most single organ system examination templates: performance and documentation of at least 12 elements • "Eyes" and "Psychiatric" examination templates: performance and documentation of at least 9 elements
	Comprehensive	• General examination template: perform all and document at least 2 elements for at least 9 organ systems • All single organ system examination templates: perform all elements and document every element in shaded boxes and at least 1 element in each unshaded box
Medical decision making (MDM): number of diagnoses*	Minimal, limited, multiple, extensive	• For a problem with established diagnosis, record should indicate status (eg, resolved, improved, persisting, worsening, etc) • For a problem without an established diagnosis, may list the differential diagnoses (eg, possible, probable, or rule out)
Medical decision making (MDM): Number of management options*	Minimal, limited, multiple, extensive	• Document initiation of, or changes in, treatments • Treatments include medications, therapies, nursing instructions, patient instructions, referrals
Medical decision making (MDM): Number and/or complexity of data to be reviewed*	Minimal (or none), limited, moderate, extensive	• Includes ordering tests; reviewing tests; discussion with physicians interpreting tests; and direct review and interpretation of actual images, tracings, specimens • Includes decision to obtain old records; review and documentation of actual findings in old records (note: not sufficient to just document "reviewed old records")
Medical decision making (MDM): Risk of significant complications, morbidity, and/or mortality	Minimal, low, moderate, high Also includes underlying diseases but only when they increase the risk and/or complexity of MDM	Provides a "table of risk" that: • Subdivides risk into 3 categories: — Risk of presenting problem(s) — Risk of diagnostic procedures ordered — Risk of management options selected • Provides examples, in each category, of minimal, low, moderate, high risk • Provides that "the highest level of risk in any one category . . . determines the overall risk"[1]

* These descriptors were not quantified by the *Documentation Guidelines.*

The *Documentation Guidelines* also further emphasize the importance of the NPP, underscoring our conclusion that the NPP warrants equal weight in E/M coding with the medical history, physical examination, and MDM. For example, in describing documentation of the medical history, the *Documentation Guidelines* advise that "the extent of history of the present illness, review of systems, and past, family, and/or social history that is obtained and documented is dependent upon clinical judgment and the *nature of the presenting problem(s)* [italics added for emphasis]."[2] It provides similar advice concerning the type and content of the physical examination, recommending that these "are based upon clinical judgment, the patient's history, and the *nature of the presenting problem(s)* [italics added for emphasis]."[2]

The *Documentation Guidelines* also present a set of "general principles" of medical record documentation. These principles introduce several requirements that elaborate upon the CPT coding system. Two of these general principles warrant further discussion because they address an issue that challenges a significant percentage of physicians:

- The medical record should be complete and legible.
- The documentation of each patient encounter should include date and legible identity of the observer[1] (ie, the notes must be legibly signed).

In other words, *illegibility is noncompliant*! Of even greater importance, illegible records interfere with quality of care. When a medical record is shared with other health care personnel who are unable to read the important medical information, and/or when a clinician is unable to read his or her own documentation, patient care may be compromised. Furthermore, in the event of an E/M audit, a reviewer may simply downcode an illegible chart because he or she is only able to give credit for care that is legibly documented. The final problem related to legibility is that illegible notes create serious obstacles in the event of medicolegal litigation.

The Case of the Miraculously Transcribed Scrawl

On one occasion, I served as an expert defense witness in a legal case against a physician who had died after the case had been filed, but 3 years before the case came to trial. His charts were completely illegible. Fortunately, the physician had realized this problem, and he had dictated every medical note in the patient's medical record, word for word, before his death. Only this dictated record allowed us to win a verdict in the case.

EVOLVING TO PRACTICAL E/M: CONNECTING THE *DOCUMENTATION GUIDELINES* WITH LEVELS OF CARE

Let's examine how correlating the objective measures from the *Documentation Guidelines* with the CPT codebook's descriptors for E/M code levels can assist physicians with E/M documentation and coding compliance matched to the physician's assessment of the medically indicated level of care. The commonly used initial visit office code 99203 provides a good illustration of how this correlation is able to guide physicians' care and documentation. As shown in Table 5.2, the quantitative values provided by the *Documentation Guidelines* clearly communicate the amount of care physicians must meet (or exceed) to justify the submission of a code for this level of service.

T A B L E   5.2

Analysis of Documentation Requirements for E/M Code 99203

CPT Code	E/M Qualitative Analysis	*Documentation Guidelines* **Quantitative Analysis**
99203:* Outpatient initial visit, level 3	Detailed history — Chief complaint — Extended HPI — Pertinent PFSH — Extended ROS	CC Chronology with 4 or more HPI Elements One or more elements from 1 of 3 areas Responses for at least 2 of 14 systems
	Moderate-severity NPP	
	Detailed examination	Document at least 12 examination elements[†]
	Low-complexity MDM	Two of the following: — Limited number of diagnoses or treatment options — Limited amount/complexity of data — Low risk of complications/morbidity

* For 99203, all three key components and NPP must meet or exceed these requirements.

[†] For general examination and most single–organ system exams. Eye and psychiatric examinations require documentation of at least 9 examination elements.

Reflecting Practical E/M methodology, the table shows that the physician should first consider the NPP immediately after obtaining the medical history, to establish the level of care warranted for the patient's illness. As will be shown in the remaining chapters of Part 2, Part 3, and Part 4, IMR's "documentation prompts" present the physician with this critical information to provide guidance during patient care for all types of service that involve the key components and the NPP.

SUBJECTIVE MEASURES IN E/M CODING

The numerical values introduced by the *Documentation Guidelines* to the history and examination sections have created objective guidelines that can assist both physicians and auditors. For example, an extended HPI is defined as one that requires documentation of a chronological description of the course of the illness that includes at least four of the eight elements defined for the present illness. A degree of subjectivity remains in the various subsections of MDM and also in the NPP. For example, neither the CPT codebook nor the *Documentation Guidelines* explain how many diagnoses must be documented to be considered "limited," "multiple," or "extensive." To provide physicians with a complete methodology that can be both practical and reliable, we need to present and accept reasonable objective descriptions for these remaining subjective elements, in a manner that is compatible with the approach used in the *Documentation Guidelines*.

Medical Decision Making

While certain components of MDM require some degree of subjectivity (eg, complexity of data reviewed), the subsections for "*number* of possible diagnoses and/or the *number* of management options" and "*amount* of data to be reviewed" seem most naturally to call for a *number* to quantify their level of complexity. Instead, the

CPT coding system and the *Documentation Guidelines* leave us only with the subjective assessments of minimal, limited, multiple (or moderate), and extensive. Practical E/M offers a recommendation to resolve this issue in Chapter 16.

Nature of Presenting Problem

The NPP is the CPT coding system's E/M vehicle for evaluating medical necessity. For most types of service, the E/M descriptors report an appropriate degree of severity of NPP for each level of care. For example, in the outpatient initial visit type of service, descriptors for level 3 (ie, code 99203) include the recommendation that "usually the presenting problem(s) are of moderate severity."[1]

The CPT codebook offers only qualitative (ie, subjective) descriptions of this critical factor (NPP), as shown in Table 5.3, and there is no further clarification in the *Documentation Guidelines*. Fortunately, however, the Clinical Examples appendix in the CPT codebook provides enough examples to guide physicians to make reasonable interpretations of the subjective descriptors. The CPT codebook's definitions of the five levels of NPP, listed in Table 5.3, are based on the natural course and prognosis of disease(s), risks of morbidity or mortality without treatment, and probability of prolonged functional impairment.

T A B L E 5.3

Descriptions for NPP

Minimal	A problem that may not require the presence of the physician, but service is provided under the physician's supervision
Self-limited or minor	A problem that runs a definite and prescribed course, is transient in nature, and is not likely to permanently alter health status OR has a good prognosis with management/compliance
Low severity	A problem where the risk of morbidity without treatment is low; there is little to no risk of mortality without treatment; full recovery without functional impairment is expected
Moderate severity	A problem where the risk of morbidity without treatment is moderate; there is moderate risk of mortality without treatment; uncertain prognosis OR increased probability of prolonged functional impairment
High severity	A problem where the risk of morbidity without treatment is high to extreme; there is moderate to high risk of mortality without treatment OR increased probability of severe, prolonged functional impairment

Source: American Medical Association. *Current Procedural Terminology,CPT® 2008*. Chicago, IL: American Medical Association, 2007.

The E/M section of the CPT codebook introduces one additional consideration related to NPP that we need to address to successfully guide the documentation process. The descriptors for the various levels of E/M care present two additional "mid-level" classifications of NPP: low to moderate severity (eg, CPT code 99213) and moderate to high severity (eg, CPT code 99204). However, the CPT codebook does not provide a precise definition of either of these classifications. Specifically, does "moderate to high" mean that (1) the NPP lies partway between "moderate severity" and "high severity," or does it indicate that (2) the severity may run the entire range from moderate to high (ie, including both moderate severity and high severity)?

On the basis of the way these mid-level classifications are used in the CPT codebook to describe levels of care, plus multiple discussions with medical directors, coders, and physicians, we recommend following the first interpretation of low to moderate and moderate to high. Therefore, we believe it would be beneficial to add two additional definitions for NPP (see Table 5.4).

TABLE 5.4

Proposed Definitions for Mid-Level NPP Descriptions*

Low to moderate severity	A problem where the risk of morbidity without treatment is low to moderate; there is low to moderate risk of mortality without treatment; full recovery without functional impairment is expected in most cases, with low probability of prolonged functional impairment
Moderate to high severity	A problem where the risk of morbidity without treatment is moderate to high; there is moderate risk of mortality without treatment; uncertain prognosis OR increased probability of prolonged functional impairment

* These descriptions are offered as logical suggestions. They do not appear in the CPT codebook.

VIGNETTES AND E/M CODING

Vignettes have been an integral part of E/M coding since its inception. These brief "thumbnail" narratives appear as the "clinical examples" in Appendix C of the CPT codebook.

It is noteworthy that the Centers for Medicare and Medicaid Services (CMS) and the American Medical Association (AMA) have made several efforts to broaden the concept of vignettes and allow them to dominate the principles of documentation and coding. The most recent attempt took place in 2002 to 2003. After considerable effort, reviewing physicians and specialty societies concluded that a vignette-based system did not offer the consistent results required for it to become a reliable basis for E/M coding. The main reason for this unreliability is inherent in the nature of the vignette: it describes only the severity of a patient's condition (ie, the NPP), without describing the amount of cognitive work that should be appropriately performed by the physician in evaluating and caring for a given condition.

SUMMARY

The definitions and descriptions in the CPT codebook and the *Documentation Guidelines* provide the compliance rules that create the foundation of Practical E/M and IMRs. The vignettes in the Clinical Examples appendix of the CPT codebook fill the important role of relating E/M code levels to medical necessity (as represented in E/M by the NPP). The Clinical Examples appendix also presents the important concept that the NPP guides the level of care and documentation warranted by the severity of the patient's illness. This integration of medical judgment about the severity of patient illness with appropriate levels of care, documentation, and coding should transform our impression of E/M coding. It is not simply a reporting mechanism for purposes of reimbursement. Rather, as presented in Practical E/M, it can offer a logical and coordinated medically based methodology to promote quality of care and caring for our patients.

References

1.   American Medical Association. *Current Procedural Terminology CPT® 2008.* Chicago, IL: American Medical Association; 2007.

2.   Health Care Financing Administration. *Documentation Guidelines for Evaluation and Management Services.* Chicago, IL: American Medical Association; 1997.

Practical E/M Methodology

As discussed in previous chapters, the conventional approach to the evaluation and management (E/M) coding system presents physicians with a number of obstacles to achieving compliant coding and documentation. As a result, physicians generally perceive the processes of documenting the medical record, accurately selecting E/M codes, and compliance as being disconnected from, and unrelated to, the provision of patient care.

Practical E/M methodology circumvents this issue by building the medical record on a foundation of compliance. It accomplishes this by incorporating all of the documentation requirements and coding rules into the intelligent medical record (IMR) framework. Since these compliance principles are based on the diagnostic process physicians are trained to follow to promote optimal patient care, as detailed in the *Bates' Guide* textbook,[1] the structure of this framework is familiar to every physician. For this reason, this structure is also able to provide effective guidance during each step of the care process, reflecting quality care principles at the same time that it ensures compliant documentation. Individual physicians can further customize this basic structure to incorporate specialty-specific features and personal practice preferences.

Using this approach enables physicians to provide high-quality, comprehensive medical care at the same time that it ensures documentation and coding compliance. Physicians generally adapt to this process quite easily, because the *Documentation Guidelines for Evaluation and Management Services*[2] actually follow the principles of the comprehensive history and physical (H&P) taught early in medical school, with only a limited number of additional considerations. Although the demands for volume and speed during residency training and practice have often "trained" many components of comprehensive care out of physicians' standard H&P, the IMR streamlines the process so that this level of care can be incorporated and accomplished efficiently.

TWO UNDERLYING PRINCIPLES OF COMPLIANCE

Medical chart reviews by Medicare carriers include two fundamental principles that are essential to understanding Medicare's compliance requirements. One of these principles is found in the Centers for Medicare and Medicaid Services (CMS) *Carriers Manual*,[3] and the other is incorporated in the Social Security Act.[4] They therefore function as integral components of the CMS protocol. Most commercial insurance companies have also adopted these concepts as rules.

The first CMS compliance concept is based on Section 7103.1(I) of the CMS *Carriers Manual*. This rule indicates that if medical care is not documented in the medical record, it is treated as if it had not been performed. This principle underscores the necessity of having thorough written documentation for all portions of the patient encounter in the medical record.

Templates That Guarantee Documentation

The concept of "it wasn't documented, therefore it wasn't done" is the reason we reject charting techniques that present patients with "selection lists." These preprinted lists of symptoms or illnesses, with instructions that ask the patient to circle any items on the list that pertain to them, result in significant errors in the documentation process. This is because the items on the list that are not circled are deemed not to be documented. That is, the absence of documentation is not the equivalent of *documenting* a negative response. No one (including auditors or even a physician seeing the patient) can tell from reading the chart whether the patient considered or understood the items that were not circled. Auditors effectively view the failure in documentation that results from the use of selection lists as a failure to perform a service. In other words, "if it wasn't documented, it wasn't done." For this reason, we recommend using only forms that require a "yes" or "no" response to every inquiry, and therefore result in documentation of the patient's response for every question asked (see Figure 10.1 in Chapter 10).

A second fundamental CMS compliance concept that deals with the important area of medical necessity is found in Section 1862 of the Social Security Act.[4] This section prohibits payment for services that are not "medically necessary." This concept has had a broad impact on determining which services the Medicare and Medicaid programs cover and which they do not. For example, until recently, preventive care services were defined as "not medically necessary." Additional Congressional legislation was required to authorize coverage for such services as screening colonoscopy, mammography, and prostate-specific antigen testing.

The principle of medical necessity also applies to E/M coding. For coding to be considered compliant, the level of care (ie, E/M code) submitted must not exceed the level of care that is medically necessary. For example, extensive documentation of the medical history and physical examination during any follow-up visit could be coded (on the basis of the key components alone) to a level 4 or level 5 established patient visit. However, if a patient presents with only a minor problem, such as a small rash or recent mild upper respiratory tract infection, it is compliant for the physician to submit an E/M code for a low level of care. A low-level code would be required in this case regardless of the amount of care documented for the three key components, because only a low level of care is "medically necessary" for the minor nature of the illness.

Examining the Other Side of the Two Underlying Principles of Compliance

While compliance experts emphasize the precautionary aspects of these two underlying principles of compliance, Practical E/M also emphasizes the powerful advantage of incorporating these principles into the compliant documentation guidance of IMRs. This approach enables the IMR forms to utilize the "flip side" of these principles, which assist and protect physicians because:

1) **When the care has been *documented*, then it has been performed.** This principle provides assurance that accurately documented IMR charts will pass audit, because every aspect of medical history, physical examination, medical decision making, and medical necessity (based on the nature of presenting problem, or NPP) have been documented. Under these circumstances, as long as the documentation is reasonable for the patient's medical condition, auditors are required to give credit for the care performed.

2) **When the care is medically necessary, then payment is mandatory.** When the physician has *documented* an appropriate assessment of the NPP, which is also supported by documentation of levels of risk and all the key components, auditors must acknowledge the medical necessity of the care provided, eliminating the potential for misinterpreta-

---

continued

tion of medical necessity and resultant downcoding. *(Note: documenting levels of medical necessity that are clearly "unreasonable" would lead to a high risk of an auditor identifying "false claims," with accompanying severe penalties.)*

It is also noteworthy that coders and auditors appreciate having this documentation present in medical records. Its presence eliminates their discomfort with being required to make a judgment about subjective medical issues related to risk and medical necessity.

ROLE OF MEDICAL NECESSITY IN COMPLIANT E/M CODING

The NPP is the component of E/M coding that is used to evaluate medical necessity. The Current Procedural Terminology (CPT®) coding system formally defines five levels of severity for NPP (listed in Table 5.3 in Chapter 5) and lists two additional levels ("low-to-moderate" and "moderate-to-high") among the descriptors for various types of service. The CPT codebook describes how each level of NPP relates to the natural course of the illness, the severity of the illness, the risks of morbidity and/or mortality without treatment, and the probability of prolonged functional impairment. The CPT codebook also indicates that the NPP should be factored into all types of E/M service where it is cited as one of the descriptors.[5] Because each code level for the types of service that consider the three key components also include a measure of NPP, this pivotal feature should be included in the documentation requirements for each of these types of services. The CPT descriptors demonstrate that higher levels of E/M care are consistently associated with higher severity of NPP. This correlation confirms that NPP is an indicator of the complexity of care warranted by the severity of an illness.

THE SIGNIFICANCE OF CLINICAL EXAMPLES IN THE CPT CODING SYSTEM

The relationship between NPP (medical necessity) and appropriate E/M code levels is well illustrated by the clinical examples in Appendix C of the CPT codebook.[5] As noted in Chapter 5, Practical E/M shares the methodology suggested in that section, which matches the severity of NPP to an appropriate level of care (ie, E/M code) and also requires that the indicated amount of medical history, physical exam, and medical decision making (MDM) for that level of care "must be met [ie, provided] and documented in the medical record to report a particular level of service."[5]

INTERRELATING NPP, CODING, CARE, AND DOCUMENTATION

It is helpful to invoke a nonmedical analogy to explain how medical necessity (or NPP) can be incorporated into the patient care process to establish an appropriate code level, which then guides the minimum amount of care that is medically indicated for that code. The pole vault track-and-field event provides a metaphor for how we use NPP to ensure compliance in the coding and documentation process. In the pole vault event, the bar is set at a measured height, which in turn sets the level of achievement that will be credited to the athlete for successfully clearing the bar on his or her jump. When we are watching the Olympics, in the preliminary portion of the pole vault event, the bar is set at a relatively low level. For example, let's assume they start with the height of the bar set at 15 feet above the ground. What happens if an athlete jumps only 13 feet? He does not get credit for jumping 15 feet even though that is the height of the bar. On the other hand, even if he jumps 6 feet over the bar he will only get credit for clearing the measured height of 15 feet. The athlete is allowed to jump as high over the bar as he can, but the amount of credit given is limited by the height of the bar.

In E/M coding, NPP (or medical necessity) sets the height of the bar. That is, it tells us the maximum level of care warranted by the severity of the patient's illnesses at the time of the visit. Because this is the case, it makes sense that the physician should first consider the NPP after completing the medical history, when he or she has sufficient information to form an initial judgment of the severity of the patient's illness. In Practical E/M, this approach is effective and reasonable, because the design of the IMR guides the documentation of a comprehensive medical history at the beginning of every visit. This allows the physician to assess the severity of the patient's illnesses (ie, NPP), and then follow the IMR's documentation prompts for NPP (which convey the CPT codebook E/M descriptors) to identify the indicated level of care, just as illustrated in the Clinical Examples appendix in the CPT codebook. Appendix A of this book presents illustrative examples of abbreviated medical records for a series of patients with upper airway symptoms whose warranted level of care (ie, the height of the pole vault bar) rises, level by level, with progressively more severe symptoms and more ominous examination findings.

Practical E/M methodology requires that the medical record provide documentation prompts to assist the physician in correctly accomplishing these two critical tasks. First, the prompts convey the CPT coding system's definitions for severity of NPP. Then, they relate the selected severity of NPP to the indicated level of care, based on the CPT descriptors of NPP for the type of service under consideration. (Sample documentation prompts for the NPP are illustrated in Figures 14.1 and 14.2.)

The definitions and code levels reported in the documentation prompt provide the CPT guidelines for the physician to set the height of the bar (ie, appropriate level of care) on the basis of the NPP. Once the physician has selected an appropriate level of care, the IMR provides additional prompts that indicate the amount of care and documentation required by CPT guidelines to "jump over the bar." For example, for an initial outpatient visit, if a patient's NPP warrants the 99203 level of E/M care, the documentation prompts will indicate the number of elements of history of present illness (four or more), number of elements of examination (12 or more), level of severity of risk (at least low), and number of diagnoses or treatment options (two or more) that must be documented in the medical record to justify using this code.

No Documentation Prompts Needed for PFSH or ROS

In the IMR, no coding prompts are required for the past, family, and social history (PFSH) and review of systems (ROS). Instead, IMR design ensures documentation of a *complete* PFSH and ROS for every visit, and this level of care is sufficient to support any coding level warranted by the NPP, including level 5 care, for any type of service. In other words, the amount of care documented is sufficient to "clear the bar" for these elements at any height set by the NPP.

If a physician were unable to include sufficient elements of one of the key components to meet the level of care set by the NPP, then he or she would have to reduce the code submitted to the code level that was actually documented. For example, if a patient's NPP warranted the 99203 level of E/M care, but the physician only performed and documented a problem-focused examination (eg, by documenting only one to five elements of examination instead of 12 or more), then the documentation would only support submitting a 99201 level, as shown by the documentation prompt. However, the IMR is designed to prevent this situation from occurring, because the documentation prompts guide the physician to provide and document the amount of care warranted by the NPP (in this case, 12 or more elements of the examination for most exam templates).

Conversely, what happens if a physician elects to provide and document a greater amount of care than the minimum warranted by the NPP? Just as in the pole vault, the maximum E/M code level that can be submitted is limited by the NPP. In the previous example, if a physician documented both history and examination at the comprehensive level and the MDM as detailed, coding based on the three key components alone could support 99204. However, the physician should submit only code 99203, because that is the maximum level of care warranted by the nature of the patient's illness. Essentially, if a physician chooses to (or happens to) clear the height of the coding bar by providing more than the minimal care requirements for that code, compliance dictates that the code level remains limited by the height of the bar (ie, the NPP).

Types of Service Requiring Only Two of Three Key Components

The CPT coding system descriptors state that only two of the three key components must meet or exceed the warranted level of care for established patient visits. That is, to clear the bar, the physician must provide and document sufficient care in only two of these sections. In the Practical E/M approach, a comprehensive history will be documented for every visit, so either the exam section or the MDM section will require documentation of a sufficient level of care to support the code indicated by the NPP.

PRACTICAL E/M METHODOLOGY AND QUALITY CARE

The recommended approach of considering the NPP and selecting the appropriate level of care after obtaining the complete medical history ensures compatibility of the care provided with the level of medical necessity, the documentation of that care, and the E/M code selected; it thereby systematizes the process of achieving compliance.

Summary of Practical E/M Methodology

1) Select the correct type of service.
2) Perform and document a comprehensive medical history (for every visit).
3) Make a preliminary determination of the NPP and identify the level of E/M care medically indicated for this severity of illness (according to CPT guidelines).
4) Perform and document the physical examination, guided by documentation prompts for the medically indicated level of care.
5) Document *all* elements of MDM, guided by documentation prompts for the medically indicated level of care.
6) Document the final impression of an appropriate level of the NPP at the conclusion of medical record documentation.

Role of the *Documentation Guidelines* in Ensuring Appropriate Levels of Examination

Practical E/M philosophy is based on providing the level of care medically indicated by the severity of illness, not "care for coding's sake." When the CPT codebook code descriptions show us, for example, that a detailed or comprehensive examination is

continued

medically appropriate for the level of care warranted by the NPP, the *Documentation Guidelines* serve two critical roles in helping the physician meet these indications.

First, the guidelines show the physician the precise criteria approved by our own medical societies for defining the extent of examination (or history) appropriate to meet the CPT coding system standards for "problem-focused, expanded problem-focused, detailed, and comprehensive" levels of care. The IMR's documentation prompts assist the physician by providing this exact information on the medical record; physicians do not have to look up (or memorize) the requirements for each type of service while they are providing care.

Second, the specified examination guidelines can be incorporated into the medical record template, with check boxes for rapid documentation of whether each defined area examined was found to be normal or abnormal. With this design element, an IMR eliminates physicians' greatest obstacle to performing the indicated levels of examination, which has been the time required to document the *normal* findings. In addition to promoting efficient documentation, this type of medical record structure also serves as a reminder to physicians of the specific examination components that their own medical specialty societies determined are warranted for that care.

These features of the *Documentation Guidelines* are so helpful to physicians, in both providing and documenting medically indicated history and examination, that Practical E/M advocates creating similar quantitative *Documentation Guidelines* for several components of MDM. Chapters 16 and 27 consider this concept in greater detail.

The IMR design, including the documentation prompts, facilitates efficiency and productivity. It is also appropriate to consider the effectiveness of this overall system in terms of quality of care, to verify that matching the amount of care with the severity of the medical condition provides an optimal process for working with patients, as well as a reliable tool for ensuring E/M compliance.

We can illustrate the medical care benefits of this approach by analyzing a hypothetical episode in which we (or a family member) are on the other side of the white coat, as a patient. In this circumstance, we expect our physician to assess the probable and potential seriousness of the condition (ie, the NPP) and then provide an appropriate level of care.

For example, if we need medical attention for a small laceration, and a good medical history confirms that we are otherwise healthy, then *problem-focused* or *expanded problem-focused* care is both appropriate and acceptable. Our physician should inquire about the circumstances of the injury, assess the advisability of a tetanus shot or antibiotics, clean the wound, and apply the bandages that are indicated. This situation does not medically indicate the need for a comprehensive examination or complex MDM. In fact, as an otherwise healthy patient, we would likely find it inappropriate and a waste of our time if the physician made such an effort for this type of problem.

On the other hand, if we were to visit an appropriate specialist because we had 6 weeks of intermittent but progressively increasing chest or abdominal distress, we would expect and require a comprehensive medical history to provide the basis for a sophisticated and directed differential diagnosis, including all possible related conditions. We would expect and require a complete examination to be sure that all areas are assessed, that no potential etiology is overlooked, and to discover whether a minor problem (e.g., muscle strain or chondritis) might be the cause of the symptoms. And finally, we would absolutely require complex MDM, to ensure that our physician can rule out (or detect, if present) any potentially serious or life-threatening problems.

As physicians we want the level of care we receive for ourselves and our families to be appropriate for the NPP. Clearly, this is also the approach we want to provide for our own patients. This is the philosophy presented in the Clinical Examples appendix in the CPT codebook, and it is precisely the core philosophy advocated by Practical E/M.

The Value of the Comprehensive Medical History

The quality-of-care standard endorses choosing and providing an appropriate level of medical care on the basis of the severity of the patient's NPP. It also supports Practical E/M's recommendation for providing the physician with a comprehensive history for every patient visit. As we see later in this book, IMR design makes this an efficient process for the physician by guiding the patient to document this information for initial patient visits and by having the physician's medical staff document this information for established patient visits.

Let's consider how this policy can increase quality of care in our first example, that of the patient with the small laceration, who may report feeling otherwise healthy. Despite the patient's initial statement that he feels otherwise healthy, the encounter also provides the physician with an opportunity to obtain a "health profile" to make sure the patient has no other medical problems. For example, perhaps further inquiry reveals he has had recent shortness of breath, or an unintended 30-pound weight loss, or sweating at night. These symptoms clearly allow the physician to begin investigating what could be more significant health problems, either directly or by referral to an appropriate clinician. It is noteworthy that under such circumstances, this increased severity of illness raises the NPP, and with the appropriately increased extent of physical exam and MDM, the E/M code reaches a higher level. As an added benefit, the physician's reimbursement increases appropriately for the increased quality and level of care.

PRECAUTION REGARDING PARTIAL USE OF IMR FORMS OR THE USE OF PARTIAL IMR FORMS

The design of the IMR form results from a completely integrated and interdependent relationship among the four mandatory elements of E/M documentation and coding: medical history, physical examination, MDM, and NPP (the E/M system's measure of medical necessity). To ensure compliance in the context of quality medical care, proper utilization of these forms *requires* completion of all sections of the forms combined with the use of the Practical E/M methodology, which was summarized above.

Partial utilization of the forms, or insertion of a portion(s) of an IMR form into another medical record form, violates both the intent and the integrity of the Practical E/M approach. Such improper utilization carries with it significant risk of noncompliant documentation and coding. In the event of an external audit, this could result in significant financial penalties and/or the designation of "false claims," which could result in even greater financial loss.

SUMMARY

The clinical examples in the CPT codebook direct us to a coding and documentation paradigm that is practical and compliant and that facilitates appropriate medical care. Practical E/M advises a similar approach, with an additional recommendation for obtaining and documenting a comprehensive history at the beginning of every patient visit. This process proceeds from the medical history to judging the severity of the NPP. Documentation prompts, based on CPT coding system descriptors, help the physician identify the level of E/M care warranted by the severity of the patient's NPP. Once the physician has identified the appropriate level of care, he or she performs and documents this amount of care (or greater) for the physical examination and MDM.

This Practical E/M approach strictly follows the principles outlined in the CPT codebook, including the important insertion of the assessment of NPP into the patient care process. It also incorporates the E/M coding and documentation compliance process into the IMR's design. By ensuring E/M compliance, this methodology allows the physician to concentrate on the care he or she considers to be clinically indicated and in the patient's best interest. As a result, at the conclusion of the patient visit, the care and documentation will be compliant for the E/M code, which was appropriately selected on the basis of NPP.

The remainder of Part 2 examines each section of the medical record in detail, illustrating the design features of the IMR that facilitate not only compliance but also efficiency and quality.

References

1. Bickley LS, Szilagyi PG. *Bates' Guide to Physical Examination and History Taking.* 8th ed. Philadelphia, PA: Lippincott Williams & Wilkins; 2003:783-787.

2. Health Care Financing Administration. *Documentation Guidelines for Evaluation and Management Services.* Chicago, IL: American Medical Association; 1997.

3. Centers for Medicare and Medicaid Services. *Carriers Manual*, Section 7103.1(I). http://www.cms.hhs.gov/Manuals/PBM/itemdetail.asp?filterType=none&filter ByDID=99&sortByDID=1&sortOrder=ascending&itemID=CMS021921&intNum PerPage=10. Accessed July 14, 2008.

4. *The Social Security Act*, Section 1862. http://www.ssa.gov/OP_Home/ ssact/title18/1862.htm. Accessed June 27, 2008.

5. American Medical Association. *Current Procedural Terminology CPT® 2008.* Chicago, IL: American Medical Association; 2007.

The Practical E/M Experience for Physicians at the Point of Care

In this chapter we look at how using the Practical Evaluation and Management (E/M) methodology plus an intelligent medical record (IMR) facilitates accomplishing the tasks involved in a patient encounter, beginning with the physician picking up the medical chart and concluding with the end of the patient interaction. Demonstrating how an IMR can assist physicians at the point of care provides a constructive context for understanding the logic underlying its design and functionality.

Following this overview, the chapters in Part 3 delve into a more thorough explanation of the step-by-step process of creating and using an IMR. This includes examining the involvement of patients and medical staff in the processes of patient care and documentation, as well as explaining how individual physician preferences and requirements influence the development of an IMR.

A CLINICIAN'S OVERVIEW OF A PRACTICAL E/M ENCOUNTER

Arriving outside the examination room, the physician opens the patient's chart and reads the medical information that has already been entered on the IMR form by the patient and/or the staff for today's visit.

- For a new patient visit, this information will include the patient's chief complaint; past, family, and social history (PFSH); and review of systems (ROS). For physicians working with a nurse or medical technician, it is likely that a number of the background details of the presenting illness will also already be documented.

- For an established visit, the physician will first review the medical decision making (MDM) page of the previous visit to refresh his or her memory of the impressions, treatment recommendations, and test(s) ordered. In some cases, the MDM section may also contain notations the physician made to indicate future treatment plans, possible responses to specific laboratory test results, and/or alternative approaches if the patient does not respond to the initial therapy. The physician will also check any laboratory reports, x-ray reports, and communications noted in the chart since the last visit. After reviewing these previous records, the physician will turn to the IMR form for the current visit and review the information that the nurse or medical assistant will already have obtained from the patient and documented in the record. This information updates the status and any changes in the patient's PFSH and ROS since the last visit, lists the patient's current medications and allergies, and reports the chief complaint as well as some brief information about the status of the patient's present illness (history of present illness, or HPI).

After entering the room and greeting the patient, the physician will complete the medical history. This includes first obtaining and documenting further details for any of the significant positive responses in the PFSH and ROS, and then conducting a detailed inquiry into the symptoms related to the patient's present illness(es).

On the basis of this comprehensive medical history, the physician should be able to make a reasonable appraisal of the severity of the patient's active medical problems, formulate a preliminary differential diagnosis, and identify potential diagnostic tests and treatment options. With this assessment, and guided by the IMR's documentation prompts, the physician can mentally select a preliminary nature of presenting problem (NPP) and a level of care (E/M code) medically appropriate for the severity of these suspected medical conditions.

The physician will next perform the physical examination. The IMR's documentation prompts will guide the physician during the physical exam. This helps ensure that the exam is sufficiently comprehensive to be appropriate for the severity of the patient's illnesses, as indicated by the NPP. This extent of examination will also meet or exceed the Current Procedural Terminology (CPT®) coding system requirements for this medically indicated level of care. At this point, if the exam findings have ruled out the more serious potential problems in the differential diagnosis or, conversely, discovered more serious problems than expected, the physician will mentally adjust the severity of the NPP and the indicated level of care—and E/M code—down or up accordingly.

Turning to the last page of the IMR (see Appendix D, page 344), the physician will then complete the documentation of all sections of the MDM and the NPP. This process is once again guided by documentation prompts that ensure sufficient documentation of diagnostic options, treatment options, and severity of risk to adequately address the patient's medical problems and to meet the CPT coding system requirements for the medically indicated level of care. Any data reviewed and/or ordered will be recorded as well, although usually soley on the basis of reporting the care without particular consideration from a compliance perspective. In the impressions and treatment recommendations sections, the physician may also choose to write some guiding thoughts, to help in reorienting himself or herself (or other clinicians who might evaluate the patient) to the subtleties of the physician's impressions about the patient at the start of the next visit. This option is unrelated to compliance, but it often improves the physician's efficiency and the usefulness of the medical record, as well as the quality of care the physician is subsequently able to provide.

The medical portion of the encounter is now complete, and the medical record documentation is simultaneously finished as well. The physician completes the "superbill" form, indicating the E/M code selected during the patient care process and identifying the documented diagnoses, and he or she is ready to move to the next appointment.

The physician may have completed the documentation solely by writing or could have chosen to supplement written material with some dictation. (The adaptation of this scenario to IMR-compatible electronic records is discussed in Chapter 23.)

In either case, the E/M code has been selected appropriately for the NPP, thereby fulfilling the requirements of medical necessity. Furthermore, the guidance of the documentation prompts ensured that the physician's care and documentation met or exceeded the requirements for compliance as an integral part of the patient care process. Clinicians become comfortable with this Practical E/M routine very quickly, since the IMR assists and facilitates their provision of care at every step and because this approach duplicates, with far greater efficiency, the optimal diagnostic process they practiced at the outset of their training.

Assessment of the Efficiency of This Practical E/M Visit

A patient visit that makes use of the Practical E/M approach generally requires about the same amount of time the physician usually needs to complete his or her patient care. There is generally significantly less physician time required for obtaining and documenting the medical history and far less time documenting the normal findings on physical examination. Some of this time saving is spent on the more thorough documentation of MDM, but the time to document thoughts about future care generally pays significant dividends in efficiency and quality during subsequent visits.

Having described the big picture, we can take an analytical look at Practical E/M methodology and then discuss in greater depth how the IMR can help physicians implement this approach during patient care. We then examine each step of the process in its own individual chapter to provide greater detail about the exact process.

IMPACT OF USING IMR FORMS ON PATIENT CARE

A natural question at this point is, "How much physician time do IMR forms require?" On the basis of the experience of many physicians, it is reasonable to say that physicians currently using written records will spend approximately the same amount of time per patient. However, they will immediately notice a significant improvement in the quality of their medical record documentation, compliance, and often their productivity as well.

There should be a more dramatic positive impact on efficiency for physicians who currently employ transcription as the primary format for their medical records. In their current system, these physicians generally dictate the entire history and physical for each patient visit. In most cases, this approach requires that physicians find time between patients or at the end of their work day to dictate their records. Integrating IMR paper templates as the documentation for much of the medical history, normal findings on the physical examination, and portions of the MDM significantly reduces the amount of dictation required, thereby decreasing both their time spent and their transcription costs.

Looking at the Change in My Own Record Keeping With IMR

Before the introduction of E/M coding and documentation guidelines, my own medical records as an otolaryngologist were documented on 5 × 7-inch index cards. For new patients, I preprinted some fill-in-the-blank sections for past medical history and social history on the index cards. Otherwise, I documented all care as free-text narrative. There was usually insufficient time for me to personally elicit and document a thorough family history or ROS as free text, so this feature of medical history had commonly been compromised in my records and my care. Established-patient visit charts generally contained history information only for the HPI, unless the patient volunteered information about an unrelated health problem. My physical examination and MDM were extensive and well documented, although they did not specifically document the risk and NPP components that are included as part of Practical E/M.

At the end of most visits, initial patient care filled up an average of one and one-half sides of a single index card. Established patient care documentation occupied less than one side of a similar card. Under these circumstances, I provided care for five to six patients per hour (one to two initial visits and the remainder as established patients). My honest self-assessment was that I was providing the best care possible.

---

continued

Following the introduction of Practical E/M methodology and IMR templates, this is what happened:

■ I continued to provide care for five to six patients per hour, with the same mix of initial and established patient visits.

■ Each initial visit had documentation on four sides of 8.5 × 11-inch paper.

■ Each established visit had documentation on one and a half sides of 8.5 × 11-inch paper.

■ The amount of medical history information obtained and documented had vastly increased (through the patient-completed check box and short-answer templates for initial visits and the PFSH and ROS updates for established patient visits).

■ Because of the increased history, I knew much more about my patients, including the identification of additional medical problems both related and unrelated to otolaryngology.

■ I actually had more time (and more leisurely time) to talk with my patients.

■ My honest self-assessment is that *now* I really was providing the best care possible.

■ My enjoyment of the practice of medicine definitely increased. The significant expansion of medical history information snapped me out of the routine of problem-focused care. It *automatically* brought with it the ability to appreciate each patient's entire health care picture and to evaluate and work with more than just the patient's presenting problem. This included addressing related ear, nose, and throat problems, getting referrals for unrelated health concerns, and addressing issues of good health and disease prevention. It's a reminder of the idealistic reasons why motivated students go to medical school in the first place.

■ Patient appreciation increased.

And all of this happened in the same amount of time I used to spend on problem-focused care and completing documentation on a 5 × 7-inch index card.

SUMMARY

The bottom line on delivering medical care using Practical E/M is that it feels similar to the comprehensive level of care physicians learned and practiced early in medical school. However, it takes the physician far less time, because an optimally designed IMR provides the physician with a predocumented complete PFSH and ROS, plus the ability to rapidly document normal exam findings and data. Although there are "new" documentation elements required by the CPT coding system (the NPP, the three elements of risk, and complexity of data), the IMR design enables the physician to enter this information efficiently.

The added benefits of Practical E/M derive from (1) data entry efficiency, (2) consideration of the severity of medical illness as a factor in determining the indicated extent of care, and (3) integrating the elements of compliance into the structure of the medical record and the patient care process. At the conclusion of each visit, the physician will have achieved compliant E/M coding and documentation, as well as providing a level of care appropriately matched to the nature of the patient's illnesses.

PART 3

Designing and Using an Intelligent Medical Record

To assist with these chapters, readers are advised to print sample intelligent medical record (IMR) forms for outpatient initial and established-patient visits appropriate to their own specialty from Part 1 or Part 2 of the accompanying CD-ROM. Alternatively, readers using IMR forms that include the general multisystem examination can make a photocopy of the forms in Appendix D. Important guidance is also available by referring to the appropriate sections of Appendix E while reading each chapter.

Selected reading for an abridged overview of Practical E/M and the effective use of IMR:

Chapter 8
■ *Summary*

Chapter 9
■ *Entire chapter*

Chapter 10
■ *Entire chapter*

Chapter 11
■ *Entire chapter*

Chapter 12
■ *Entire chapter*

Chapter 13
- *Goals for Design: Introduction*
- *Goals for Design: Design for Compliance Requirements*
- *Using the HPI Section of the IMR*
- *Summary*

Chapter 14
- *Entire chapter*

Chapter 15
- *Entire chapter*

Chapter 16
- *Goals for Design: Introduction*
- *Goals for Design: Design for Compliance Requirements*
- *Using the MDM Section of the IMR*
- *Summary*

Chapter 17
- *Introduction*
- *Goals for Design: Design for Compliance Requirements*
- *Using the Time, Counseling, and Coordination of Care Section of the IMR*
- *Summary*

Chapter 18
- *Entire chapter*

Model for Analyzing Medical Record Designs

Analyzing the structure and function of each subsection of medical record systems in general, and of the intelligent medical record (IMR) in particular, calls for the introduction of new terminology and perspectives on several features of the medical record that have not been highlighted in the past. This terminology includes the different types of *interface* between the medical record and the person entering data, identification of the most appropriate *data entry personnel*, and the choice of *formats* available for entering data and for storing and retrieving data. Each of the design options available in each of these categories has features that may have positive and/or negative consequences for most of the criteria we use, including quality, efficiency, compliance, productivity, and usability of medical records. It will be helpful for physicians to appreciate these comparisons when considering the features of medical records they choose to meet their own practice needs and personal preferences.

EVALUATING THE MEDICAL RECORD INTERFACE

Interface describes the design features used to enter information into the medical record. Selecting an appropriate interface for each section of the record directly impacts the physician's efficiency, the potential for data input by nonphysicians, and the usefulness of the information entered.

There are two distinct medical record interface categories, each with significantly different strengths and weaknesses. In a *graphic* interface, the person entering information selects appropriate responses from a preprinted list or, alternatively, enters short written responses and descriptions in response to specific questions. The graphic interface works best for sections of the history and physical (H&P) where significant information can be entered accurately by using brief objective descriptions (eg, "yes or no," "normal or abnormal") or concise complete answers. The *narrative* interface is a series of blank lines that permits recording of detailed free-text information. This interface accepts written, dictated, or typed data entry. This structure is optimal for portions of the medical visit that call for analog (expository) documentation. The IMR is designed to provide the type of interface that is best suited to the information-gathering requirements of each subsection of the medical record.

Graphic Interface

The graphic interface includes several options for quickly documenting information that can be expressed in a concise manner. These include:

- check boxes to record yes/no or normal/abnormal responses,
- blank lines for concise answers, and
- selection lists to designate positive responses.

A selection list includes multiple preprinted choices and asks the person entering data to select one or more of the items on the list that applies in response to a specific question. It should be used only under circumstances that do not require documentation of negative responses. The IMR uses selection lists effectively for physician documentation in the medical decision making (MDM) section of the medical record. For example, this approach is appropriate for indicating which of the four levels of risk applies to a patient. It is not appropriate for documentation of patient history information, such as review of systems (ROS), which requires either a positive or a negative response.

Figure 8.1 illustrates a graphic interface that uses check boxes and blank lines. This design is particularly useful for portions of the medical record that enable patients to enter their own medical history information. This interface ensures compliance with the Current Procedural Terminology (CPT®) coding system because it requires the patient to review and document a yes or no answer to each question. The blank lines provide the ability for the patient or the physician to add further details when appropriate.

FIGURE 8.1

Past Medical History: Check Boxes (Sample Form). Example of instructions and use of check boxes and short answers for documentation of past medical illnesses (diagnoses). This is specifically designed with language that allows the questions to be easily understood and answered by a patient. The italicized response illustrates how a patient might complete the form.

Past Medical History:

1) Please check the "Yes" or "No" box to indicate if you have any of the following illnesses; for "Yes" answers, please explain

	Yes	No	
Diabetes (Circle: type I / type II)	☐	☒	_____
Hypertension (high blood press)	☐	☒	_____
Thyroid problems	☒	☐	_Low thyroid diagnosed in 2005_
Heart Disease/cholesterol probs	☐	☒	_____
Respiratory problems	☐	☒	_____
Bleeding disorder	☐	☒	_____

Graphic interfaces are extremely useful and efficient for the following sections of the medical record:

- Past medical history
- Family history
- Social history
- ROS
- Physical examination (normal findings)
- MDM (including data ordered, complexity of data, risks of illness/tests/treatments)
- Nature of presenting problem (NPP)

For portions of the MDM section, any of the three types of graphic interface may be used, as all of them satisfy the four primary criteria discussed in the previous section (compliance, efficiency, user friendliness, and quality care). The IMR uses only check-box and short-answer graphic interfaces in the medical history and physical exam sections of the record, as these allow for documentation of "negative" or "normal" responses.

Compliance and Quality Barriers to the Use of a Selection List Interface When Patients Enter Data

The *Documentation Guidelines* requirement for complete documentation of the past medical history is that "at least one specific item. . . must be documented."[1] The requirement for a complete ROS is documentation of at least one response (positive or

continued

negative) to questions related to each of 10 or more organ systems. However, if the patient has no positive responses, a selection list interface would not provide any documentation of a response, leaving only a preprinted list of illnesses or symptoms.

From the perspectives of both compliance and quality of care, there is no means of determining whether a patient even considered the questions. The physician cannot reliably determine the meaning of a nonresponse; the patient could have overlooked the question or even skipped entire portions of the template. For this reason, the IMR employs only check-box and short-answer graphic interface designs that require a documented "yes" or "no" response for portions of the medical record that permit direct patient documentation.

Narrative Interface

The narrative interface relies on free text for both obtaining and documenting complex medical information. A narrative approach is essential for thorough and in-depth recording of significant medical history and specific abnormal physical examination findings. This interface enables the documentation to reflect the way physicians delve, layer by layer, into the details of the medical history. In the process of obtaining a detailed history of the present illness (HPI), at each step in the dialogue the patient's response to an initial question or questions directs the content of the physician's next set of questions. This process leads to responses that are unique to each patient and each encounter, and this individualized information is optimally documented by means of a descriptive narrative. The restricted yes/no or linear vocabulary of the graphic interface is not suited to "tell a story" of each patient's unique medical history or to adequately describe the nuances that distinguish each patient's abnormal physical exam findings.

The narrative interface is optimal for several sections of the compliant medical record:

■ HPI,
■ positive responses to inquiries in the ROS (these function like "mini" HPIs),
■ positive findings on the physical examination, and
■ descriptive details and qualifying remarks for the "impressions" and "plans" sections in the MDM portion of the medical record.

Electronic Records and Narrative Sections of the Medical Record

To date, almost all electronic health records (EHRs)* I have reviewed have used *graphic* interfaces ("pick lists" or preformed macros) for the four portions of the medical record that I believe are best suited to a narrative approach. In nearly every case, this has resulted in one or both of the following problems:

1. A serious obstacle to physician usability, which results from the attempt to force information-rich narrative descriptions into the limited vocabulary of a graphic interface

2. A less informative record, which is due to entry of generalized descriptions that do not adequately portray the uniqueness of each patient's individualized H&P findings or convey the physician's judgment about the relative merit of each of the possible differential diagnoses and treatment options

---

*The two terms *electronic medical record (EMR)* and *electronic health record (EHR)* "are very commonly used interchangeably by different members of the medical and information technology communities to describe an electronic version of a physician's typical paper chart. . . . Some members of the information technology community have advocated differentiating these two terms. They prefer to use the phrase EMR to describe fully functional systems whose information remains local, within the medical practice. . . [the phrase] EHR is generally applied to systems that have additional features to permit interconnectivity and interoperability with programs and networks outside of a medical practice. . . [and] capability to 'other care-related activities directly or indirectly via interface – including evidence-based decision support, quality management, and outcomes reporting.'"[2] Because most currently available electronic records include these advanced capabilities, the term *EHR* will be used throughout the remainder of this book to collectively describe all electronic record systems that permit digital entry, storage, and retrieval of clinical information.

OPTIONS FOR DATA INPUT BY MEDICAL PERSONNEL AND PATIENTS

Another extremely successful tool to increase the efficiency with which data is entered into the medical record is to designate the optimal data entry person for each component of the medical record. The interface for each section must be designed to accommodate the data entry person's level of training and abilities, while retaining the features that ensure quality of care, compliance, and usability.

Is it necessary for the clinician to obtain and enter all of the information into the medical record personally? While each physician must ultimately decide this question for himself or herself, the *Documentation Guidelines* specify that "the ROS and PFSH [past, family, and social history] may be recorded by ancillary staff or on a form completed by the patient."[1] The effort to increase physician efficiency and productivity suggests examining each portion of the medical record to determine whether nonphysician input can be appropriate.

My analysis leads to the conclusion that the physician's expertise is essential for performing and documenting the following four elements of medical care:

- asking specialized questions related to symptomatic portions of the medical history (usually HPI and positive responses to symptoms in the ROS),
- determining the NPP (severity of patient illness),
- conducting a physical examination, and
- performing MDM, including determining the differential diagnosis and the medical plan (diagnostic studies and treatment options).

Achieving the most effective use of the physician's time with the patient calls for using physician extenders (such as nurses, assistants, and patients) to provide and/or enter as much of the other medical information into the chart as possible. In an IMR, carefully designed graphic interfaces facilitate having the patients themselves function as the data entry persons for the chief complaint, PFSH, and ROS. The physician then reviews this information and expands upon it when appropriate.

Physician Extenders

The term *extenders* includes personnel who perform medically related tasks and thereby "extend" the physician's ability to provide care. This term conventionally refers to members of the doctor's staff, such as physician assistants, nurse practitioners, nurses, medical technicians, laboratory technicians, radiology technicians, audiologists, and so on. Practical E/M expands the population of physician extenders to include the patients themselves when they perform the task of entering a portion of their medical histories into their medical records.

Past History, Family History, and Social History

The PFSH includes information about previous illnesses, previous operations, medications, allergies, personal habits, and family medical problems. Figure 8.1 illustrated a sample graphic interface design for the initial visit past medical history that prompts the patient to provide details about previous illnesses by using the checkbox and short-answer graphic interface. Similarly, straightforward short-answer questions allow patients to document their previous operations and current medications and allergies, as illustrated in Figures 8.2, 8.3, and 8.4.

FIGURE 8.2

History of Operations: Short Answer (Sample Form). Example of a "previous operations" section of the past medical history using a short-answer graphic interface.

> **2) Please list any operations (and dates) you have ever had (including tonsils & adenoids):**

FIGURE 8.3

Medications: Short Answer (Sample Form). Example of the "medications" section of the past medical history, using a short-answer graphic interface.

> **3) Please list any current medications (and amounts, times per day);**
> *(include aspirin, antacids, vitamins, hormone replacement, birth control, herbal supplements, OTC meds including sinus/allergy/weight loss meds):*

FIGURE 8.4

History of Allergies: Short Answer (Sample Form). Example of an "allergies" section of the past medical history using a short-answer graphic interface. The IMR addresses inhalant allergy information in the past medical illnesses section, as illustrated on page 1 of the initial visit form shown in Appendix D.

> List any ALLERGIES TO MEDICATIONS:

Patients can provide and document the pertinent information about their social history and family history by using a check-box interface similar to Figure 8.1. (Samples of these templates are illustrated in Chapter 10.)

Review of Systems

The ROS presents another opportunity for patients to enter their own medical information. The IMR provides a preprinted list of medical signs and symptoms, and patients check boxes to indicate whether they do or do not have each item on the list. Evaluation and management (E/M) coding compliance requirements mandate inquiry about one or more symptoms for at least 10 of the organ systems defined by the *Documentation Guidelines* to ensure sufficient information for a complete ROS.[1] From a quality care perspective, Practical E/M recommends a complete ROS for all initial patient visits, regardless of the severity of the patient's chief complaint. Using this approach provides physicians with extensive information about the patient's current general health status and may uncover additional health issues unrelated to the reason for the current visit.

On a practical note, many offices using patients as data entry personnel advise their new patients to arrive at the office 15 minutes prior to their scheduled appointment to complete these forms, as well as forms for their billing and insurance information. Physicians can also introduce alternative options, such as mailing or faxing forms to a patient before the visit, or even providing these forms via a secure Internet connection, where patients may either download the forms or directly enter responses into the forms on screen.

Documentation of the modified ROS and PFSH for *established* patients also lends itself to a short-answer graphic format, and therefore permits documentation to be performed by either the physician, his or her staff, or the patient. The options for this specialized portion of the medical record are detailed in Chapter 11.

Chief Complaint

The chief complaint is a short description, in the patient's own words, of the reason for his or her medical visit. With an appropriate question about the reason(s) for the visit, the patient can easily provide this information on a short-answer form.

History of Present Illness

Obtaining and documenting most of the data-rich and multitiered information of the HPI warrants a narrative approach, which is most appropriately completed by a clinician (ie, physician, nurse practitioner, or physician's assistant). However, patients' responses to inquiries about three of the eight elements of the HPI (designated by the *Documentation Guidelines*) generally result in sufficiently concise answers to offer the opportunity for a nurse or medical technician, when available, to obtain and document this information. Questions about (1) duration, (2) timing (eg, Is the symptom constant or intermittent? How long does it last?), and (3) severity elicit pertinent information that is helpful in investigating most disease processes. The physician reviews the patient responses documented by the staff and then obtain an appropriately detailed history that includes review of the time course of the patient's illness. These details will also include inquiry about one or more additional elements of the HPI.

MEDICAL RECORD FORMAT OPTIONS

I use the term *format* to describe the medium used for collecting and storing medical record information. The conventional presentation of medical record formats offers three classifications:

- Written records
- Transcription (aka dictation)
- Electronic

In addition to recognizing these formats, the concept of Practical E/M differentiates between the two functions of (1) data input and (2) data storage and retrieval when considering the relative benefits and drawbacks of different formats. This foreshadows my consideration of hybrid formats, which maximize the strengths and minimize the weaknesses of each format to achieve optimal IMR functionality that is tailored to each physician's personal preferences.

What Is *Functionality*?

Functionality is not a conventional dictionary term. However, its meaning is readily available on numerous Internet sites that describe software. The best definition I found was on the US Department of State Web site (http://usinfo.state.gov/products/pubs/intelprp/glossary.htm), which defines functionality as "that aspect of design that makes a product work better for its intended purpose, as opposed to making the product look better or to identifying its commercial source."

Written and Dictated Records

Traditionally, clinicians have entered data into their medical records either by writing on paper or by dictation. Each of these two modes of data entry has its own advantages and disadvantages. However, because the product of transcription is generally a paper document, the data storage and retrieval format used for both of these approaches is identical. Until recently, physicians have usually stored these paper records in the form of physical charts that are generally compiled into $9\frac{1}{2} \times 12$-inch manila folders that they keep in their offices.

Electronic Records

It is also critical when evaluating medical records to consider their evolution into an electronic environment. Currently, both the US Government and private industry are calling for increased use of EHRs. Potential benefits of EHRs include improved patient safety, improved quality of health care, and lower health system costs, all of which will hopefully be accomplished through the electronic sharing of medical information and the elimination of information errors. While investigators are devoting a great deal of effort to the potential uses for data that have been entered into EHRs, designers of these programs must also ensure that the data being entered is meaningful to practitioners, and that these systems have the ability to efficiently record high-quality individualized information that is accurate, meaningful, patient-specific, and visit-specific. If the EHR software systems do not facilitate and guarantee high standards for data entry, they face the same risk that threatens the quality of all information systems: "garbage in, garbage out."

FORMAT OPTIONS FOR DATA INPUT

Writing

Information input by writing offers multiple advantages. It is a highly efficient format for entering information in the graphic interface of an IMR, using check boxes and short answers to record responses. As noted earlier in this chapter, writing enhances efficiency by creating opportunities for information gathering and medical record data entry by extenders. Writing can also be a concise approach to documenting those portions of the medical record in which a narrative interface is optimal. For most physicians, writing during the patient encounter does not interfere with the flow of the visit or disrupt the patient-physician relationship. In addition, the written format is generally the least costly means of entering information into the medical record.

The one obvious potential drawback of directly writing information in the medical record is the issue of legibility (or, rather, the lack of legibility). In the *Documentation Guidelines*, the first general principle of medical record documentation states, "the medical record should be complete and legible."[1] That is, if the record is not legible, it fails the standard of compliance. It will also fail an audit on the basis of the fundamental principle that "if it wasn't documented, it wasn't done," because when auditors cannot read the physician's notes, they commonly conclude that either the information was not documented or the care was not performed at all. Therefore, to meet compliance requirements, physicians whose handwriting is illegible must chose from among several possible solutions: (1) use dictation for the narrative and MDM portions of the record, (2) perform data entry on a keyboard, or (3) practice and achieve legible handwriting.

Dictation/Transcription

The dictation format also works extremely well for reporting the narrative sections of the medical record: the HPI, details of positive ROS responses, abnormal examination findings, and the impressions and recommendations portions of MDM. Its greatest advantage, of course, is that transcription is always legible. For physicians who prefer dictation, IMR integrates transcription for these narrative sections of the medical record with written graphic forms that are utilized for the rest of the medical chart. When the physician is dictating each narrative section, Practical E/M suggests that he or she check the section's preprinted box labeled "see attached dictation." The dictated pages are placed in the chart with the paper forms when completed. This *hybrid* of written graphic templates and dictated narrative descriptions reduces both the cost and the amount of time required to complete dictation when compared to dictating the entire medical record.

Hybrid #1: Writing Plus Dictation

In 2008, most physicians are using some form of template for obtaining PFSH and ROS information from their patients. Some of those who dictate portions of their records also enter these written templates into their medical record without repeating the template information in their dictation. However, many physicians actually do a "complete" H&P dictation, repeating the written data into the recorder to transfer it from the forms into the transcription, thereby reducing efficiency and increasing their transcription costs.

It is important that the written component of the IMR hybrid include the graphic interface fields that document complexity of data ordered/reviewed, the three types of risk, and the NPP.

Keyboard Entry

The advent of computerized medical records has brought with it another format option for data entry: keyboard and/or "point-and-shoot" entry using mouse clicks. It is intriguing that from the earliest appearance of EHRs, two basic features have dominated the process used by these systems for data entry:

- For keyboard entry, the physician is required to be the data entry person.
- In most systems, there is little or no provision for the narrative entry of information. Instead, those sections of the medical record for which a narrative description is most appropriate are compiled only by some variation of a graphic format (ie, "pick list" or macros that contain preloaded clinical information).

These two typical features of most currently available EMRs and EHRs create obstacles to the quality of medical information entered into the medical record, to achieving optimal efficiency in entering that information, and to creating compliant medical documentation. The inability to enter complex narrative data as free text significantly limits the physician's ability to describe details that individualize a patient's symptoms, examination abnormalities, treatment plan and that uniquely distinguish one patient's illness and medical status from another's. Even those systems that have now introduced voice recognition software, which does permit the option of free-text dictation, have generally failed to eliminate the flawed options of pick lists and preloaded generic macros. The requirement that the physician enter all the data eliminates the efficiency gained in the written format of having the patient enter his or her own chief complaint, PFSH, and ROS on paper. Chapter 23 assesses these concerns and reviews options for addressing them.

FORMAT OPTIONS FOR DATA STORAGE AND RETRIEVAL

Paper Charts

The traditional data storage system is a "chart system" of paper records stored in folders. This includes copies of transcribed material, laboratory reports, radiology reports, and other correspondence. The theoretical advantages of data storage using paper are that the system is thought to be "low tech," easy to use, and low cost. In to-day's medical environment, we have come to appreciate that these presumed advantages often no longer hold true. Paper storage incurs significant costs for materials, storage space, shredding, and personnel time. It can also create a significant hassle factor in gaining convenient access to records at all times, particularly for larger groups and facilities with multiple medical personnel, testing departments, and/or offices in multiple locations. There is also the risk of paper information being mis-filed, separated from the record, or otherwise lost.

Electronic Scanned Images

A direct scanning system can now eliminate many of the costs of a paper storage system and provide ready access to patient records at any time. All of the paper images are scanned into a server that files the images into a "folder" for each patient. This type of system scans not only the paper from written or transcribed medical records, but also images of laboratory reports, x-ray reports, and correspondence.

Although the scanning approach reduces costs and allows convenient access to the medical record, it lacks the features of a true EHR for data mining and interconnectivity with laboratory and pharmacy software. In addition, the quality of the E/M documentation and coding in this approach is clearly limited to the quality of the paper record used.

Electronic Medical Records

True EMRs and EHRs have appeared over the last 20 years, and they are currently receiving increasing amounts of attention and development. Among the advantages these programs offer are ready access to patient records at all times, reduced filing costs, and search functionality (to collect and analyze data for evidence-based medicine studies). As EMRs evolve, these systems bring the promise of interoperability with other electronic systems, such as electronic ordering of pharmaceuticals, electronic ordering and reporting of laboratory tests, electronic ordering and reporting of radiology tests, and importing of quality standards and "best-practices" guidelines at the point of care.

However, most of the current EMRs also have several disadvantages. There are financial issues related to both startup and maintenance costs. These financial issues ultimately may be addressed either as costs come down over time through the development of less expensive in-office systems or by Internet-based application service provider (ASP) systems. Furthermore, the structure and functionality of current software systems have also created significant hurdles for physicians in attaining optimal documentation, efficiency, and usability at the point of care. Finally, most current EMR systems have fallen short of optimal documentation and coding compliance standards. Among their commonly encountered deficits in E/M coding compliance are:

1. a lack of documentation of NPP and multiple elements of the MDM,
2. templated (or pick-list–generated) history and exam elements that compile similar information for all patient encounters,

3. the inability to document consideration of alternative (ie, "rule out") diagnoses and management options, and

4. automated coding calculations based solely on the three key components without consideration of medical necessity.

Introducing the ASP

An application service provider (ASP) system is built upon an Internet-based server, or memory storage unit. The physician sends information to the ASP Internet site and gains access to the stored information by logging onto the secure ASP Web site with any computer. These systems have monthly access fees but save a significant portion of the costs incurred by the purchase of computer hardware, technical support for in-house systems, maintenance for both hardware and software, and software upgrades.

THE VALUE OF ADHERING TO PRACTICAL E/M PRINCIPLES WITH MEDICAL RECORDS IN ALL FORMATS

In their earliest clinical training, physicians learn the importance of accurate documentation in their medical records to reflect the care they perform. The *Documentation Guidelines* emphasizes that the quality of this documentation is an important element contributing to high quality care. The medical record facilitates:

- The ability of the physician and other health care professionals to evaluate and plan the patient's immediate treatment, and to monitor his/her health care over time;

- Communication and continuity of care among physicians and other health care professionals involved in the patient's care;

- Accurate and timely claims review and payment;

- Appropriate utilization review and quality of care evaluations; and

- Collection of data that may be useful for research and education"[1, p 2]

The primary characteristic of medical records in the first two-thirds of the 20th century was that physicians simply recorded their observations and recommendations on blank pieces of paper. However, the potential for the design of medical records to directly influence care appeared in 1968 with Dr Lawrence Weed's development of the "problem-oriented medical record" (POMR). This design concept not only added a new perspective to the part of the record we now call MDM but also affected the way physicians approached patient care.

During the 16 years since the introduction of the E/M coding system, the complexity of its documentation principles plus economic and time pressures from current payment systems have combined to compel the introduction of increasingly sophisticated medical record documentation tools. These include structured templates in paper records, preloaded word-processing templates and macros for transcription, and a variety of tools in EHRs (eg, copy-forward capabilities, copy-and-paste capabilities, drop-down menus, and macros with preloaded clinical information).

Accompanying these increasingly sophisticated medical record tools are significant influences on the patient care process, including both potential benefits and potential disruptions. Practical E/M presents a methodology based on physicians' optimal workflow, and it strives to present only tools that support and reinforce the medical diagnostic process.

Appendix E in this book underscores the importance of medical record designs that follow these principles, whether using data entry by writing, dictation, or electronic mechanisms. This appendix illustrates the potential dangers for compliance, quality, and liability concerns when physicians fail to follow these principles for documentation in each component of the medical record, regardless of whether the source of the problem is flawed medical record design or improper physician use of a compliant design. Readers are encouraged to refer to the appropriate portions of the tables in Appendix E while reading each chapter of Part 3 of *Practical E/M*.

SUMMARY

This chapter introduces terminology to define elements of medical record design, particularly as applied to the IMR. The descriptions of graphic and narrative interface demonstrate how the documentation requirements for each section of the medical record dictate the optimal structure for obtaining and entering the medical information. Identifying optimal data entry personnel for each subsection of the medical record increases physician efficiency and can influence the amount and quality of information obtained. The characteristics of the three different formats for medical records (writing, dictation, and electronic) must each be evaluated in terms of how they fulfill the separate functions of data entry and data storage/retrieval. The advantages of each of these formats can be maximized by combining them in hybrid solutions.

Reference

1. Health Care Financing Administration. *Documentation Guidelines for Evaluation and Management Services*. Chicago, IL: American Medical Association; 1997

2. Levinson S. Practical EHR: Electronic Record Solutions for Compliance and Quality Care. Chicago: American Medical Association, 2008, page 8–9.

Identifying the Correct Type of Service for Each Visit

The first step in compliant documentation and coding is identifying the correct type of evaluation and management (E/M) service that applies to each patient encounter. The Current Procedural Terminology (CPT®) codebook[1] labels these as "categories and subcategories" of service. The categories define a general feature of several types of care, such as outpatient services, inpatient services, or nursing home services. The actual codes appear in approximately 40 subcategories for type of service that are distinguished by their location (outpatient, hospital observation, nursing facility, and so on), characteristics of care (critical care service, preventive medicine service, discharge service, and so on), and/or a patient's classification (new patient, established patient, neonatal, and so on). In reality, most physicians use only four or five different types of service for 99% of the care they provide. The majority of physicians most frequently use the following three office outpatient visit codes:

- Initial visits (CPT codes 99201-99205)
- Established patient visits (CPT codes 99211-99215)
- Office consultations, new or established patients (CPT codes 99241-99245)

Some physicians may use emergency department services for new or established patients (CPT codes 99281-99285), or the following most common hospital care codes:

- Initial hospital care (CPT codes 99221-99223)
- Subsequent hospital care (CPT codes 99231-99233)
- Inpatient consultations, new or established patients (CPT codes 99251-99255)

Although this chapter and the remaining chapters in Part 3 focus on the three most commonly used outpatient services, the basic principles presented also apply the other types of E/M service that depend on key components and nature of the presenting problem (NPP). These will be examined in Part 4.

Types of E/M Service for Which Practical E/M Methodology Does Not Apply

Code selection for a variety of E/M services is not determined by consideration of the three key components and NPP. Instead, these types of service are defined by factors that may include patient health status, patient age, initial or established patient visit, and/or location of care. Even though these services do not require complex coding calculations to determine levels of care, physicians can benefit significantly from the use of well-designed forms to help them efficiently meet the significant documentation requirements while supporting, rather than interfering with, the patient care process. These advantages are illustrated in Chapter 20, which presents IMR tools for two of the more commonly provided services of this type: critical care services (CPT codes 99291-99292) and preventive medicine services (CPT codes 99381-99397).

OUTPATIENT INITIAL VISIT AND ESTABLISHED PATIENT VISIT SERVICES

In the outpatient office setting, it is usually the administrative staff that identifies the category of a patient's visit. They select among an initial visit, an established patient visit, and a consultation. (The nurse and/or the physician may also double-check the type of service, which is particularly helpful in finding out whether the patient's physician had requested a consultation.) For outpatient services, Practical E/M recommends using two different forms: one for initial visits and a second for established patient visits. The CPT coding system distinguishes between these two types of service by placing a three year criterion on the date of a patient's most recent care within a practice. Specifically, it defines a new patient as one who has not received any professional services from the physician, or another physician of the same specialty in the same group, within the last three years. A patient who has been seen within the last three years is classified as an established patient.[1] Consultations may be appropriate for either new or established patients; the requirements for this type of service are discussed later in this chapter. Identifying the correct type of service enables the administrative staff to identify which intelligent medical record (IMR) form to put in the medical chart for each visit.

The IMR forms for new and established patients differ with respect to the details of the documentation prompts in the history of present illness (HPI) and examination sections, and the content of the templates for past, family, and social history (PFSH) and review of systems (ROS). Each form is labeled with its type of service and has design and documentation prompts that are matched to the CPT requirements for that type of care.

Postoperative Patients

For patients returning for postoperative care for which no E/M code will be submitted (because the value of the care is included in the "global period" after surgery), there are no defined documentation requirements. However, I recommend that physicians routinely use an established patient visit form, which has several advantages.

First, from a quality perspective, it is always appropriate to inquire whether there has been any change in PFSH or ROS since the patient's previous visit. It is valuable to know whether the patient is being treated for a new problem, has changed medications, or has new symptoms that may or may not be related to the surgical procedure.

The second advantage of using the established patient visit form is that if the patient has a new problem, an additional problem unrelated to the procedure, or a complication related to the surgery, CPT guidelines advise the physician to submit a request for payment by using the appropriate E/M code for the service appended by modifier 24. Using the established patient visit form not only facilitates discovering these circumstances, it also facilitates appropriate documentation and coding of such encounters when they occur.

OUTPATIENT CONSULTATIONS

On the basis of the descriptions in the CPT codebook for different levels of care, the documentation prompts for an outpatient consultation are almost all identical to the prompts for an initial office visit, differing only in the fact that low-moderate severity NPP is required to warrant level 2 care for an initial outpatient visit, while low severity NPP warrants level 2 for an outpatient consultation. This enables physicians to use the initial visit template in documenting a consultation, while being cognizant of the minor variation in the levels of NPP. However, physicians also have an added responsibility to *document* the conditions that qualify their care as a consultation. Specifically, the CPT coding system describes consultations as "a type of service provided by a physician whose opinion or advice regarding evaluation and/or management of a specific problem is requested by another physician or other appropriate source."[1]

The part of this definition that refers to "another physician" is easy. However, the CPT coding system does not provide an explanation or a set of examples for defining the "other appropriate source," beyond specifying that this category does not include patients themselves or members of their families. The August 2001 issue of the *CPT Assistant* newsletter provides significant guidance, stating, "Some common examples include a physician assistant, nurse practitioner, doctor of chiropractic, physical therapist, occupational therapist, speech-language therapist, psychologist, social worker, lawyer, or insurance company."[2] In addition, for further clarification about which sources qualify as "other appropriate source," physicians may call the Centers for Medicare and Medicaid Services (CMS) and request a list of the professionals it qualifies as "other appropriate source(s)."

Applying the guidance of the August 2001 issue of the *CPT Assistant* newsletter, my suggested guideline for "other appropriate source" is that the request for consultation should be made by a medically related professional who might reasonably discover, and be concerned about, potential medical problems in the consultant's specialty. As an otolaryngologist, I have included nurse practitioners, dentists, audiologists, speech therapists, chiropractors, and psychologists as "other appropriate [requesting] sources."

It is also noteworthy that CMS has added one more qualification for using the E/M consultation codes. This requires that the requesting physician not be transferring complete care of the patient to the second physician. In practical terms, this feature most often enters into consideration when an emergency department physician sends a patient to another physician for follow-up care. Because the emergency department physician is not planning to provide ongoing care of the patient, he or she is therefore transferring that care to another physician. In this circumstance, a consultation service is not appropriate, and the treating physician must use an initial or established outpatient visit, whichever is appropriate. Of note, coders, auditors, and insurance company medical directors generally concur with this CMS stipulation.

Frequently Asked Questions About Consultation Services

The CPT coding system does not directly address the question of whether the requesting physician must have requested a specific consultant, or just generally recommended seeing a physician with expertise in a particular specialty. For several reasons, it is logical to consider the general recommendation sufficient. First, the CPT coding system does not specify that the requesting physician name a particular doctor to perform the consultation. Further, physicians often advise their patients to choose among a selection of physicians, which is qualitatively the equivalent of asking them to see one of the specialists in the area. Most important, from the perspective of medical quality, the requesting physician anticipates receiving a written summary from the consultant to assist with ongoing care of the patient.

Another common question is, "Does another physician's request for a consultation 'count' as a true consultation if the consultant has treated the patient within the last three years (the normal requirement for an established patient visit)?" The straightforward answer is *yes*. The subheading under "office or other outpatient consultations" in the CPT codebook directly states that it includes a "new or established patient."[1] Looking one layer deeper at this issue, we should also apply the measure of reasonableness. If the patient has previously been discharged from ongoing care, then a reasonableness test would certainly warrant classification of a requested evaluation as a consultation. If an existing patient (who has been seen within the last 3 years) is advised to obtain care for a new or unrelated problem, the reasonableness test will also warrant use of a consultation code. In contrast, if the consultant is providing ongoing care for a problem, and another physician advises a reassessment of that same problem sooner than the regularly scheduled visit, then treating this request as an established patient visit seems more appropriate (and reasonable).

The next logical question to address is whether the physician should use an initial visit template or an established patient template to document a legitimate consultation service for a patient whom the physician has treated within the last three years. From a practical standpoint, it may be inappropriate to have the patient fill out another complete PFSH and ROS form typically used with an initial visit. Therefore, in those circumstances it seems advisable to use the established patient form and obtain the updated PFSH and ROS information in the same way it is done for an established patient visit.

Change in the Documentation Prompts for a Consultation When Using the Established Patient Form

When using the established patient form for a consultation, the physician must be aware that the IMR's documentation prompts for HPI and physical examination on this form do not match the CPT requirements for consultations. In this circumstance, physicians should refer to the corresponding documentation prompts on page 3 of the initial visit form. An alternative solution is to create an additional form, which would incorporate these two correct documentation prompts for consultations performed on established patients.

Fulfilling Compliance Requirements for Consultations

The CPT codebook mandates the following two documentation requirements for consultations:

- The physician must document the *written or verbal* request for consultation in the medical record.[1]
- "The consultant's opinion and any services that were ordered or performed must also be documented in the patient's medical record and communicated by written report to the requesting physician or other appropriate source."[1]

The IMR recommends satisfying the first requirement, verification in the medical record, by adding a preprinted statement at the top of the page containing the HPI. As shown in Figure 9.1, this brief statement ensures compliance by documenting the request for consultation, and it maximizes efficiency by incorporating wording that includes everything needed for compliant documentation. It also allows the staff to simply fill in the name of the requesting physician (or other appropriate source).

F I G U R E **9.1**

Documentation Template for Consultation. The section designed for documenting the request for consultation appears in the upper right-hand corner of page 3 of the initial visit form (because pages 1 and 2 are completed by the patient) and at the top of page 1 of the established visit form.

Patient States Consultation Requested By: _____

The administrative staff, the clinical staff, or the physician documents the consultation request simply by writing in the name of the requesting physician or other appropriate requesting source. Including the verbiage "patient states" acknowledges the CPT guideline that the request may be "verbal."[1] In practice, a patient may often just report that his or her physician requested the consultation. They do not bring a written consultation form with them, and physicians do not have the time to call and request an authorization form. Because the consultant also cannot know whether the requesting physician has adequately documented the request in his or her own records, attributing the statement to the patient adds a reasonable level of protection in the event of an audit. If desired for further documentation, physicians may additionally add check boxes to indicate whether either of the following events occurred:

- Requesting physician's office called to schedule appointment for the patient
- Written consultation request received

Wording the Documentation for Optimal E/M Audit Protection

Clarifying phrases such as "patient states" are incorporated into the IMR because of anecdotal tales from physicians. This particular verbiage was derived from an insurance company audit of charts on which the consultation documentation read, "Consultation requested by_____." When the hired review company found complete compliance of the physician's own E/M documentation, they turned their attention to investigating whether the requesting physicians had documented a request for consultation in their own records (even though this is not a CPT requirement). Some requesting physicians had failed to document their requests, leading to a brief "gotcha" moment. Of course, that moment didn't last long, after one of the consultant physicians (and his attorney) pointed out that the only point the reviewers had proven was that the consultant documented well, and the requesting physician documented poorly.

However, it's much nicer to avoid "gotcha" moments than it is to have the aggravation of dealing with them. Therefore, the IMR form has added "patient states" to the preprinted statement to document that the consultant is relying, reasonably, on the patient's credibility concerning the request.

The second documentation requirement is a written report to the requesting physician. Appendix B of this book presents two efficient and effective sample templates that incorporate the content of conventional dictated consultation letters into structured forms with an organization preferred by requesting physicians. One design is formatted as a fax form. The second design is appropriate for dictation or electronic record formats and permits data merge functionality to incorporate information documented in the physician's history and physical (H&P). However, these samples are based on experience rather than specific guidelines. Both the CPT coding system and the *Documentation Guidelines for Evaluation and Management Services*[3] are silent concerning the content and form of such written reports, and this leads to several commonly encountered questions:

1. In the event of an audit, can the consultant's documentation of an encounter include both the office notes and his or her letter to the requesting physician?
   - This answer is a definite *yes*. The letter is part of the physician's medical record, and any review of documentation should include all parts of that record.
2. Can the consultant use the letter to the requesting physician as his or her *sole* documentation of the encounter?
   - This policy is acceptable for documentation purposes because the consultation is part of the medical record. However, the amount of

documentation in these letters is usually not sufficient to justify higher levels of service, and this option will likely yield poor results in the event of an audit. This is because the common consultation letter format leaves out too much documentation that is required under E/M coding and documentation guidelines (eg, complete PFSH, complete ROS, normal examination findings, and portions of the medical decision making [MDM]). Audits of records that have nothing more than a consultation letter generally result in a level 1 or level 2 consultation code because of CPT documentation requirements, even though the NPP may warrant a higher level of care (and justify a higher-level E/M code).

3. Can the consultant simply send (or fax) a copy of the office history and physical (H&P) form as the "written report to the requesting physician" (with or without a cover letter declaring "I have attached a copy of my office records on patient so-and-so")?

   ■ Most coders agree that the answer to this question is *no*. First, this would not be a "written report"; it is simply a copy of the office medical record and therefore does not fulfill the CPT coding system's definition of a consultation.[1] Second, consultation codes are credited with significantly higher relative value units (RVUs) than initial or established visits; medical directors and consultants generally concur that this additional value is based on the added effort and responsibility for creating a meaningful consultation report; this requires more than the use of a photocopy or fax machine.

4. Are there different requirements for consultation letters among physicians in a group practice with a shared medical record?

   ■ The CPT codebook does not make a separate distinction for this circumstance. The CMS does provide some guidance in Chapter 12 of the *Medicare Claims Processing Manual*, which states that in such practices with a shared record "it is acceptable to include the consultant's report in the medical record documentation and not require a separate letter. . . . The written request and the consultation evaluation, findings and recommendations shall be available in the consultation report."[4, p 54]

   ■ However, CMS does not define or clarify whether the physician's usual H&P form meets the requirements of being the consultant's "written report," or whether this provision still requires a *separate* written consultation report but simply does not require it to be sent to the requesting physician. Practices are advised to get a written opinion about this detail from their own Medicare carrier's medical director.

5. Have other recent CMS modifications to the consultation section of the *Medicare Claims Processing Manual* altered documentation requirements for consultations?

   ■ One modification has imposed an additional requirement that the request for consultation must be "included in the requesting physician plan of care."[4, p 54]

   ■ The CMS also dramatically changed the definition and intent of the phrase "transfer of care" in its recent modifications, by adding the three words "for the condition." The *Manual* now advises that "a transfer of care occurs when a physician or qualified NPP (nonphysician practitioner) requests that another physician or qualified NPP take over the responsibility for managing the patient's complete care *for the condition* and does not expect to continue treating or caring for the patient for that condition. . . . In a transfer of care the receiving physician or qualified NPP shall not report a consultation service."[4, p 51]

The Problems Imposed by Medicare's New Consultation Rules

The new requirement that a request for consultation be documented in the requesting physician's medical record has created a new obstacle for consulting physicians. The only way they can be assured that such documentation exists in the requesting physician's own record is to require the patient to bring a written document from that physician's office as a means of proof.

The new CMS definition for "transfer of care" directly contradicts the CPT criteria for a consultation. More importantly, when interpreted literally, this provision eliminates all consultation services. By the *Carrier Manual*'s own definition, the patient requires care "beyond the requesting physician's knowledge."[4, p 51] Under this circumstance, it would violate the standard of care for the requesting physician to resume caring for the patient's problem; a written message from a neurosurgeon would not qualify an internist to care for a patient's brain tumor. On the other hand, the internist does need to know (by a consultant's written report) the extent of the problem and the care provided so that he or she can continue providing optimal ongoing care for the patient. Further, of the three examples of the policy in the Carrier Manual, two directly contradict this policy and the third appears to promote care below the medical standard.

By attempting to eliminate reimbursement that covers physicians' expense for creating consultation reports, this policy provides negative incentives that interfere with communication among physicians about their patients. This action conflicts with quality care and is contradictory to medical ethics. It is also particularly inappropriate and ironic because CMS currently professes a desire to promote the use of electronic health records to facilitate communication about patients' health records. Physicians are advised to get a written letter from their own carrier's medical director clarifying this policy and to report any instances where a carrier's nonpayment for a medically indicated consultation violates quality care standards.

OTHER TYPES OF SERVICE

The specific descriptions of the many other types of service are listed in the E/M section of the CPT codebook. Because these other categories of care do not occur in the physician's office, the clinician is responsible for identifying the appropriate type of service and matching this with the appropriate IMR template.

The CPT coding system provides different descriptors for the levels of history, examination, MDM, and NPP for each type of E/M service. As a result, several separate IMR forms are required to accurately match the design features and documentation prompts to each type of service. Therefore, each physician will commonly have several forms to cover the services he or she ordinarily provides (eg, separate forms for initial outpatient visits, established outpatient visits, subsequent inpatient care, and so on).

For many physicians, the types of service used most often, in addition to office outpatient visits, are hospital inpatient visits (including initial care, subsequent care, initial consultations, etc). It is convenient that the outpatient consultation IMR form can be used for inpatient consultations, because these two types of service have identical CPT descriptors for the levels of care.

The Hospital Consultation and IMR Forms

Currently, most standard hospital consultation forms offer one blank page to the consulting physician, who then writes or dictates a free-text manuscript. This limitation invites problem-focused care and problem-focused documentation. Physicians commonly document an HPI and a problem-focused examination, which is followed by MDM that may be straightforward or quite complex, depending on the physician and the

continued

patient's condition. However, the lack of documentation of PFSH, ROS, and either a detailed or comprehensive physical examination in the text of the consultation results in a report that supports only a low-level consultation code (ie, 99251 or 99252). In contrast, the NPP for most inpatient consultations warrants moderate or high-level care (ie, 99253, 99254, or 99255). The result is a quandary for the physician, resulting from the fact that the design of the standard hospital consultation form commonly leads to quality and productivity that are both lower than warranted by the severity of patients' illnesses.

The structure of the outpatient consultation IMR template is exactly matched to the compliance requirements of inpatient consultations. In practical terms, it is also permitted, and usually most efficient, to obtain PFSH, ROS, and data information directly from the hospital chart and enter in onto the IMR form, augmenting any missing material from the patient or family (or documenting "not accessible because . . ." if the patient is unable to respond). Therefore, as presented in Chapters 19 and shown in the accompanying CD-ROM, the inpatient consultation IMR form includes additional features to document the source(s) of the documented history information in each case. In summary, using an IMR form for inpatient consultations is more efficient than using the traditional hospital consultation form, and it almost always results in providing and documenting a more appropriate level of care plus imporved E/M coding compliance.

Physicians must have a different form for hospital inpatient initial care visits, because there are only three levels of care for this type of service (99221, 99222, and 99223), and different documentation prompts are required. Subsequent hospital care visits also require a different form, not only because this type of service also has only three levels of care, but also because the CPT coding system provides completely different descriptors for the NPP. This requires a documentation prompt with different wording for this section of the medical record. In addition, the PFSH section may be eliminated from this template (or simply ignored if the physician prefers), because the CPT coding guidelines do not require daily updates of this information for this type of service.[1]

Inpatient Subsequent Care Visits: NPP and the Level of Care

For the inpatient subsequent care service, CPT coding guidelines show that the NPP directly mandates the appropriate level of care. The patient with a "stable" NPP warrants level 1 care (ie, code 99231), and the CPT coding system defines the amount of care and documentation required for two of the three key components to support this service. Similarly, an NPP of "patient is responding inadequately to therapy or has developed a minor complication"[1, p 13] warrants care appropriate for 99232. Finally, an NPP of "unstable, significant complication, or new problem" warrants 99233 care and documentation. (See Figure 14.2 in Chapter 14 for an example of this documentation prompt. There is also a sample form for this type of service in the accompanying CD-ROM.)

For all other types of service, such as emergency department visits, nursing home care, and so on, physicians must evaluate whether the CPT coding guidelines allow them to adapt an existing form, or whether they must create separate forms. These decisions will depend on both the E/M coding guidelines and the frequency with which a physician employs each particular type of service. Physicians generally prefer to have individualized IMR forms for each type of service that they provide frequently.

SUMMARY

Selecting the appropriate type of service for a patient visit is the first step in accomplishing compliant coding and documentation. The CPT coding system describes approximately 40 types of E/M service that are codified for patient care. Identifying the type of service provides the first four digits of the five-digit E/M code, while the level of care determines the fifth digit. For example, in code 99203, the digits "9920" specify that the care is provided for an outpatient initial visit, and the digit "3" indicates the level of care.

This chapter concentrates on the three most common outpatient services. This includes a discussion of the special requirements for defining and documenting consultation services. It is noteworthy that for most outpatient office encounters, the staff rather than the physician identifies the type of service. The physician has two responsibilities related to type of service for outpatient office visits: (1) confirming the type of service and (2) providing a consultation letter to requesting physicians for consultation services.

The CPT guidelines relating the NPP to the extent of care, and even to the required components of care, vary for different types of service. Therefore, IMR design must take these variations into consideration to ensure that the foundation of the medical record is compliant for each patient visit. This requires physicians to have several different templates for the services they perform frequently, each form identified by the type(s) of service for which it is appropriate. These design customizations are reflected in both the content of the templates and the guidance of the documentation prompts.

References

1. American Medical Association. *Current Procedural Terminology CPT® 2008.* Chicago, IL: American Medical Association; 2007.

2. American Medical Association. Consultation: answers to perplexing questions. *CPT Assistant.* 2001;11(8):1–4.

3. Health Care Financing Administration. *Documentation Guidelines for Evaluation and Management Services.* Chicago, IL: American Medical Association; 1997.

4. *Medicare Claims Processing Manual,* Chapter 12, section 30.6.10. http://cms.hhs.gov/manuals/downloads/clm104c12.pdf. Accessed March 7, 2008.

Obtaining and Documenting Background Medical History: Initial Patient Visit

The past, family, and social history (PFSH) and review of systems (ROS) convey the patient's background medical information, enabling the clinician to obtain a complete picture of the patient's health and ask pertinent questions related to positive responses. To strive toward the goal of optimal efficiency for obtaining and documenting medical information, it is not necessary for the physician to be the data entry person for this portion of medical care. It is often more efficient for an extender, preferably the patient, to enter the "yes" or "no" responses to a list of medical conditions and symptoms into the medical record. The intelligent medical record (IMR) form is therefore designed to enable patients to enter their own medical history information directly into the chart. This interface design should be easy not only for the patient to understand and complete, but also for the physician to quickly scan and identify significant responses. If the patient is unable to enter the information, the design also helps the physician or staff by providing the questions to ask and an efficient means of entering the patient's responses.

Figure 10.1 illustrates page 1 of a sample IMR form, which contains the PFSH, for an internist's initial patient visit. The design of this template ensures efficiency, ease of use, and compliance. It also enables each physician to modify the specific questions to suit his or her specialty and personal preferences. For example, a pediatrician would likely want to employ a different list of medical illnesses in the past history, inquire about different issues related to the social history, and investigate different illness related to the family history than would an internist. However, such changes have no effect on the template's functionality, thereby maintaining the IMR goals of compliance and efficiency.

CHIEF COMPLAINT

Design for Compliance Requirements

The Current Procedural Terminology (CPT®) coding system and the *Documentation Guidelines for Evaluation and Management Services* both define *chief complaint* as "a concise statement describing the symptom, problem, condition, diagnosis or other factor that is the reason for the encounter, usually stated in the patient's own words."[1] The *Documentation Guidelines* also requires that "the medical record should clearly reflect the chief complaint."[2] To fulfill this requirement, the IMR form includes a space at the beginning of the initial visit medical history section that prompts the patient to record the chief complaint.

FIGURE 10.1

Sample Initial Visit IMR Form for General Medical Care (Page 1)

Patient Name:_____   Account No._____   DOB:____/____/____

Initial Visit Form (p. 1):   Please provide the following medical information to the best of your ability:

Date:	Age:	List any ALLERGIES TO MEDICATIONS:
What problems are you here for today?		

Past Medical History:
   1) Please check the "Yes" or "No" box to indicate if you have any of the following illnesses; for "Yes" answers, please explain.

	Yes	No			Yes	No
Diabetes (Circle: type I/type II)	☐	☐		Stomach or Intestinal problems	☐	☐
Hypertension (high blood press)	☐	☐		Allergy problems/therapy	☐	☐
Thyroid problems	☐	☐		Kidney problems	☐	☐
Heart Disease/cholesterol probs	☐	☐		Neurological problems	☐	☐
Respiratory problems	☐	☐		Cancer	☐	☐
Bleeding disorder	☐	☐		Other Medical Diagnosis	☐	☐

   2) Please list any operations (and dates) you have ever had *(including tonsils & adenoids)*:

   3) Please list any current medications (and amounts, times per day):
      (include aspirin, antacids, vitamins, hormone replacement, birth control, herbal supplements, OTC meds including sinus/allergy/weight loss meds):

Social History:	Yes	No		Please list details below:
Do you use tobacco?	☐	☐	List type and how much:	
If no, did you use it previously?	☐	☐	List type and how much:	When did you quit?
Do you drink alcohol?	☐	☐	List type and how much:	
Do you use recreational drugs?	☐	☐	List type and how much:	
What is your occupation?				

Family History:
   Please check the "Yes" or "No" box to indicate whether any relatives have any of the following illnesses:
   If yes, please indicate which relative(s) have the problem.

	Yes	No	
Heart problems/murmurs	☐	☐	
Allergy	☐	☐	
Diabetes	☐	☐	
Cancer	☐	☐	
Bleeding disorder	☐	☐	
Anesthesia problems	☐	☐	

☐ See attached dictation | Reviewed by:

Design for Efficiency and Quality Care

The chief complaint can be elicited by a brief inquiry into the patient's reason(s) for the current visit. As this calls for a concise response, the IMR form employs a short-answer graphic interface that enables patients to enter the information themselves. This provides the added assurance that the chief complaint will be "stated in the patient's own words." The graphic interface for short answers is simply one or two blank lines, attached to an appropriate question. To enable patients to provide the information without medical assistance, it is important to use terminology that patients can understand readily (eg, having the chart form ask "What is your chief complaint?" does not fulfill this requirement). Although there are many reasonable questions that would be acceptable, we have found success using the inquiry, "What problems are you here for today?" Patients readily understand the question and generally respond to it with brief, direct answers. The phrasing also invites patients to list more than one problem, which ensures that the physician is aware of all of their concerns. Figure 10.2 highlights the sample chief complaint section of the sample initial visit IMR form.

F I G U R E **10.2**

Graphic Interface Appearance for Chief Complaint (Sample Form)

Date:	Age:
What problems are you here for today?	

PAST MEDICAL HISTORY

Design for Compliance Requirements

The *Documentation Guidelines* define *past medical history* as "the patient's past experiences with illnesses, operations, injuries and treatments."[2] The CPT codebook provides a more comprehensive summary, listing the following[1]:

- Prior major illnesses and injuries
- Prior operations
- Prior hospitalizations
- Current medications
- Allergies (eg, drug, food)
- Age-appropriate immunization status
- Age-appropriate feeding/dietary status

The *Documentation Guidelines* advises that, for initial patient visits, physicians can fulfill the requirement for a "complete" PFSH by documenting "at least one specific item from each of the three history areas"[2] (ie, past medical history, family history, and social history). Most physicians would not consider the asking of merely one question in each of these sections (eg, "do you have any allergies") as being sufficient to qualify for obtaining a comprehensive medical history and providing quality medical care. However, this is the minimum requirement physicians must satisfy to meet the criterion for E/M compliance.

Design for Efficiency and Quality Care

Although compliance and productivity criteria are satisfied with documentation of only one element of past medical history, the IMR interface is also designed to allow physicians to obtain sufficient information to meet their own personal standards for providing their patients with quality care. To accomplish this, the IMR employs a series of graphic interfaces that enable patients to enter their information directly into the medical record. This approach affords the physician the opportunity to include all medically pertinent concerns on the template, to elicit as much information "free" of significant physician time input as he or she determines is beneficial to providing optimal patient care. This structure promotes maximal efficiency plus maximum information for the physician.

Compliance Is a Beginning, Not an End

The ability to incorporate all the information the physician desires into the past medical history section is a prime example of the fact that fulfilling compliance requirements is only the starting point for IMR design. Beginning with the solid foundation of E/M compliance, physicians are able to build additional structure into an IMR form, based upon their personal goals for quality care for their patients.

There are multiple subsections to the past medical history section of the IMR form. The IMR designs each component with a graphic interface (and patient instructions) that is optimal for obtaining accurate information. Figure 10.3 illustrates an example of a past medical history section, which physicians are able to modify according to the information they want to include in their own medical records. Because the CPT coding system and the *Documentation Guidelines* require only one element to achieve a "complete" past medical history, physicians have complete freedom to accept, modify, delete, or add any specific past medical history information they prefer, while working within the compliant framework of the IMR.

SOCIAL HISTORY

Design for Compliance Requirements

The CPT coding system describes the social history as including some of the following specific information, which is structured to be appropriate for the medical specialty, the patient's age, and the physician's practice[1]:

- Marital status; living arrangements
- Education
- Current employment
- Employment history
- Substance use
- Sexual history

As with the past medical history, the *Documentation Guidelines* requires notation of only one item from the social history to satisfy the requirements for a "complete" PFSH.[2]

Template for Past Medical History (Sample Form). This template satisfies (and significantly exceeds) the past medical history component of the *Documentation Guidelines* requirement for comprehensive medical history, which is documentation of at least one element of the past medical history. It also incorporates CPT coding system recommendations and parallels the comprehensive past medical history taught to medical students. It may be adapted to each physician's preferences by changing the illnesses listed in the check box section. (Details for the medical illnesses checked as "yes" should be listed in the lines next to and/or below the check boxes.)

Patient Name:_____   Account No._____   DOB:___/___/___

Initial Visit Form (p. 1): Please provide the following medical information to the best of your ability:

Date:	Age:	List any ALLERGIES TO MEDICATIONS:
What problems are you here for today?		

Past Medical History:

1) Please check the "Yes" or "No" box to indicate if you have any of the following illnesses; for "Yes" answers, please explain.

	Yes No			Yes No	
Diabetes (Circle: type I/type II)	☐ ☐	_____	Stomach or Intestinal problems	☐ ☐	____
Hypertension (high blood press)	☐ ☐	_____	Allergy problems/therapy	☐ ☐	____
Thyroid problems	☐ ☐	_____	Kidney problems	☐ ☐	____
Heart Disease/cholesterol probs	☐ ☐	_____	Neurological problems	☐ ☐	____
Respiratory problems	☐ ☐	_____	Cancer	☐ ☐	____
Bleeding disorder	☐ ☐	_____	Other Medical Diagnosis	☐ ☐	____

2) Please list any operations (and dates) you have ever had *(including tonsils & adenoids)*:

3) Please list any current medications (and amounts, times per day):
(include aspirin, antacids, vitamins, hormone replacement, birth control, herbal supplements, OTC meds including sinus/allergy/weight loss meds):

Design for Efficiency and Quality Care

The IMR graphic interface provides the ability to obtain this information efficiently, directly from the patient. This enables and encourages physicians to include questions on their template about any social history information that they feel has the potential to assist them in providing quality care for their patients. Figure 10.4 illustrates some of the possible questions physicians can use as a starting point for identifying the social history information they want to include in their own customized medical records. Because the CPT coding system and the *Documentation Guidelines* require only one element to achieve a "complete" social history, within this design physicians have complete freedom to accept, modify, delete, or add any specific material they wish. This example includes check boxes for efficient documentation of those inquiries that are suitable for a "yes or no" response. The blank lines provide space for details and short descriptive answers.

F i g u r e   10.4

Template for Social History (Sample Form). This template satisfies (and exceeds) the social history portion of the *Documentation Guidelines* requirement for comprehensive medical history, which is documentation of at least one element of the social history. It also incorporates CPT coding system recommendations and parallels the comprehensive social history taught to medical students. It should be modified to suit each physician's personal preferences.

Social History:	Yes	No		Please list details below:
Do you use tobacco?	☐	☐	List type and how much:	_____
If no, did you use it previously?	☐	☐	List type and how much:	_____ When did you quit?
Do you drink alcohol?	☐	☐	List type and how much:	_____
Do you use recreational drugs?	☐	☐	List type and how much:	_____
What is your occupation?				_____

FAMILY HISTORY

Design for Compliance Requirements

The CPT coding system describes the family history section of the medical history as including significant information about the following[1]:

- health status of parents, siblings, and children;
- cause of death of parents, siblings, and children;
- diseases related to the patient's problems, as identified in the chief complaint, history of present illness (HPI), or ROS; and
- diseases that may be hereditary and provide insight about the patient's health.

As with the past medical history and social history sections, the *Documentation Guidelines* require notation of only one item from the family history to satisfy the requirements for a "complete" PFSH.[2]

Design for Efficiency and Quality

The IMR graphic interface provides the ability to obtain this information efficiently, directly from the patient. This allows and encourages physicians to include questions on their template about any family history information that they feel has the potential to assist them in providing quality care for their patients. Figure 10.5 illustrates some of the possible questions physicians can use as a starting point for identifying the family history information they want to include in their own customized medical records. Once again, because of the *Documentation Guidelines* requirements, they have complete freedom to accept, modify, delete, or add any specific material they wish. The blank lines permit short descriptive answers for details, as requested. The "reviewed by" line fulfills the *Documentation Guidelines* requirement for physician signature (or initials) indicating that he or she has reviewed all portions of the PFSH. (This section is commonly the last portion of the PFSH page of IMR forms, where it provides documentation of review of the entire page.)

Template for Family History (Sample Form). This template fulfills (and exceeds) the family history component of the *Documentation Guidelines* requirement for comprehensive medical history, which is documentation of at least one element of the family history. It also incorporates CPT coding system recommendations and parallels the comprehensive family history taught to medical students. It should be modified to suit each physician's personal preferences.

Family History:
Please check the "Yes" or "No" box to indicate whether any relatives have any of the following illnesses:
If yes, please indicate which relative(s) have the problem.

	Yes	No	
Heart problems/murmurs	☐	☐	
Allergy	☐	☐	
Diabetes	☐	☐	
Cancer	☐	☐	
Bleeding disorder	☐	☐	
Anesthesia problems	☐	☐	
		☐ See attached dictation	Reviewed by:

SYNOPSIS AND ANALYSIS OF CHIEF COMPLAINT AND PAST, FAMILY, AND SOCIAL HISTORY

Table 10.1 summarizes the IMR design for the chief complaint and PFSH sections of an initial patient visit.

TABLE **10.1**

Synopsis of IMR for Chief Complaint and PFSH for an Initial Patient Visit

Component	Interface Options	Data Entry	Format Options	Comments
Chief complaint	Graphic (with short answer)	Patient	Writing	Patient entry; supports all E/M levels
PFSH				
Yes/no (and short-answer) questions	Graphic (with check boxes and short answers)	Patient	Writing	Patient entry; supports all E/M levels
Investigation of "yes" responses	Graphic (with short answers) or brief narrative	Physician	Writing or dictation	Usually, brief description for added detail

The IMR ensures *compliance* for the chief complaint and PFSH sections of every initial patient visit because it structures the medical record for each of these elements upon the standards required to support all levels of E/M codes, up to and including level 5. For this reason, the chief complaint and PFSH sections do not require documentation prompts. *Efficiency* is as high as possible because the patient can complete all the preliminary information; the physician gains significant information while investing only minimal time to review the form and place initials in the "reviewed by" box. Investigation and documentation of positive responses involves additional physician input to provide details, using the short-answer graphic format (or dictation). Most important, this extensive medical history information provides critical background information, which helps physicians provide quality care.

Compliance Basis for Patients Entering Information Into the Medical Record

Having patients enter their own history into the medical record is definitely *compliant*. The *Documentation Guidelines* specify that "the ROS and PFSH may be recorded by ancillary staff or on a form completed by the patient. To document that the physician reviewed the information, there must be a notation supplementing or confirming the information recorded by others."[2]

REVIEW OF SYSTEMS

Design for Compliance Requirements

The ROS presents another opportunity for physicians to obtain, free of significant physician time input, a considerable amount of medical information that offers extensive benefits for patient care. Similar to the design for the PFSH, the IMR form employs a graphic interface with "yes" and "no" check boxes for the ROS. The design permits the patient to perform the data entry, which is facilitated by using a paper format for the preprinted template.

The CPT codebook describes ROS as "an inventory of body systems obtained through a series of questions seeking to identify signs and/or symptoms which the patient may be experiencing or has experienced."[1] The CPT coding system and the *Documentation Guidelines* recognize 14 different systems for potential review, which are listed in the left-hand column in Figure 10.6. To meet Practical E/M's goal of a complete ROS for every initial patient visit, the *Documentation Guidelines* requires documentation of at least one response for each of at least 10 of these systems, including "positive or pertinent negative responses."[2] By documenting information for 10 or more of these systems for every initial visit, the IMR ensures that the level of medical history obtained will support whatever level E/M code is warranted by the nature of presenting problem (NPP), up to and including level 5.

Review of Systems or Past Medical History?

There is often confusion among physicians and reviewers about whether a particular medical history inquiry relates to the ROS or to the past medical history. Many medical record templates fail to distinguish the inquiries appropriate for ROS from those appropriate for past medical history. We can differentiate between the questions that are most appropriate for each of these two medical history categories by identifying whether the question asks about a *diagnosis* (which belongs in the past medical history category) or about a *medical sign or symptom* (which belongs in the ROS category). For example, asking whether a patient has "allergies" refers to a *diagnosis* and should appear in the past medical history section. Asking whether the patient has sneezing fits or rashes refers to *signs and symptoms* and should appear in the ROS section.

Design for Efficiency and Quality Care

Although compliance and productivity criteria are satisfied by the documentation of only one question about signs or symptoms for each of 10 or more of the 14 organ systems, Practical E/M again emphasizes that the quality care issue compels physicians to obtain more than this required minimum amount of clinical information. Because the IMR uses a graphic interface for ROS and allows the patient to enter the data directly into the medical record, the design provides the physician with the opportunity to obtain as much information, without significant physician time investment, as he or she determines is beneficial for providing optimal patient care. Practical E/M starts with two or more symptom inquiries for each of the 14 organ systems, and physicians are encouraged to customize additional questions based on their specialty and personal preferences.

Designing the ROS

When customizing the ROS template, a physician should first insert appropriate screening questions related to all areas of his or her own specialty. These relevant inquiries can be inserted under various organ system categories other than the physician's own specialty. For example, the relevant ear, nose, and throat question about headache is reasonably placed in the "neurology" system; postnasal drip can be placed in "allergy"; and heartburn (for reflux) naturally appears in the gastrointestinal system. The physician may insert additional relevant questions in any of the other categories as well.

Figure 10.6 illustrates a sample ROS section of an IMR form. Once again, physicians are able to modify these questions according to the information they want to include in their own medical records. They will maintain full compliance as long as they continue to include at least one question for each of ten or more systems.

FIGURE 10.6

Template for Review of Systems (Sample Form).

Date____/____/____

Patient Name:_____   Account No._____   DOB:____/____/____

Outpatient Initial Visit Form (p. 2): Please provide the following medical information to the best of your ability:

Review of Systems:
  1) Please check the "Yes" or "No" box to indicate whether you presently have any of the following symptoms:
  2) For any "yes" responses, please check the "Current" box if this symptom relates to the reason for your visit today.

		Yes	No	Current		Yes	No	Current
GENERAL	chills	☐	☐	☐	weight loss or gain	☐	☐	☐
	fatigue	☐	☐	☐	daytime sleepiness	☐	☐	☐
ALLERGY	environmental allergy	☐	☐	☐	sneezing fits	☐	☐	☐
NEURO	headache	☐	☐	☐	weakness	☐	☐	☐
	passing out	☐	☐	☐	numbness, tingling	☐	☐	☐
EYES	eye pain/pressure	☐	☐	☐	vision changes	☐	☐	☐
	watery or itchy eyes	☐	☐	☐				
ENT	hearing loss	☐	☐	☐	ear noises	☐	☐	☐
	dizziness	☐	☐	☐	lightheadedness	☐	☐	☐
	nasal congestion	☐	☐	☐	sinus pressure or pain	☐	☐	☐
	hoarseness	☐	☐	☐	problem snoring, apnea	☐	☐	☐
	throat clearing	☐	☐	☐	throat pain	☐	☐	☐
RESPIR	cough	☐	☐	☐	coughing blood	☐	☐	☐
	wheezing	☐	☐	☐	shortness of breath	☐	☐	☐
CARDIAC	chest pain	☐	☐	☐	palpitations	☐	☐	☐
	wake short of breath	☐	☐	☐	ankle swelling	☐	☐	☐
GI	difficulty swallowing	☐	☐	☐	heartburn	☐	☐	☐
	abdominal pain	☐	☐	☐	nausea/vomiting	☐	☐	☐
	bowel irregularity	☐	☐	☐	rectal bleeding	☐	☐	☐
GU	frequent urination	☐	☐	☐	painful urination	☐	☐	☐
	blood in urine	☐	☐	☐	prostate problems	☐	☐	☐
HEME/LYM	swollen glands	☐	☐	☐	sweating at night	☐	☐	☐
	bleeding problems	☐	☐	☐	easy bruising	☐	☐	☐
ENDO	feel warmer than others	☐	☐	☐	feel cooler than others	☐	☐	☐
MSK	joint aches	☐	☐	☐	muscle aches	☐	☐	☐
SKIN	rash	☐	☐	☐	hives	☐	☐	☐
	itching	☐	☐	☐	skin or hair changes	☐	☐	☐
PSYCH	depression	☐	☐	☐	anxiety or panic	☐	☐	☐

PLEASE STOP HERE   ☐ See attached dictation

Reviewed by:

As shown in Figure 10.6, the IMR provides an additional efficiency feature to help the physician identify whether any of the positive responses relate to the patient's presenting illness or to an unrelated problem. The form includes an additional box labeled "Current," with the following attached instruction: "For any 'Yes' responses, please check the 'Current' box if this symptom relates to the reason for your visit today." Any positive boxes that are also identified with the present illness (by a check in the "current" box) can be investigated further in the HPI section of the history. The physician will also review and document further detail for all other symptoms with positive responses (ie, those unrelated to the HPI) by writing on the blank lines at the bottom of the page or by dictation. After this, the physician must sign the "Reviewed by" line at the bottom of the page to document review of all the patient's responses.

Eliminating the Negative Consequences of "All Others Negative"

Many physicians who do not use compliantly structured records and/or patients to document answers to ROS questions make other attempts to decrease the time they spend obtaining and documenting the ROS for new patients. Often these physicians' records document actual "associated signs and symptoms" only related to the presenting problem, usually in the HPI section of the record. Then, for the ROS section, they will write (or dictate) "all others negative."

This statement derives from the instruction in the *Documentation Guidelines* for a *complete* ROS that states "For the remaining systems, a notation indicating all other systems are negative is permissible."[2(p 8)] However, in nearly all charts where this statement appears, the physician has failed to fulfill the additional care and documentation requirements that must be met for a complete ROS before reporting "all others negative":

■ The physician must ask "a series of questions seeking to identify signs and/or symptoms which the patient may be experiencing or has experienced"[2(p 8)] in an inventory of 10 or more organ systems.

■ The physician must individually document positive and *pertinent negative* responses from any of those organ systems. This includes individual documentation of the questions asked and the patient's responses for all organ systems that might be pertinent to the problem identified in the HPI (eg, for a patient complaining of chest pain, systems documented in detail should include not only the cardiovascular system, but also pulmonary, gastrointestinal, musculoskeletal, skin, constitutional, hematologic, neurologic, and psychiatric).

The IMR's design of the ROS section provides a superior approach, eliminating significant physician time and effort and also avoiding potential problems with compliance, quality of care, and even liability issues that can arise from substituting the generic statement "all others negative" for performing and documenting a complete ROS.

SYNOPSIS AND ANALYSIS OF ROS

Table 10.2 summarizes the IMR design for the ROS section of an initial patient visit.

TABLE 10.2

Synopsis of IMR for ROS for an Initial Patient Visit

Component of ROS	Interface	Data Entry Options	Format Options	Comments
Yes/no questions	Graphic (with check boxes)	Patient Nurse/tech Physician	Writing	Patient entry
				Ensures complete ROS; supports all E/M levels
Investigation of "yes" responses	Narrative	Physician	Writing or dictation	Narrative interface is essential to explore details of individual symptoms

The IMR ensures *compliance* for the ROS section of every initial patient visit, because it structures the template upon the standards required to support all levels of E/M codes, up to and including level 5. For this reason, the ROS section does not require documentation prompts. *Efficiency* is as high as possible for the portion of this section completed by the patient; the physician gains significant information while investing only minimal time to review the form and place initials on the "Reviewed by" line. In some cases, investigation and documentation of positive responses may involve a moderate amount of physician documentation, because effectively investigating new patient problems calls for a more sophisticated narrative approach. In return, this additional effort often reveals significant medical information, which as a secondary benefit may also have a positive impact on *productivity*. Additional medical issues identified in the ROS become additional "presenting problems," which will increase the "number of diagnoses" component of medical decision making (MDM) and contribute to documentation for the medically indicated level of care. Depending on their severity, one or more of these additional problems may also increase the "risk of presenting problem(s)" and the severity of the NPP. The effect on productivity therefore includes both the potential for an appropriately higher-level E/M code for this initial visit (based on the level of NPP) and possible additional care visits to fully address these added problems.

The discovery of additional medical issues in the ROS creates a positive impact on quality of care. The comprehensive ROS provides so much information about the patient, with so little added physician time required, that it underscores the quality care benefits of the Practical E/M philosophy. There is a substantial benefit from having in-depth insight into as much of the patient's health history as possible, and the IMR design for PFSH and ROS enables physicians to obtain that insight. It catalyzes the process of identifying and treating previously undiscovered patient illnesses. It promotes early intervention and prevention counseling. It generates tremendous appreciation from our patients and promotes a positive patient-physician relationship. It creates a feeling of satisfaction and enjoyment for physicians, fulfilling much of the promise that drew us to medicine as a profession.

HISTORY OF PRESENT ILLNESS

Design for Compliance Requirements

The IMR design for the HPI portion of the medical chart has several special compliance features, as illustrated in Figure 10.7. The first line provides a documentation prompt that reminds physicians of the HPI requirement for recording a "chronological description"[1(p 3)] of the patient's illness; ie, the HPI must be an actual *history*, not just a description of the details of the chief complaint. It also relates the number of elements of the HPI that must be included in the history to report the various code levels for the indicated type of service. The example in this figure shows the prompt for an outpatient initial visit. Different types of service will have modified documentation prompts based upon CPT coding system guidelines (eg, for an outpatient established visit, one to three elements will support up to a level 3 visit). Practical E/M philosophy recommends obtaining and documenting four or more elements of the HPI during every visit. Not only does this ensure compliance with every level of service, but also the amount of information that can be obtained in this way generally contributes to higher-quality care.

The documentation prompt on the second line of the HPI lists the eight elements of the HPI, as defined by the *Documentation Guidelines*.[2] Whenever possible, I suggest having a nurse or medical assistant document the first three of these elements at every visit. They lend themselves to short direct answers and provide valuable background information in every case. Also, the next (ie, fourth) element that the physician describes as part of the true history will provide enough documentation to qualify as an "extended" HPI, as defined by the *Documentation Guidelines*.[2] An extended HPI provides a level of care sufficient to support any level E/M code that is indicated by the NPP. Of course, when an assistant is not available, the elements of the HPI can be obtained and documented by the clinician while guiding the patient to describe the events of the course of the illness. Alternatively, as provided by the 1997 edition of the *Documentation Guidelines,* an extended HPI may be documented by indicating the status of three chronic or inactive conditions.[2] This HPI approach is often appropriate for an established patient who is being monitored for ongoing management of several health problems (eg, hypertension, congestive heart failure, and diabetes).

FIGURE 10.7

HPI Template for Initial Outpatient Visit With E/M Documentation Prompts (Sample Form).

Design for Efficiency and Quality Care

Although the critical portions of the HPI require direct physician involvement as part of the development of a differential diagnosis (ie, physicians' "diagnostic process"), the IMR template for the HPI includes an optional section for preliminary free-text documentation by a nurse or medical assistant. I suggest that this begin with documentation of the HPI elements of duration, timing, and severity as they pertain to the patient's chief complaint. These three elements generally result in short-answer responses, so they are easily documented in the free-text area provided. The nurse can also add any further history information he or she obtains. The remaining information (ie, location, quality, context, modifying factors, associated signs and symptoms, and/or other details), obtained by the physician, will likely involve documentation of multiple variables and multiple levels of inquiry as part of investigating of the actual historical course of the patient's illness. This degree of detail is best documented by using a narrative interface. (This feature is discussed in greater detail in Chapter 13.)

USING THE INITIAL VISIT HISTORY SECTION OF THE IMR

In the most common scenario for an outpatient initial visit, the physician's administrative staff will give pages 1 and 2 of the medical record to the patient to complete in the waiting room prior to the visit. These can be printed on opposite sides of a single sheet of paper. They include most of the medical history: the chief complaint, PFSH, and ROS. The medical staff should make sure that the patient has fully completed all of the questions. The office staff should advise patients to arrive 15 minutes before the scheduled appointment time to complete their forms (unless they have filled out this form in advance).

Completing Information Forms in the Electronic Era

If there is sufficient time in advance of an appointment, the staff can have the option to mail, fax, or e-mail the forms to the patient so that he or she may complete the forms at home and bring them to the appointment. As the electronic age moves forward, physicians may even have patients who will prefer to complete this material directly on their physicians' secure Web sites. If patients are eventually maintaining their own personal electronic health records, then they will be able to download all this background information to their physicians, either electronically or by printout.

Before the physician comes to the examining room, the nurse or medical assistant can review this information with the patient and document additional detail about positive responses when appropriate. The assistant may also obtain some of the HPI information by asking the patient about the duration, timing, and severity of the symptoms, as directed by the documentation prompt for this section. The assistant may add any additional history information in the free-text area designated for his or her input as well. Otherwise, physicians who practice without a nurse or assistant will perform these tasks.

SUMMARY

Because the design of the IMR ensures a complete PFSH and a complete ROS for every initial visit, IMR forms do not require documentation prompts for these first two pages of the record. The care and documentation that are built into the structure of the IMR are sufficient to support whatever evaluation and management code the NPP indicates. Even more important, the comprehensive PFSH, ROS, and HPI provide the physician with an in-depth perspective on the patient's general health and current conditions, facilitating both quality care through the development of a comprehensive differential diagnosis, and the physician's ability to derive a reasonable assessment of the severity of the patient's illness and NPP.

References

1.   American Medical Association. *Current Procedural Terminology CPT® 2008.* Chicago, IL: American Medical Association; 2007.

2.   Health Care Financing Administration. *Documentation Guidelines for Evaluation and Management Services.* Chicago, IL: American Medical Association; 1997.

Obtaining and Documenting Background Medical History: Established Patient Visit

For established patients, the past, family, and social history (PFSH) and review of systems (ROS) document and alert the physician to changes in the patient's background medical information. Once again, it is not necessary for the physician to be the data entry person for the medical information gathered in this portion of the visit. It is more efficient for an assistant (when available) to directly obtain and document the patient's responses to an inquiry about changes in general health status or symptoms that have occurred since the date of the previous visit. The goal is to provide this information to the physician in the most efficient manner possible, so that he or she receives an updated picture of the patient's health and can then ask pertinent detailed questions related to any positive responses. Note, however, that this update of PFSH and ROS does not include information related to the present illness, which is covered in the history of present illness (HPI) section of the established visit record.

PAST, FAMILY, AND SOCIAL HISTORY AND REVIEW OF SYSTEMS

Design for Compliance Requirements

For outpatient established visits, the compliance requirements for both obtaining and documenting the PFSH and ROS can be satisfied without asking the patient the same questions that were asked during the initial visit and without redocumenting all the information recorded during previous visits. The *Documentation Guidelines for Evaluation and Management Services* provides a reasonable mechanism for obtaining PFSH and ROS information that both ensures compliance and elicits valuable medical information. It states, "A ROS and/or a PFSH obtained during an earlier encounter does not need to be rerecorded if there is evidence that the physician reviewed and updated the previous information."[1] The *Documentation Guidelines* further advises that these requirements may be satisfied by "describing any new ROS and/or PFSH information or noting there has been no change in the information; and noting the date and location of the earlier ROS and/or PFSH."[1]

A Caveat About Updating PFSH and ROS, Regarding Levels of Care

The extent of these history elements cannot exceed the level of PFSH and ROS documented at the previous visit. For example, if the patient's initial visit chart recorded review of only one system of the ROS (by definition, a problem-pertinent ROS), then an update that documents "no change since" can support only that same level of

---

continued

problem-pertinent ROS, as it is an update of only the systems previously documented. This is compliant coding, but the physician must recognize that it does not support higher levels of care. In traditional approaches to medical records, to increase the level of PFSH and/or ROS above that of the previous visit, the physician would have to ask additional relevant questions and document the responses.

The Practical E/M approach builds coding compliance for the medical history into every established patient visit. Because every initial visit includes a complete PFSH and ROS, the documentation of "no change since" for an established patient visit in the Practical E/M system documents a complete PFSH and ROS, which supports any level of care, up to and including level 5, that is medically indicated by the nature of presenting problem (NPP).

The *Documentation Guidelines* offers additional instructions that apply to the PFSH for certain types of service. Specifically, it states, "It is not necessary to record information about the PFSH. . .for subsequent hospital care. . . . and subsequent nursing facility care."[1] Therefore, intelligent medical record (IMR) templates for these services do not necessarily include the PFSH section, unless the physician wishes to do so on the basis of his or her own personal preferences.

Design for Efficiency and Quality Care

The IMR maximizes the efficiency of documenting the established patient update by employing a short-answer graphic interface template. This design permits the PFSH and ROS update information to be obtained and documented by the physician's medical assistant, who asks the patient whether there has been any change in his or her medical history or health symptoms since the previous visit. The physician reviews the documented information, obtains further details of any changes, and confirms the review by signing or initialing on the signature line provided.

The IMR template also includes a provision for documenting additional medical history data that is not required by the CPT coding system guidelines or the *Documentation Guidelines*. This supplemental information appears in the lower part of the PFSH section of Figure 11.1. Specifically confirming and recording the patient's medications and allergies at the beginning of each visit improves quality care and patient well-being by providing the physician with immediate access to this information before he or she adds a new medication or modifies the dosage of an existing treatment. This saves the physician time that would otherwise be needed to search through old records, and it may prevent errors by helping the physician to avoid prescribing a medication to which the patient has previously advised he or she is allergic. It also helps avoid medication duplications and/or interactions. These optional sections can be eliminated from the PFSH update if the patient's medical chart has a formal (and updated) "patient profile" section that includes medication lists and allergy lists readily available elsewhere in the medical record.

Graphic Interface for Established Visit PFSH and ROS Updates*

Date: ___/___/___	PMH/SH/FH	no change since last visit date: _____
Except:		
New Allergies: _____	Existing allergies:	
Current Medications: _____		
		Reviewed by:

ROS	no change since last visit date: _____
Except:	
	Reviewed by:

*The section of the PFSH update for documentation of new allergies, existing allergies, and current medications is suggested by the *Documentation Guidelines,* but this information is not required for compliance.

Figure 11.1 illustrates the upper portion of page 1 of a sample IMR template for an established patient visit. Because the questions asked for the purpose of updating the medical history are of a general nature, this template is applicable for any medical specialty.

SYNOPSIS AND ANALYSIS OF PFSH AND ROS UPDATE

Table 11.1 summarizes the medical record design used in the sample IMR form for the PFSH and ROS sections of an established patient visit.

T A B L E 11.1

Synopsis of IMR for PFSH and ROS for an Established Patient Visit

Component	Interface	Data Entry Options	Format Options	Comments
PFSH and ROS				
Short-answer questions	Graphic (with short answers)	Medical staff or Physician	Writing or dictation	Supports all E/M levels
Investigation of "yes" responses	Graphic (with short answers)	Physician	Writing or dictation	Usually brief description for added details

The IMR ensures *compliance* for this section of every established patient visit, because it structures the PFSH and ROS update on the standards required to support all levels of E/M codes, up to and including level 5. This relies on the fact that the Practical E/M approach calls for documentation of a complete PFSH and ROS on all initial visits; therefore, the updates also provide a complete PFSH and ROS. *Efficiency* is high because of the short-answer interface and the fact that the medical staff can obtain and document the medical update. The physician gains pertinent information about the patient while investing only the time required to review the form and place initials on the "Reviewed by" line. When the patient reports positive responses, the physician also focuses on these issues and documents the details.

USING THE PFSH AND ROS UPDATE SECTION OF THE IMR

When an established patient returns for a follow-up visit, it would be impractical and inappropriate to repeat the detailed patient PFSH and ROS questionnaires used for the initial visit. This would be an inefficient use of time for both the patient and the physician, and it would not effectively contribute to the patient's care.

Fortunately, the *Documentation Guidelines* has introduced the concept of an update, which is incorporated into the IMR to allow rapid documentation. First, the assistant (or physician) fills in the date of the last visit in the preprinted PFSH and ROS sections on the form. If there have not been any changes in health since the last visit, then no further documentation is required for a complete PFSH and ROS. The assistant (or physician) documents any reported changes that have occurred, in the brief narrative area following the word "Except." If a nurse or medical assistant completes this update, the physician must review the findings, document additional details about the health changes, and initial the "Reviewed by" line for each of the two sections shown in Figure 11.1.

How we ask patients about changes in their health since the last visit is an important factor in determining whether we are able to obtain meaningful information. This is the major reason that Practical E/M designates that a staff member or physician ask the patient the questions, rather than have the patient fill out a form, as they did for the initial visit. If we were to hand the patient a form with the straightforward question, "Have there been any changes in your general health since the last visit?" in many cases the patient's automatic response would be "no" (even if changes had actually occurred). The question, when asked this simply, usually does not promote sufficient consideration by patients to elicit all the details pertinent to their medical care. Therefore, eliciting meaningful information requires either the use of a more complex questionnaire, or designating the physician or a medical assistant to ask the question in a more sophisticated fashion. Using a more thought-provoking inquiry, which includes some examples of the type of information we want to obtain, can stimulate patient recall.

An example of an effective inquiry for the PFSH update is, "Since your last visit on March 5th, have you had any significant change in your medical status? For example, have you seen any other physicians, been hospitalized, had an operation, or changed any of your medications?" Following the patient's answer to this question, it is often helpful to review the listed medications and allergies from the previous visit with the patient. It can also be helpful to redocument this information in the medical record for the current visit. Although not mandated by the *Documentation Guidelines*, adding these details does provide the physician with reference information that is particularly useful when he or she adds or modifies medications at the end of the visit.

When updating the ROS, an example of an effective inquiry is, "Also, since your last visit, have you had any significant new medical symptoms, such as chest pain, shortness of breath, headache, or fatigue?"

UPDATING THE HISTORY OF PRESENT ILLNESS

As with initial patient visits, we encourage (when possible, and unless contradicted by new CMS policy) having the nurse or medical technician obtain a portion of the HPI after completing the update of the PFSH and ROS for established patients. This includes an update of the progress of symptoms related to the present illness, responses to medications, side effects, and the three elements of duration, timing, and severity. The physician will then build on this information in a more detailed review of the HPI that leads to a reassessment of the patient's differential diagnosis.

OVERVIEW OF MEDICAL STAFF INVOLVEMENT IN THE MEDICAL HISTORY

During both initial patient visits and established patient visits, there are a number of advantages to be gained from involving nurses and medical assistants in obtaining medical history information. First, the staff is immediately drawn into the care process as participating members of the health care team. It offers them more opportunities to interact with the patient directly and establish a relationship. The staff can contribute additional time to obtaining preliminary information and also eliciting detailed information that the patient might not otherwise have time to (or choose to) share. Their input can prepare physicians to focus on specific patient issues in greater depth, and it enables physicians to optimize the use of their time with patients.

Staff participation also improves office morale by encouraging the nurses and technicians to exercise the skills that attracted them to the medical profession. In addition, patients appreciate the staff being involved in their treatment. They generally feel as if more time has been spent addressing their health concerns, and they commonly take away an increased sense of caring from the practice.

How Nurses Respond to Obtaining Medical History

In my own office, the use of IMR always involved the nurses and medical assistants in direct patient care, and I always appreciated how their involvement contributed to their work enjoyment and job satisfaction. During a consultation several years ago at a multiphysician practice where I was introducing the physicians to IMR, I had the opportunity to appreciate the importance our staffs attach to this opportunity for in-depth involvement in direct patient care.

While in the clinical area, I met with the head nurse and discussed the effect of the IMR on workflow in the practice. When I cautiously inquired how the nurses would feel about being responsible for some added time to update the medical history for all of the follow-up patients, her response startled me. She said, "Doctor, that would be *wonderful*. Please tell our doctors how much we want to help them care for the patients, not just answer phone calls and move patients in and out of rooms. There are so many things we can do to help if the physicians will only let us." This perspective reinforces the beneficial impact that this type of workflow policy can have on office morale, while simultaneously providing significant improvements in patient care quality and efficiency.

SUMMARY

The two short response boxes for updating the PFSH and ROS, which appear at the top of page 1 of the IMR's established patient visit form, have several compliance and patient care benefits. The original purpose for including this material was to ensure that physicians obtained and documented a comprehensive history for E/M compliance purposes, thereby supporting any level of E/M care that the physician determined to be appropriate for the NPP. However, the crucial benefit of obtaining this updated health information is that, with a minimal investment of time by either the staff or the physician, it contributes meaningful medical information to every visit. It provides the physician with an ongoing gauge of the patient's health as a setting for the specific concerns of the visit, and it ensures that no significant information is overlooked.

If the patient's general health and medications have not changed significantly since the previous visit, the physician can reasonably interpret that any specific health changes, for better or worse, relate directly to the problems he or she is addressing for the patient. On the other hand, if there have been unrelated new health issues, the physician can factor this information into the care he or she is providing for the patient. For example, if a patient presents a new symptom, it is important to know whether there was a new medication prescribed by another physician two weeks ago. The symptom may be quickly identified as a side effect of the new medication. In some cases, the side effect can present significant health danger to the patient. In others, awareness of this potential etiology for the patient's new symptoms can eliminate a patient's distress, as well as saving both the physician and the patient significant time, effort, and cost that would otherwise be spent attempting to discover the cause of the new problem.

As related anecdotally in the Chapter 1 sidebar titled "The Insight Moment," updating information about the patient's general health at the beginning of every follow-up visit not only paints a meaningful background picture but, in many instances, also contributes critical information that solves some medical problems and prevents others from occurring. This feature clearly illustrates the positive impact that integrating compliance into the medical record can have on the quality of patient care.

References

1.   Health Care Financing Administration. *Documentation Guidelines for Evaluation and Management Services.* Chicago, IL: American Medical Association; 1997.

2.   American Medical Association. *Current Procedural Terminology CPT® 2008.* Chicago, IL: American Medical Association; 2007.

Reviewing Chief Complaint; Past, Family, and Social History; and Review of Systems

The next step in the physician/patient encounter, regardless of whether the patient is established or this is his or her first visit to the office, is the physician's review of the chief complaint and past, family, and social history (PFSH).

PRIOR TO ENTERING THE EXAMINATION ROOM

The physician should review the completed information on the medical chart before entering a patient's examining room. Looking over the PFSH and review of systems (ROS) provides a comprehensive background summary of the patient's general health. The completed information also identifies the patient's reason for the visit, and it provides the physician with some details about this problem from information documented in both the history of present illness (HPI) and the portion of the ROS related to the physician's specialty.

This initial assessment also identifies any positive responses in the ROS and PFSH that merit further investigation and documentation when the physician is talking with the patient. For example, if the symptoms reported in the chief complaint began six months ago, it will be important to ask the patient when he or she started using each of the medications documented. If the onset of symptoms coincided with the start of a medication, a quick visit to the *Physicians' Desk Reference* often solves an otherwise perplexing problem, and may save not only time, but also hundreds or thousands of dollars in expensive tests (all of which would likely prove negative).

Practical E/M and Medication Side Effects

While this example of medication side effects might sound rare or far-fetched, the opposite is true. In my own practice, immediately after reading the patient's chief complaint, our nurses would always ask (and document) when the patient had started his or her medications. They would then check the *Physician's Desk Reference* and identify which of the patient's medications' recognized side effects were potentially responsible for the presenting symptoms. I could then evaluate this etiology in detail during the visit. Incredibly, medication side effects were responsible for patients' reported symptoms an average of *5 to 10 times per day*. It was truly amazing; patients would arrive with complex and challenging head and neck symptoms, such as dizziness, headache, swallowing problems, dry mouth, abnormal taste, abnormal sense of smell, etc. The "normal" workup of these symptoms would have been extensive and expensive.

Instead, with the guidance of the intelligent medical record (IMR), many times the nurses were able to identify the cause of the problem before I even saw the patient. All I

---

continued

had to do was walk into the room, review the open *Physician's Desk Reference*, complete the review of the medical history and perform the appropriate level of physical examination to make sure there was no significant pathology present, document the chart, and have the very pleasant task of advising the patient that there was probably nothing seriously wrong: "Mr Jones, I'm happy to tell you that so far it appears likely that there is nothing seriously wrong. In fact, based on when your dizziness began, it is very likely that this represents a side effect of your medication, X. Certainly, that's where we should start. I will contact Dr ABC (who prescribed the medication), and he'll advise what options you have for an alternate treatment or dosage. I'll want to recheck you in 6 weeks to make sure everything has returned to normal. If it has not, we can evaluate further at that time to determine what might be going on and help to make you better. Of course, call sooner if the problem starts to get worse."

The previous sidebar illustrates how encouraging medical personnel to obtain and/or review elements of the history can save physician time and provide information that might otherwise be overlooked, usually because of time pressures physicians face in our present health system. It also demonstrates how adhering to Practical Evaluation and Management (E/M) practices by obtaining a complete PFSH not only assists with Current Procedural Terminology (CPT®) coding requirements, but also yields critical information that leads directly to enhanced quality of care.

When the patient's symptoms prove to be secondary to medications, the effect this has on coding is completely dependent, as it should be, on the severity and risk of the side effect for each particular patient. In the event of a minor symptom, with anticipated rapid resolution after changing medications, the nature of presenting problem (NPP) and selected level of care (E/M code) should be low. This would usually then warrant performing an expanded problem-focused or detailed examination and only low complexity of medical decision making (MDM). On the other hand, if the side effect were severe or life threatening (eg, aplastic anemia or renal failure), the NPP and selected level of care (E/M code) would be high. This high level of the NPP then appropriately warrants performing and documenting a comprehensive physical examination and a complex MDM.

For an initial visit, the IMR's ROS includes questions pertaining to 10 or more of the 14 organ systems described in the *Documentation Guidelines for Evaluation and Management Services*.[1] The patient's responses provide the physician with specific information concerning signs and symptoms related to his or her specialty, and they also present a reasonably thorough background picture of the patient's overall health. Some of the positive responses for these questions will relate to the present illness and be marked by a check in the "Current" box.

The Medical Value of Complete PFSH and ROS

In January 2002, I witnessed an extreme example of the power of the ROS template in eliciting important medical information from patients. A 48-year-old patient came to our office for an initial visit. He completed the patient portion of our IMR form, including the chief complaint, PFSH, and ROS sections. The patient's presenting complaint was "ears clogged" for several weeks, a typical symptom for a patient whose ears are probably obstructed with earwax. The figure on the next page shows the check box portion of this patient's ROS.

My medical technician, who had worked with me for three years, went into the patient's examination room to obtain some preliminary information about the HPI. The information she obtained and documented on duration, timing, severity, location, modifying factors, and associated signs and symptoms all strongly confirmed that the patient's underlying problem was probably impacted earwax. However, she also reviewed

continued

1. Please check the "Yes" or "No" box to indicate if you have any of the following symptoms.
2. For any "Yes" responses, please check the "current" box if this symptom relates to the reason for your visit today.

		Yes	No	Current		Yes	No	Current
GENERAL	Chills	☐	☒	☐	Weight loss or gain	☒	☐	☐
	Fatigue	☒	☐	☐	Daytime sleepiness	☒	☐	☐
ALLERGY	Sneezing fits	☒	☐	☐	Postnasal drip	☒	☐	☐
NEURO	Headache	☐	☒	☐	Passing out	☐	☒	☐
Eyes	Eye pain / pressure	☐	☒	☐	Watery/Itchy eyes	☒	☐	☐
ENT	Ear pain of itch	☒	☐	☐	Ear drainage	☒	☐	☒
	Hearing loss	☒	☐	☒	Ear noises	☐	☒	☐
	Dizziness	☐	☒	☐	Lightheadedness	☐	☒	☐
	Nasal congestion	☒	☐	☐	Sinus pressure or pain	☒	☐	☐
	Sense of smell problem	☐	☒	☐	Prob snoring, apnea	☒	☐	☐
	Hoarseness	☐	☒	☐	Throat pain	☐	☒	☐
	Throat clearing	☒	☐	☐	Throat dryness/itch	☒	☐	☐
RESPIR.	Cough	☒	☐	☐	Coughing blood	☐	☒	☐
	Wheezing	☒	☐	☐	Shortness of breath	☒	☐	☐
CARDIAC	Chest pain	☐	☒	☐	Palpitations	☐	☒	☐
GI	Difficulty swallowing	☐	☒	☐	Heartburn	☒	☐	☐
GU	Frequent urination	☐	☒	☐	Painful urination	☐	☒	☐
HEME/LYM	Swollen glands	☐	☒	☐	Sweating at night	☐	☒	☐
	Bleeding problems	☐	☒	☐	Easy bruising	☐	☒	☐
ENDO	Feel warmer than others	☐	☒	☐	Feel cooler than others	☐	☒	☐
MSK	Joint aches	☐	☒	☐	Muscle aches	☐	☒	☐
SKIN	Rash	☒	☐	☐	Hives	☐	☒	☐
	Itching	☒	☐	☐	Skin or hair changes	☐	☒	☐
PSYCH	Depression	☐	☒	☐	Anxiety or panic	☐	☒	☐

the ROS, with its many positive responses, only two of which had checks in the "Current" boxes to indicate that they were directly related to the present illness. On the basis of her review, when I arrived outside the patient's room she handed me the medical record and told me, "I have the patient reading our information sheets for allergy, sinus problems, laryngopharyngeal reflux, and snoring/obstructive sleep apnea." She had inferred these potential diagnoses on the basis of the positive responses in the ROS, specifically the following:

■ The allergy impression resulted from the patient's positive responses to "sneezing fits, watery eyes, nasal congestion."

■ The sinus problems impression resulted from the patient's positive responses to "nasal congestion, sinus pressure or pain."

■ The laryngopharyngeal reflux impression resulted from the patient's positive responses to "throat clearing, postnasal drip, cough, heartburn."

■ The snoring/obstructive sleep apnea impression resulted from the patient's positive responses to "problems snoring/apnea, fatigue, daytime sleepiness."

In addition to obtaining a more detailed HPI, the majority of the time I spent obtaining this patient's medical history consisted primarily of in-depth questions about

continued

all of the positive ROS responses. I determined that the NPP was high, because of the symptoms strongly suggestive of severe obstructive sleep apnea, a potentially life-threatening illness. The documentation prompts guided an appropriate comprehensive physical examination, and a high-complexity MDM was readily documented because of the high risk of the medical problem and the patient's extensive diagnoses and potential treatment options. I submitted an appropriate E/M code of 99205.

It is sufficient to state that my medical technician's clinical impressions were 100% valid. The patient had both history information and physical examination findings that strongly supported her interpretations. Diagnostic testing subsequently confirmed that the patient had severe, potentially life-threatening obstructive sleep apnea (respiratory disturbance index of 60 apneic episodes per hour and severe oxygen desaturation). Over the next two months, appropriate medical care and weight loss intervention gave this patient relief of all his symptoms, including those related to obstructive sleep apnea.

The patient arrived with current symptoms related to earwax, but the medical record drew out and recorded information that led to the discovery, and subsequent treatment, of far more significant and health-endangering conditions. The obvious conclusion from this case is that the intelligence of the medical record serves as a highly effective information gathering and reporting tool, sufficient to direct a clinician toward multiple significant medical diagnoses. My medical technician certainly deserved (and was given) tremendous credit for her ability to formulate a reasonable set of diagnoses from the IMR's report of the patient's symptoms. This stage of care was completed efficiently and compliantly. It also positively affected productivity (the patient arrived to be treated for a low-level chief complaint, but following the ROS was determined to have disease processes with a high-severity NPP, leading to an appropriately high-level E/M visit). However, the critical message is how this information affected the quality of care for this patient. For a patient presenting with a simple problem of earwax, the thorough ROS completed by the patient helped us identify, diagnose, and successfully treat several major health issues.

AFTER ENTERING THE EXAMINATION ROOM

The Practical E/M approach recommends that before beginning an investigation of the HPI, the physician should address all of the positive responses documented by the patient in the PFSH and ROS template, except those related to the patient's present illness. These questions are fresh in the patient's memory from filling out the IMR form, and it is most effective to inquire about this background medical information first.

The physician must investigate and document the pertinent medical details related to any of the positive responses recorded by the patient. Not only is this required to meet the standards of E/M compliance, but it is also important for quality of care and critical to help prevent potential liability problems. Each positive response is a possible additional "presenting problem," at least until further evaluation proves it to be insignificant or already being adequately treated. For example, in the past history section, if the patient has checked the "Yes" box for thyroid problems, the physician should inquire about the nature of the thyroid problem and document all relevant information (such as whether the patient has been diagnosed with hyperthyroid or hypothyroid condition, when this was diagnosed, how well it is controlled with treatment, the name of the physician following the condition, and so on).

Each of the positive symptoms and signs recorded in the ROS can be treated as a "mini" HPI, requiring details about the chronological course of the patient's symptoms, including additional questions about severity, timing, duration, and so on. This information is best obtained and documented by writing in the narrative interface that appears as a series of blank lines below the check box interface. For physicians who prefer to dictate, there is an appropriate check box, "See attached dictation," to document that the information will be transcribed on a separate page.

Some of the patient's symptoms may be minor or may even have resolved. For these, the physician's responsibility is simply to document this status. Alternatively, some of the symptoms identified in these sections may present significant and untreated medical issues. Those that relate to the physician's specialty will become additional active problems, and they may be of even greater health concern than the problem that brought the patient to the office. These will be categorized along with the patient's presenting complaint as active problems in the "impressions" portion of the MDM section. The risks and potential morbidity and mortality of these additional active problems should be included as part of the physician's assessment of the NPP and factored into the selection of the appropriate level of care (ie, coding) for the visit.

Multiple Positive Responses

Occasionally the PFSH and particularly the ROS will have an abundance of significant positive responses. While the physician must do preliminary assessment of these issues, if there are too many for the time of the visit, some of the nonacute problems may be noted and deferred for further evaluation during a subsequent visit.

In addition, the broad brush stroke of IMR's comprehensive ROS (reviewing at least 10 of the 14 designated systems) may also lead physicians to discover symptoms of significant systemic illnesses that are unrelated to their own field of expertise, eg, thyroid dysfunction (feeling warmer or cooler than others, skin changes, hair changes, fatigue, etc), panic disorder, heart disease (chest pain, shortness of breath), chronic obstructive pulmonary disease, or malignancy (weight loss, dysphagia). Under these circumstances, the physician should ask whether each condition is under care by a physician and, if not, the physician should determine whether the symptoms are of sufficient concern to warrant referral to an appropriate specialist for evaluation.

For those symptoms and conditions that are currently being treated, the physician should also obtain further details to determine whether, in his (her) best judgment, the patient is responding appropriately to the therapy. If he (she) feels that this is not the case, it is appropriate to have the patient contact the physician who is caring for that condition and schedule reevaluation, or even to contact the other physician directly when medically indicated. Of course, all of the additional history information obtained from the patient should be documented in the narrative portion of the ROS section. Additionally, all of the clinical impressions and recommendations for follow-up care with another physician should be documented in the "impressions" and "plans" sections of the MDM.

Finally, on rare occasions, the positive symptoms in the ROS may present an acute problem, such as chest pain, that prompts the physician to interrupt the visit and arrange for immediate urgent care.

Personal Experience With the ROS and Quality Care

When physicians are designing their IMR, Practical E/M encourages them to include multiple appropriate questions for each of the 14 systems defined by the *Documentation Guidelines*.[1] Negative responses by the patient add no time or effort for physicians, while positive responses often help us to help our patients by providing better care through early identification of significant illness. In eight years of experience working with an IMR as an otolaryngologist, I encountered patients with significant symptoms in 13 of these 14 systems. Some of the previously undiagnosed diseases I helped identify in

continued

fields unrelated to my own specialty include cerebral aneurysm (severe headache of recent onset), asthma, chronic obstructive pulmonary disease, congestive heart failure, myocardial infarction, gastric ulcer, and lymphoma of the abdomen (weight loss without dieting and night sweats).

On more than one occasion, I stopped an office visit within several minutes of meeting a patient for the first time, after asking the patient a few questions about his or her positive response in the ROS to "chest pain." In most such cases, further questions revealed information along the lines of, "My physician follows me for this, it's been worked up, I'm on medication, and there has been no change," which I would document in the narrative section of the ROS and proceed with the visit. However, in those circumstances when the patient instead reported, "It started yesterday, I've never had it before, it's severe at times, and there's pain in my left arm and jaw," I would discontinue the visit, call the patient's internist, and convey his or her instructions to the patient— sending the patient immediately to either the physician's office or the hospital.

When these instances of disease with high NPP occur, unless the physician is going to perform a comprehensive examination and document complex MDM related to the heart problem, from a coding perspective, I recommend not even submitting this as an E/M visit. Although the patient has a severe problem, it's not in your specialty. You certainly don't want to take the time to address the patient's less-than-life-threatening chief complaint for the otolaryngology visit. Get the patient into the proper medical hands as soon as possible. The patient will certainly return when his or her heart condition has stabilized, and then you can provide appropriate initial visit care related to the problem that brought the patient to your office. This is also more productive than submitting a low-level initial visit if you didn't have time to complete the HPI, physical examination, and MDM.

ADVANTAGES OF OBTAINING THE PFSH AND ROS BEFORE ADDRESSING THE HPI

Having a completed picture of the patient's PFSH and ROS before beginning to investigate the patient's HPI impacts the physician's approach to the entire care process. Approaching the history in this fashion provides the physician with significant insight into the patient's overall health and the context for the current problem. The physician can also correlate how known diagnoses and symptoms relate to the present illness. From a quality perspective, this encourages a more comprehensive or holistic approach.

In contrast, the traditional approach of evaluating the HPI first, followed by the remainder of the medical history, may encourage problem-focused care. This results from the fact that when the elements of the medical history are completed in this sequence, physicians focus their attention immediately on the current problem or problems. Completing and considering the PFSH and ROS are then easily viewed more as chores that must be completed for coding purposes rather than as essential components of patient care. Under this circumstance, physicians tend to see the PFSH and ROS as background information to a central present illness, rather than perceiving the present illness as one aspect of the patient's overall health picture, which is a perspective that is most compatible with quality care.

Why Practical E/M Recommends Addressing the PFSH and ROS Before the HPI

Having used IMR since 1995, I always had the PFSH and ROS information available before entering the patient's room and before investigating the HPI. Therefore, my evaluation of patients always started with a reasonable understanding of their general

continued

health, including active medical problems and treatments, before I turned my attention to the problem for which they were being seen (ie, the HPI). This approach automatically orients the physician toward a perspective of first considering the patient as a whole, and then as someone who also happens to have a current illness that has brought them to the current appointment.

Several years ago, I identified a common suboptimal effect of the usual practice of investigating the HPI before reviewing the PFSH and ROS. This insight followed my review of one of my daughter's medical school exercises, which consisted of a history and physical on a "standardized patient" whose primary complaint related to a urinary tract symptom. Her H&P consisted of a rather remarkable eight printed pages of comprehensive care and researched assessment. As in most, if not all, medical schools, the traditional teaching of medical evaluations has taught physicians to obtain the HPI first, followed by the rest of the medical history. Her medical record was documented in this same order.

I was struck by the contrast of reading the HPI before the PFSH and ROS. I felt disoriented, as if I were evaluating an illness that happened to have a patient attached, rather than the other way around. As I was reading the HPI, I found myself struggling to picture the whole patient. Is there diabetes in the family? Does she have polyuria? Has she ever had abdominal or gynecological surgery? What medications is she on? Has she had a recent weight change? Once I had finished the HPI and then read the PFSH and ROS, it all came together and made sense. However, this approach to understanding the patient was much more of a struggle, because the medical information related to the patient's current problem was disconnected from the overall health setting of the patient.

I then reread the report, but started with the PFSH and ROS and then proceeded to the HPI. What a difference! Knowing the background information first made it so much easier to visualize the patient and understand the "right" questions that needed to be asked about the presenting problem. I compare it to piecing together a jigsaw puzzle. We can do a much better (and more efficient) job when we have a picture of the nearly completed puzzle in front of us from the start, rather than trying to put together puzzle pieces with no initial concept of what the whole image actually looks like.

SUMMARY

The PFSH and ROS portions of the medical history provide extensive insight into the patient's current health, and they help the physician arrive at a correct diagnosis related to the present illness. Also, positive symptoms in the physician's specialty, but unrelated to the present illness, can help the physician identify additional health problems that may benefit from diagnosis and treatment. Almost as important is the fact that the negative ROS responses complete the picture of the patient's medical background by indicating many medical problems that may be ruled out. Finally, a thorough medical history also offers physicians the opportunity to identify potential medical issues unrelated to their own specialty or beyond their expertise, and provide referrals whenever appropriate.

After reviewing the patient's completed PFSH, ROS, and portions of the HPI documented by staff, the physician has a good sense of the patient's specialty-specific medical issues and the background setting of the patient's overall health. This is the optimal time to address the medical issues related to the patient's chief complaint.

Reference

1.   Health Care Financing Administration. *Documentation Guidelines for Evaluation and Management Services*. Chicago, IL: American Medical Association; 1997.

Documenting the History of Present Illness

GOALS FOR DESIGN

Ideally, documentation of the history of present illness (HPI) should concisely tell an in-depth story that enables the physician, and/or others reviewing the patient's chart, to appreciate the nature and severity of the patient's medical problem(s) and the factors that point to the final differential diagnosis. To achieve this ideal efficiently, the intelligent medical record (IMR) employs a narrative interface for documentation of the HPI.

The narrative interface allows free-text entry of the history as it evolves, step by step, through a process of logical investigation into the chronological course of the illness and the feature contributing to each phase of the patient's medical problems. This design, and the natural evolution it allows for documenting the history, enables physicians to convey the detailed characteristics that individualize each patient's illnesses and to describe the impact of those illnesses on the patient.

The narrative interface lends itself to data entry by writing or dictation. (The options for physicians using electronic health records are discussed in Chapter 23.) The IMR forms provide a check box for physicians to indicate when some or all of the information has been entered into the record by dictation. Separate sections may also be provided for input by the medical staff and the physician.

The Role of the HPI in the Medical Diagnostic Process

Physicians learn the fundamentals of the medical diagnostic process from their earliest introduction to clinical medicine. This long-established approach, taught to physicians as the optimal method for evaluating the patient's medical conditions and developing a valid differential diagnosis, is the fundamental method that physicians apply in pursuit of true quality care, which begins with making an accurate diagnosis.

While the diagnostic process includes consideration of all the elements of the comprehensive history and physical (H&P), it begins the assessment of a patient's medical problems by obtaining a thorough medical history, including background information (past, family, and social history [PFSH] and review of systems [ROS]) and a meaningful HPI. Physicians usually begin taking the HPI with an open-ended question to the patient about how the problem began. The responses to initial questions will suggest possible underlying diagnoses and an initial clinical appraisal of the severity of the patient's illness. This initial impression triggers a dynamic process in which physicians use increasingly precise questions (often related to the "eight elements of the HPI") while tracing the time course of the patient's symptoms. The interaction concludes when physicians are comfortable that they have established a probable diagnosis, a set of alternative diagnoses, and a reasonable assessment of the severity of their patient's illness (ie, the nature of presenting problem [NPP]).

This interweaving of diagnostic reasoning as a component of obtaining the medical history is an advanced medical skill. As noted in the *Bates' Guide*, "[b]ecause assessment takes place in the clinician's mind, the process of clinical reasoning often seems inaccessible and even mysterious to the beginning student. . . .As you gain experience, your thinking process will begin at the outset of the patient encounter, not at the end."[3(pp 783-784)] Accurately documenting the HPI requires a narrative approach to record the details of the course of a patient's illness and also to convey the physician's thought process during this component of the diagnostic process.

Design for Compliance Requirements

The Current Procedural Terminology (CPT®) codebook and the *Documentation Guidelines for Evaluation and Management Services* define the HPI as "a chronological description of the development of the patient's present illness from the first sign and/or symptom to the present."[1,2] They also cite that the HPI includes information about eight identified elements:

- Location
- Quality
- Severity
- Duration
- Timing
- Context
- Modifying factors
- Associated signs and symptoms[1,2]

Finally, the *Documentation Guidelines* additionally advises that "a brief HPI consists of one to three elements of the HPI," and "an extended HPI consists of at least four elements of the HPI, or the status of at least three chronic or inactive conditions."[2]

As illustrated in Figure 13.1, the IMR form provides a two-part documentation prompt for the HPI. One part lists the eight elements of the HPI to assist the physician during care. The other part first reminds that the HPI must report the *chronology* of the patient's illness and then indicates the number of elements that must be obtained and documented to meet the CPT coding system requirements for various levels of evaluation and management (E/M) care. This prompt is specific to the type of service of each IMR form.

Examples of the Elements of the HPI

The CPT codebook and the *Documentation Guidelines* do not provide detailed definitions or sample questions for the eight elements of the HPI. Although most of these should be reasonably self-explanatory, physicians sometimes request examples. The following list is just that: a smorgasbord of questions physicians can ask patients, categorized to illuminate the eight elements. However, these examples are certainly not to be considered a comprehensive inventory.

1. Duration
   - How long have you had the problem?
   - When did the problem begin?
2. Timing
   - Is the nausea constant or intermittent?
   - How often do you get the headaches? How often do you get the severe ones?

---

continued

- When you get the dizziness, how long does it last? (Dizziness that lasts for 3 seconds is very different from dizziness lasting 24 hours.)

3. Severity
   - Is the pain mild, moderate, or severe?
   - On a scale of 1 to 10, how severe is the pain?

4. Location
   - Where on your belly is the pain located?
   - Did it start there also, or has it moved?
   - Does it stay in that one spot, or does it move to other parts of your belly or back?

5. Quality
   - Describe the nature of the pain.
   - Is the pain sharp, dull, aching, pounding, or something else?
   - Describe the sensation you feel without using the word "dizzy."
   - By dizzy, do you mean lightheaded? Is there a sense of motion—up and down, side to side, or going around and around?

6. Context
   - Have you ever had a similar problem in the past?
   - What were you doing when the problem started?
   - Have you had any injuries or trauma to that part of your body?

7. Modifying factors
   - Does anything make the nausea better or worse?
   - Do antacids give you any relief?
   - Does it change in different positions?
   - Did the antibiotics you took give you any relief?

8. Associated signs and symptoms
   - Are there any vision changes or do you see flashing lights with the headache?
   - Do you have the sense that you know when the headache is coming?
   - Since you've had the sweating at night, do you notice any rashes; muscle aches or joint aches; fever; shortness of breath; lumps under your arms, in your neck, or in your groin? Any weight loss or gain?

The option to achieve an "extended HPI" by documenting the status of three or more chronic or inactive diseases is most appropriately used for follow-up care of an established patient who has several stable ongoing medical conditions controlled with medication (eg, diabetes, hypertension, asthma, and so on). The patient may have few if any symptoms, but the conditions warrant regular follow-up monitoring. Inquiry about the status of these illnesses is a compliant alternative to asking about aspects of symptoms using a chronological description and the eight elements of HPI.

A typical HPI section for an outpatient established patient visit is shown in Figure 13.1. The appearance of the HPI template is similar for all of the different types of service, but the documentation prompts are modified according to the CPT descriptors for each type of service (eg, for an outpatient established patient visit, one to three elements will support up to a level 3 visit, which is a higher level of care than one to three elements supports for an initial visit).

Despite the variations in HPI documentation requirements to achieve the various levels of care for different types of service, documenting a chronological description of the course of the patient's present illness that includes four or more of the eight HPI elements always qualifies as an "extended" HPI. This amount of care satisfies the documentation requirement for all levels of care warranted by the NPP, up to and including level 5, for all types of service. For reasons of both compliance and medical quality, the Practical E/M approach recommends documenting an extended HPI for every visit.

FIGURE 13.1

Sample HPI Template for Outpatient Established Patient Visit

PRESENT ILLNESS	Chronology with: 1. one to three elements (level 2 or 3) 2. four to eight elements; OR status of 3 chronic or inactive conditions (level 4 or 5)
	(1) duration (2) timing (3) severity; (4) location (5) quality (6) context (7) modifying factors (8) assoc. signs & symptoms
	☐ See attached dictation

Design for Efficiency and Quality Care

The IMR documentation prompt modifies the order in which the eight elements are listed in the CPT codebook, because we strongly urge physicians to obtain (or have their medical assistant obtain) the first three elements listed during every visit. Specifically, duration, timing, and severity provide valuable information relative to every patient encounter, and both the questions and the responses to these elements are usually relatively straightforward. Once the medical assistant, nurse, or physician has documented the background information obtained from the patient for these initial three elements, the next (fourth) element(s), documented by the physician as a component of a formal medical history, will ensure an "extended" HPI, as well as completing the documentation of a comprehensive medical history, for every visit.

The body of the HPI template is a free-text section that gives the physician the opportunity to document an in-depth narrative description of the course of the patient's illness, including one or more additional elements of the HPI. When investigating the patient's symptoms to determine the possible etiologies, physicians invariably ask one or more questions related to "associated signs and symptoms." This provides the fourth element, which will account for the necessary extended HPI documentation. Each of these eight elements should be investigated when indicated, on the basis of obtaining a thorough medical history and carrying out an effective "diagnostic process."

We want the HPI to "tell a story," which reveals the complexity of the medical history as it unfolds. The narrative documentation approach reflects the process whereby the history, as it evolves, guides the diagnostic process. Part of the art of medicine involves a physician comparing the course of an illness, and the nuances of the patient's symptoms, with the physician's own knowledge of the natural course of diseases. This insight is often what leads to a final differential diagnosis, which the physician then evaluates further through the physical examination and subsequent diagnostic testing. For the physician, it frequently feels like "playing detective," as he or she searches down clue after clue to arrive at the correct diagnosis. This narrative approach to documenting the HPI positively affects both quality care and optimal physician efficiency.

Why Not a Graphic Interface for HPI?

An alternative hypothetical graphic interface would simply list the eight elements of HPI and obtain one-dimensional responses to questions about each of them. However, such an approach is incapable of meaningfully recording a true medical history, which includes a chronological description of the development of the disease process. In many cases, particularly complex ones, this interface is therefore unsatisfactory for compliance as well as for quality of care and completeness of documentation.

continued

In practice, auditors have encountered written, dictated, and electronic medical records that attempt to use this approach. The result is a snapshot of the patient's major symptom rather than a history of the illness. In most cases, it conveys little more than a detailed (or extended) chief complaint rather than an actual medical history. For example, the statement "patient has three weeks of mild intermittent pain in the center of the chest" is just a detailed chief complaint that happens to include four elements of an HPI (duration, timing, severity, and location). However, there is no *history* of the illness. Therefore, this level of information fails to provide the possibility of discovering or presenting the full story of a patient's history. Instead, every patient with a given symptom will sound very similar to every other patient with that symptom. This approach fails to help the physician implement the medical diagnostic process to develop a reasonable differential diagnosis with a high probability of accuracy or insight into the severity of the patient's illness.

The graphic interface approach would also be unlikely to provide the physician with reasonable protection in the untoward event of a liability case. Attorneys counsel that a medical record that thoroughly describes a patient's illness, and documents the physician's reasons for making medical decisions, provides the physician's best defense.

SYNOPSIS AND ANALYSIS OF HPI

Table 13.1 summarizes the IMR design for the HPI section of the medical record.

TABLE 13.1

Synopsis of IMR for HPI

Section of HPI	Interface	Data Entry Options	Format Options	Comments
Nurse/ Assistant Section "Duration, timing, and severity." May include additional elements as well.	Narrative (with short answer)	• Nurse/ technician • Left blank if no extender	• Writing or dictation	The eight elements are medically useful in almost all cases.
Physician Section Detailed investigation, chronological description and details of appropriate elements of HPI	Narrative	Physician	Writing or dictation	Narrative interface is essential to explore details of individuall patient illness.

Following Practical E/M's recommendation of obtaining and documenting the chronology plus four or more elements of the HPI ensures coding *compliance* for every visit, up to and including level 5 care. The resulting "extended" HPI also encourages quality care by providing extensive information that helps physicians arrive at accurate diagnoses for their patients.

USING THE HPI SECTION OF THE IMR

As noted in the preceding chapters, the physician obtains the HPI after reviewing information related to the PFSH and ROS, which provide an overview of the patient's general health status.

The narrative interface enables a physician who is skilled in obtaining a medical history to record the relevant and meaningful clinical information efficiently, without necessarily requiring extensive writing or time. For example, the brief (34-word) sample HPI illustrated in Figure 13.2 includes all eight elements of the present illness and concisely describes a patient with the probable diagnosis of acute otitis externa. This description also provides enough clinical information to rule out the existence of both a chronic external ear problem and significant middle ear pathology.

FIGURE 13.2

Sample Narrative HPI for Patient With a Complaint of Unilateral Ear Pain (and a Diagnosis Confirmed as Acute Otitis Externa)

HPI

Five days of moderate and increasing left ear pain and tenderness. Pain is constant and sharp. No hearing loss, tinnitus, or dizziness. Patient uses cotton swabs daily. No recent swimming. No previous ear problems.

Elements of HPI

- Duration: 5 days
- Timing: Pain is constant
- Severity: Moderate and increasing
- Location: Left ear
- Quality: Sharp
- Context: No recent swimming; no previous ear problems
- Modifying factors: Patient uses cotton swabs daily
- Associated signs and symptoms: No hearing loss, tinnitus, or dizziness

---

SUMMARY

The HPI section of the IMR provides documentation prompts that report the elements of the HPI for compliance, guide initial input of information by the medical staff, and encourage the physician to perform and document an "extended" history for every patient visit. This both ensures coding compliance and promotes effective care. The HPI employs a narrative interface because it enables the physician to have complete freedom to pursue and record the course of each patient's individualized disease process. It also gives the physician the ability to accurately document the thought process whereby a directed medical history develops and narrows down a differential diagnosis.

References

1.   American Medical Association. *Current Procedural Terminology CPT® 2008*. Chicago, IL: American Medical Association; 2007.

2.   Health Care Financing Administration. *Documentation Guidelines for Evaluation and Management Services*. Chicago, IL: American Medical Association; 1997.

3.   Bickley LS, Szilagyi PG. *Bates' Guide to Physical Examination and History Taking*. 8th ed. Philadelphia, PA: Lippincott Williams & Wilkins, 2003.

Documenting the Nature of Presenting Problem

Documentation of the nature of presenting problem (NPP) is not found in traditional medical records. Similarly, traditional teaching of evaluation and management (E/M) coding has focused on the three "key" components while paying little attention to this "contributory factor."[1] However, the NPP plays a central role in Practical E/M, just as it does in the Current Procedural Terminology (CPT®) coding system and the clinical examples found in the CPT codebook.[1]

GOALS FOR DESIGN

In Practical E/M methodology, after completing the medical history, the physician performs an initial assessment of the NPP and identifies the medically indicated level of care. This assessment then guides the physician through the physical examination and medical decision making (MDM) to ensure that he or she performs and documents the appropriate amounts of care. The physician may reconsider the severity of the NPP and appropriate level of care at any time during the physical examination and MDM. The final level of the NPP will be reassessed and documented during or after documenting the MDM.

Design for Compliance Requirements

The intelligent medical record (IMR) template summarizes the CPT coding guidelines concerning the NPP in its section for NPP definitions and documentation prompts, which is located on the final page of the form. This section lists the definitions for the six or seven recognized levels of severity (depending on the type of service) to help physicians identify the severity of the NPP related to each patient's illness. The template includes the CPT coding system definitions that were previously shown in Table 5.3, plus Practical E/M's proposed definitions for mid-level NPP descriptions, which were presented in Table 5.4. These concepts are combined in Figure 14.1.

Design for Efficiency and Quality Care

The IMR uses a simple selection-list graphic interface for documentation of NPP. The templates vary with each type of service, in accordance with CPT coding descriptors for levels of care appropriate for severity of NPP. For ease of documentation, the template enables the physician to circle the level of NPP that, in his or her judgment, is most appropriate for each encounter. Figure 14.1 illustrates the NPP documentation template for an outpatient initial visit or consultation. The documentation prompts duplicate the descriptors in the CPT codebook for this type of service. For example, the NPP for E/M code 99202 is described in the CPT codebook as, "usually, the presenting problem(s) are of low to moderate severity."[1]

NPP Section, with Documentation Prompts

NATURE OF PRESENTING PROBLEM(S)

1. minor   **(level 1)**   Problem runs definite and prescribed course, is transient in nature, and is not likely to permanently alter health status; OR, has a good prognosis with management and compliance.

2. low   **(level 1)++**   Problem in which the risk of morbidity without treatment is low; there is little to no risk of mortality without treatment; full recovery without functional impairment is expected.

3. low - mod   **(level 2)**   Problem in which the risk of morbidity without treatment is low to moderate; there is low to moderate risk of mortality without treatment; full recovery without functional impairment is expected in most cases, with low probability of prolonged functional impairment

4. moderate   **(level 3)**   Problem in which the risk of morbidity without treatment is moderate; there is moderate risk of mortality without treatment; prognosis is uncertain, or there is an increased probability of prolonged functional impairment.

5. mod - high   **(levels 4, 5)**   Problem in which the risk of morbidity without treatment is moderate to high; there is moderate risk of mortality without treatment; uncertain prognosis or increased probability of prolonged functional impairment

6. high   **(level 5)**   Problem in which the risk of morbidity without treatment is high to extreme; there is moderate to high risk of mortality without treatment, or high probability of severe prolonged functional impairment.

++ For Consultation, a low NPP is equal to a level 2

*The lowest level of NPP, minimal, does not apply to the initial visit type of service; it is reserved for outpatient established patient visits, and it appears in the NPP documentation prompt for that type of service. Also, as discussed in Chapter 5, the CPT descriptors introduce the NPP levels of "low to moderate" and "moderate to high," which are not specifically defined by CPT (although we proposed definitions for them in Chapter 5), but are associated with various E/M code levels for many types of E/M service.

THE NPP TEMPLATE FOR DIFFERENT TYPES OF SERVICE

The CPT code descriptions for several types of service present different definitions for the levels of severity of the NPP from those shown in Figure 14.1. The alternative definitions appear for the following types of service:

■ subsequent hospital care

■ nursing facility services (assessments and subsequent care)

■ established domiciliary patients

Figure 14.2 illustrates the NPP template for subsequent hospital care. This type of service contains only three code levels (CPT codes 99231, 99232, and 99233), all of which have an NPP based on a patient's clinical status rather than a severity level. This status directly dictates the appropriate level of care and code level for each visit, as demonstrated by the NPP documentation prompts.

F I G U R E 14.2

Documentation Prompt Section for NPP for an Inpatient Subsequent Care Visit

NATURE OF PRESENTING PROBLEM(S)

1. Stable: **(level 1)**   Usually, the patient is stable, recovering or improving

2. Inadequate response: **(level 2)**   Usually, the patient is responding inadequately to therapy or has developed a minor complication

3. Unstable: **(level 3)**   Usually, the patient is unstable or has developed a significant complication or a significant new problem

SYNOPSIS AND ANALYSIS OF NPP

The NPP is a conceptual cornerstone of Practical E/M and the IMR. Judging the severity of the NPP for each visit guides the physician to identify the level of care (and E/M code) that is warranted by the severity of patient illness at the time of the encounter, according to CPT coding guidelines. This information then guides the extent of care (for the physical examination and the MDM) that the physician must perform and document to submit the indicated E/M code. Table 14.1 summarizes the structure selected for the NPP section of the medical record.

TABLE 14.1

Synopsis of IMR for NPP

Section of Record	Interface	Data Entry Options	Format Options	Comments
Nature of presenting problem	Graphic (selection list)	Physician	Writing	Cornerstone for compliant coding and documentation

USING THE NPP SECTION OF THE IMR

By the time a physician has completed (and documented) the patient's comprehensive medical history, he or she has usually formed an impression of the severity of the patient's illness(es), mentally compiled a preliminary list of the patient's potential diagnoses, and developed a preliminary idea about the complexity of care that may be indicated for these medical problems. This happens "automatically" for physicians who are experienced working with a good history.

The physician should next refer to the NPP section (on the last page of the IMR) and identify which level of NPP best describes the severity of the patient's illnesses at this point. Once this has been identified, the documentation prompt identifies the level of care that is appropriate for the selected NPP, which also establishes the highest-level E/M code that can appropriately be submitted for the evaluation of this patient's problems. The documentation prompts in the remainder of the IMR will further guide the physician and ensure that the amount of care provided and documented for the physical examination and MDM meets or exceeds the level of care chosen.

Review of the NPP and the Pole Vault Metaphor

Referring back to the pole vault metaphor (presented in Chapter 6), the patient's NPP has now set the height of the bar for the maximum level of care (ie, the E/M code) that should be submitted. The NPP, and its medically indicated level of care based on CPT descriptors, guides the physician regarding the extent of care that should be performed (or exceeded) to meet CPT's standard of care for an illness of this severity.

Depending on findings during the physical examination and on conclusions reached during documentation of the MDM, the physician may reassess this original impression of the NPP (and reset the height of the bar) at any time during the visit.

There are several caveats for using the NPP template and documentation prompts correctly:

1. Choose the level of NPP (low, moderate to high, etc) whose definition most reasonably matches the probable severity of the patient's illness(es).

    ■ Note that the CPT definitions for the various levels of NPP are *subjective*.

    ■ This subjectivity explains why it is important for physicians to document their clinical impression of the severity of the patient's problem(s). Assuming that the documented level of NPP is reasonable for the patient's illness, it should provide strong support for medical necessity in the event of an audit.

2. The documentation prompt associated with the selected level of NPP corresponds to the CPT coding system's assessment of the level of care (E/M code) that is medically indicated for the severity of the patient's medical problems.

    ■ The clinical examples in Appendix C of the CPT codebook provide additional guidance on identifying the appropriate level of care warranted by a patient's presenting problem(s). These help physicians interpret the severity of the NPP.

3. For new outpatient visits and consultations, an illness of "moderate severity" warrants level 3 care, while an illness of "moderate to high" severity warrants either level 4 or level 5 care. An illness of "low severity" indicates only level 1 or 2 care.

    ■ Patient records that indicate an illness of low severity (eg, cerumen or viral upper respiratory tract infection as a single diagnosis) might be challenged on the grounds of lacking "medical necessity," if the physician were to submit an E/M code higher than level 2.

4. For established patient visits, the CPT criteria for the NPP are somewhat more liberal. An illness with an NPP of "low to moderate" severity is considered sufficient to indicate level 3 care for an established visit, but merits only level 2 care for an initial visit or consultation. However, the CPT coding system still requires "moderate to high" severity of NPP to warrant levels 4 and 5 care for all three types of service.

The initial assessment of NPP and appropriate level of care is not written in stone. If the physical examination reveals an unexpected finding (eg, the exam of a "routine" stuffy nose reveals massive nasal polyps or even a tumor), the physician may revise his or her initial assessment to a more severe illness, and the severity of the NPP and the indicated level of care should be increased accordingly. Similarly, if exam findings or laboratory reports reviewed during the visit rule out the potentially dangerous problems related to the patient's symptoms, it may be appropriate to lower the NPP and level of care.

At the conclusion of the patient's visit, the physician returns to the NPP section, shown earlier in Figure 14.1, and circles the level of severity that corresponds to his or her final impression of the patient's illnesses. The documentation of NPP provides audit protection because it records the physician's impression of "medical necessity" at the time of the visit. Most important, this step finalizes the integration of appropriate levels of documentation and coding into the extent of evaluation and treatment clinically indicated for each patient's medical needs.

GUIDANCE FOR CHOOSING THE SEVERITY OF NPP AND LEVEL OF CARE

Compliant use of the NPP principles is a foundation for the concepts of Practical E/M coding and the IMR. We therefore urge that selection of the appropriate severity of NPP and the indicated level of care be fair and reasonable in every case. As discussed in Chapter 6, clinicians can gain meaningful insight into the relationship between the severity of presenting problems (ie, the NPP) and the indicated levels of care by referring to the clinical examples in the CPT codebook, which were developed by the medical specialty societies themselves.[1] Appendix A of Practical E/M also presents hypothetical examples of the significant elements of medical records for a spectrum of patients, all of whom have upper respiratory symptoms, whose severity of illness and medically indicated level of care range from low (warranting code 99202) to high (warranting code 99205).

The CPT Codebook's Clinical Examples for Outpatient Initial Visits Level 1, 2, and 3

Appendix C provides several pages of clinical examples of patients with illnesses whose severity (ie, NPP) warrants each of the five levels of care for this type of service. The following examples are representative cases from that section illustrating levels 1, 2, and 3 care:

■ 99201: "Initial office visit for a 22-year-old male with a small area of sunburn requiring first aid"[1(p 474)]

■ 99202: "Initial office visit for a 25-year-old with a single season allergic rhinitis" [1(p 475)]

■ 99203: "Initial office visit of an adult who presents with symptoms of an upper respiratory infection that has progressed to unilateral purulent nasal discharge and discomfort in the right maxillary teeth" [1(p 475)]

Distinguishing Medical Indications for Level 4 and Level 5 Care

For many types of service, such as outpatient initial visits and established visits, following the NPP guidelines alone can present a hypothetical challenge in distinguishing between level 4 and level 5 codes. This is because, for these types of service, the CPT coding system designates the NPP for both level 4 and level 5 as "moderate to high." This situation leads to the question of how physicians can reasonably select the appropriate level of care for a given encounter with a moderate to high NPP.

In these situations, the CPT codebook provides clarification for this issue in the clinical examples appendix. We recommend that physicians review these examples, with particular attention to clinical cases in their own specialty. These vignettes provide a good sense of the relative severity of various illnesses and how they are associated with the different levels of care. The introduction of the clinical examples appendix stresses that these are examples and not absolute. They are presented as guidelines, and actual clinical situations may not exactly match the level of care illustrated.

As an additional guideline for patients with a moderate to high NPP, we suggest that those patients who have the greatest probability of experiencing life-threatening consequences or significant functional impairment as a result of a serious illness warrant level 5 care. Those patients who might have a similar diagnosis, but who are less likely to suffer the most serious consequences, warrant level 4 care. Another way of looking at this approach is that if the severity of the patient's illness does not fit the worst-case scenario under consideration, then the current problem likely calls for level 4 care.

Pragmatic Considerations for Selecting Between Level 4 and Level 5 Care

1. When the physician determines (and documents) that the NPP is "high," this is a positive indication that level 5 care will likely be warranted by the severity of the patient's illness. As noted above, this will also probably correlate with a "high" risk of the presenting problem(s).

2. When the physician determines (and documents) that the NPP is "moderate to high," then realistically selecting the appropriateness of level 5 care (vs level 4 care) will most often depend on the documentation of the levels of risk in the MDM. To warrant submitting a level 5 code, the physician should reasonably be able to determine, and document, that at least one of the three levels of risk is "high." As discussed in Chapter 16, this documentation will be necessary (in most cases) to support level 5 care. If none of the three levels of risk is "high," then level 4 care will most often be the appropriate determination as well as the highest level of E/M care that can be supported by the MDM.

The CPT Codebook's Clinical Examples for Outpatient Initial Visits Level 4 and 5

The following examples are representative cases from Appendix C's clinical examples illustrating level 4 and level 5 care for outpatient initial visits:

- 99204: "Initial office visit for a 60-year-old male with recent change in bowel habits, weight loss, and abdominal pain" [1(p 475)]
- 99205: "Initial office visit for a patient with disseminated lupus erythematosus with kidney disease, edema, purpura, and scarring lesions on the extremities plus cardiac symptoms" [1(p 476)]

Becoming Proficient at Selecting Appropriate Levels of Care

An effective way for a group of physicians in the same specialty to develop a sense of the clinical conditions warranting the various types of NPP and levels of care is to conduct a "coding forum." During a coding forum, the participating physicians should first suggest and discuss five or six clinical situations, appropriate for their own specialty, that everyone agrees fall into the category of having at least moderate- to high-severity NPP and reasonably qualify as medical conditions warranting level 5 care. The physicians should include appropriate clinical situations that are described for level 5 care in the CPT codebook's clinical examples appendix and consider scenarios that are equivalent to them in severity. As a reminder, per the CPT coding system, these are medical conditions in which the risk of morbidity without treatment is moderate to high, or the risk of mortality without treatment is moderate to high, or there is a moderate to high probability of severe prolonged functional impairment.[1] For example, the majority of physicians would agree that patients with most untreated malignant neoplasms should reasonably fall into this category, as would patients with significant loss of neurological function, stroke, kidney failure, or an uncontrolled autoimmune disease.

It is also critical for the physicians involved in the coding forum to appreciate that selecting an appropriate code level depends not only on the probable diagnosis, but also on the clinical scenario on the date of the visit. For example, a patient with probable lung cancer (clinical and radiographic evidence) would certainly be a candidate for level 5 care on the initial visit. However, once the patient has had successful surgery and is clinically doing well, a routine follow-up appointment that reveals the patient is feeling well and has no evidence of active disease no longer warrants the use of a level 5 E/M code. In fact, the physician may reasonably designate the NPP for that follow-up visit as low to moderate, and this level of NPP would indicate care appropriate for a level 3 established patient visit.

After reaching a consensus on the common scenarios that in most cases warrant level 5 care, the forum participants should next review a list of clinical scenarios that they agree warrant level 4 care and coding. These are still patients who are clinically at significant risk, but the severity of the problem or likelihood of severe consequences without treatment is not as high as for level 5. As described earlier, these patients do not fit the "worst-case scenario." For instance, Appendix C in the CPT codebook cites an example of a cardiology patient warranting level 4 care, describing "an initial office visit for initial evaluation of a 63-year-old male with chest pain on exertion."[1] While this patient is certainly at risk for morbidity, we can readily describe patients with cardiac problems who have a higher degree of risk. Another reasonable rule of thumb is that most patients who are candidates for hospitalization or nonelective surgical procedures will have an NPP of moderate to high severity and will warrant level 4 or level 5 care. Finally, patients with multiple problems requiring more complex evaluation and care may also warrant level 4 services and coding (unless all the problems are of low severity).

The third coding forum exercise looks at the other end of the spectrum. The physicians should identify clinical situations that have minimal and low NPPs, which would therefore be appropriate for level 2 coding and care. As noted earlier in Figure 14.1, for initial visits these are most often illnesses that are self-limited and will improve with minimal or routine intervention. An example is a viral upper respiratory tract infection of recent onset, without signs or symptoms of significant bacterial involvement. Such visits commonly involve counseling and reassurance rather than active therapeutic intervention. For established patients, another reasonable guideline is that level 2 visits often involve patients who have responded well to treatment, whose presenting problems have completely resolved, and who will not require significant further medical follow-up for those problems.

Once the physicians are comfortable with commonly encountered clinical scenarios that reasonably meet criteria for warranting level 5, level 4, and level 2 care, they can deduce that most other situations have moderate NPP and will warrant level 3 care. For most specialties, this category appropriately encompasses the majority of their patient visits. In general, the illnesses for these patients warrant some degree of diagnostic evaluation and/or an active medical intervention to cure or stabilize the illness.

SUMMARY

The process of identifying the NPP begins when the physician formulates a preliminary differential diagnosis. This occurs after he or she has reviewed and documented the medical history, including past medical history, social history, family history, ROS, and the history of present illness.

At this juncture, the physician has enough of an impression of the patient's medical condition to refer to the NPP template, located on the last page of the IMR form, and follow CPT guidelines to establish the severity of the NPP. The documentation prompts on the template help the physician identify the level of E/M care warranted for the NPP and type of service, based on the CPT codebook's guidelines. Having identified the appropriate level of care, the physician now returns to the normal sequence of completing the physical examination and then the MDM, relying on the documentation prompts in those sections to confirm that the amount of care provided, and documented, meets or exceeds the CPT guidelines for severity of the patient's NPP.

The NPP and/or level of care (E/M code) may be adjusted at any point during the visit, if the findings in the physical examination or MDM warrant a change. The physician documents his or her final impression of severity of NPP during or after the MDM. This step completes the integration of care, documentation, and coding indicated by the severity of each patient's medical problems.

Reference

1.   American Medical Association. *Current Procedural Terminology CPT® 2008*. Chicago, IL: American Medical Association; 2007.

Documenting the Physical Examination

Achieving the efficient use of physician time and ensuring the quality of the documentation are the two primary challenges physicians face when documenting the physical examination. In medical school, physicians are taught to document a comprehensive examination, including the positive and negative physical examination findings for every organ system. In contrast to this ideal, an inspection of the physical examination that is documented by most resident physicians and practicing physicians usually reveals only a narrative description of all of the abnormal findings, and this is often confined to the organ system related to the presenting problem. When physicians are queried about this limited documentation, they generally explain that they "did a complete examination, but didn't have time to document all the normal findings." Unfortunately, this lack of documentation of the normal findings fails to satisfy the Current Procedural Terminology (CPT®) coding system requirements for higher levels of evaluation and management (E/M) coding. In addition, it is important to recognize that the absence of documented normal examination findings can (and does) create a significant problem for physicians in medicolegal cases.

GOALS FOR DESIGN

To address these problems, the first portion of the physical examination section of the intelligent medical record (IMR) provides an efficient check-box interface that helps physicians document whether each exam element they perform is "normal" or "abnormal." The second portion of this section provides a narrative interface that enables the physician to record in exact detail any abnormal findings, with a level of clarity that enables the physician or other members of the health care team to assess and monitor the progress of the patient's illness and the response to treatment.

Design for Compliance Requirements

According to Centers for Medicare and Medicaid Services (CMS) policy, physicians may choose to use either the 1995 edition[1] or the 1997 edition[2] of the *Documentation Guidelines for Evaluation and Management Services* as a standard for recording the physical examination. Both publications built their criteria upon the qualitative descriptions in the CPT coding system,[3] which are shown in Figure 15.1.

FIGURE 15.1

CPT Descriptors for Four Levels of Physical Examination

■ **Problem focused:** A limited examination of the affected body area or organ system

■ **Expanded problem focused:** A limited examination of the affected body area or organ system and other symptomatic or related organ system(s)

■ **Detailed:** An extended examination of the affected body area or organ system and other symptomatic or related organ system(s)

■ **Comprehensive:** A general multisystem examination or a complete examination of a single organ system

---

Source: American Medical Association. Current Procedural Terminology CPT® 2008. Chicago, Ill: American Medical Association; 2007.

The 1995 edition of the *Documentation Guidelines* provided only a small amount of additional information to these baseline CPT descriptors. Specifically, it noted that to qualify as comprehensive, "a general multi-system examination should include findings about eight or more of the 12 organ systems."[1] Despite this additional guidance, the descriptions of the levels of care, including "limited examination," "extended examination," and "complete examination of a single organ system," remained subjective. Therefore, the 1995 guidelines do not provide sufficient guidance to ensure compliant documentation and coding in every case. This leaves reviewers, consultants, and auditors without a uniform set of criteria for consistently evaluating the care and documentation for this portion of the medical record. It also leaves physicians without precise, quantifiable examination guidelines to use as a reference for coding and documentation, and therefore leaves them vulnerable to subjective and possibly inaccurate review by auditors.

In light of these issues, Practical E/M recommends that physicians follow the more extensive physical examination criteria included in the 1997 edition of the *Documentation Guidelines*.[2] This edition presents a general multisystem examination template and 11 single-organ-system examination templates. There are also specific quantitative values that describe the extent of documentation required to satisfy the CPT definitions for the four levels of the physical examination (problem focused, expanded problem focused, detailed, and comprehensive). We recommend that physicians select one of these 12 physical examination templates for their personal IMR based on their specialty and their clinical requirements. All of these templates provide physicians with both guidelines and audit protection. They also permit physicians to create customized medical record templates, designed with a user-friendly graphic interface that facilitates fast and easy documentation of normal findings. Figure 15.2 lists all 12 categories of examinations specified in the 1997 edition of the *Documentation Guidelines*.[2]

FIGURE 15.2

Types of Examination Defined in the 1997 Edition of the *Documentation Guidelines*

---

1. General Multisystem Examination	7. Hematologic/Lymphatic/Immunologic
Single-Organ-System Examinations:	
2. Cardiovascular	8. Musculoskeletal
3. Ears, Nose, Mouth, and Throat	9. Neurological
4. Eyes	10. Psychiatric
5. Genitourinary (Female)	11. Respiratory
6. Genitourinary (Male)	12. Skin

Source: Health Care Financing Administration. *Documentation Guidelines for Evaluation and Management Services*. Chicago, Ill: American Medical Association; 1997.

The 1997 edition also provides the guidelines that Practical E/M uses to develop reliable and authoritative documentation prompts for the examination section of the IMR. Because the *Documentation Guidelines* requirements differ for each of these 12 types of physical examination, these prompts are specific to each type of examination and service. Figure 15.3 illustrates the examination documentation prompt of an initial outpatient visit for the general multisystem examination template.

F i g u r e   15.3

Sample Physical Examination Documentation Prompt for Initial Outpatient Visit,
General Multisystem Examination

1.	Problem focused = 1–5 elements (level 1)
2.	Expanded = 6–11 elements (level 2)
3.	Detailed = 12 or more element in two or more systems, OR at least 2 elements for each of six or more systems (level 3)
4.	Comprehensive = document 2 (or more) elements in each of nine or more systems (levels 4 and 5)

The 1997 edition of the *Documentation Guidelines* also describes three additional requirements for compliant documentation of the physical examination[2]:

- Specific abnormal and relevant negative findings of the examination of the affected or symptomatic body area(s) or organ system(s) should be documented. A notation of "abnormal" without elaboration is insufficient.

- Abnormal or unexpected findings of the examination of any asymptomatic body area(s) or organ system(s) should be described.

- A brief statement or notation indicating "negative" or "normal" is sufficient to document normal findings related to unaffected area(s) or asymptomatic organ system(s).

The IMR incorporates these elements into the design of the physical examination template. A special feature facilitates documentation of the "relevant negative findings" required in the first of these requirements. The IMR adds a brief description, customized by each physician, of the normal findings for each element included in the check-box portion of the examination. These descriptions appear in lowercase letters in the column preceding the check boxes in Figures 15.4 and 15.5.

Design for Efficiency and Quality Care

The Practical E/M solution to the challenges posed by the guidelines for the physical examination section of the medical record is to use a dual approach that facilitates efficient and complete documentation of both normal and abnormal findings. The first portion of the examination section of the IMR is presented as a graphic interface, using check boxes for the physician to indicate whether the finding for each of the mandated examination elements is "normal" or "abnormal." This documentation tool enables physicians to document all the normal findings of a complete examination extremely quickly and easily (usually in 15 seconds or less). The second portion of the examination section consists of a set of blank lines for the narrative description of all of the abnormal findings and pertinent normal physical exam findings.

The benefit of using a narrative interface to describe abnormal findings is that it encourages detailed individualized descriptions of all abnormal aspects of the areas in question. This precision boosts quality of care by helping the physician monitor the progress of an illness and the response to treatment. The physician may elect to write or dictate this section, exactly as he or she would have done if there were no graphic interface to facilitate documentation of the normal findings. Figure 15.4 illustrates a sample physical examination design using the general multisystem examination template, retaining all 14 of the body areas and organ systems.

Shaded Boxes in the Single-Organ-System Examinations

For comprehensive examinations performed with one of the single-organ-system templates, the *Documentation Guidelines* requires physicians to "*perform* all elements identified by a bullet."[2] However, some of the organ systems require *documentation* of only one of their listed elements. The IMR indicates these selected organ systems by lightly shading their region of the examination template. This shading is illustrated in the Ear, Nose, and Throat examination template shown in Figure 15.5.

CUSTOMIZING EXAMINATION TEMPLATES

Customization 1: Selecting an Appropriate Exam Template

Designing an IMR that meets each physician's preferences for documentation of the physical examination does involve customization. The first step in the customization process requires the physician to select the examination template he or she wishes to use for his or her medical record. The *Documentation Guidelines* provides that "a general multi-system examination or a single organ system examination may be performed by any physician regardless of specialty."[2]

Each physician should consider two issues when selecting which of the 12 described templates is the optimal template for his or her practice. The appropriate template should include all or most of the common body areas the physician examines in the majority of his or her patients. More important, however, the template under consideration definitely must not require the physician to examine areas of the body that would be inappropriate to his or her specialty, or outside the physician's area of expertise. This is because the *Documentation Guidelines* requires that *all* the listed areas in each single-organ-system template be examined and documented to qualify as a comprehensive examination. Fortunately, this is not the requirement for the general multisystem examination.

Most physicians whose specialty is not listed among the 11 single-organ-system examination templates should choose the general multisystem template and customize it to fit their needs. Although this template provides physicians with the ability to document their findings for as many as 14 different organ systems and body areas (as shown in Figure 15.4), according to the *Documentation Guidelines*, even the highest-level examination (ie, comprehensive examination for level 5 service) only requires the physician to "include at least nine organ systems or body areas."[2]

F I G U R E   1 5 . 4

General Multisystem Examination Template. The documentation prompt is for an initial outpatient visit. Due to space constraints, the GU examination (male and female) and the remainder of the musculoskeletal examination are printed on a supplemental page. (Physicians may select the organ systems they examine the least often to appear on the supplemental page.)

Date ____/____/____   Patient States Consultation Requested By_____

Patient Name:_____   Account No._____   DOB:____/____/____

Outpatient Initial Visit Form (p. 3):

PRESENT ILLNESS	Chronology with: 1. one to three elements (level 2) 2. four to eight elements; OR status of 3 chronic or inactive conditions (level 3, 4, or 5)
	(1) duration (2) timing (3) severity; (4) location (5) quality (6) context (7) modifying factors (8) assoc. signs & symptoms

☐ See attached dictation

PHYSICAL EXAMINATION: **General Multisystem Exam**

GENERAL   (at least 3 measurements of vital signs)   HT___ft___in   WT_____lbs

BP sitting-standing ____/____mm Hg   BP supine____/____mm Hg

PULSE ____/min   regular - irregular   RESP ____/min   TEMP _____°(F-C)

			Normal/AB					Normal/AB
	GENERAL APPEARANCE	Stature, nutrition	☐ ☐	**CHEST/**	**BREAST INSPECTION**	Symmetry, color	☐ ☐
EYES	CONJUNCTIVAE & LIDS	Appearance, color	☐ ☐	**BREASTS**	BREAST/AXILLAE PALP	Nodules, masses	☐ ☐
	PUPILS & IRISES	Size, reactivity	☐ ☐	**GI/ABD**	MASSES/TENDERNESS	Palpation	☐ ☐
	OPTIC DISCS	Fundi, vessels	☐ ☐		LIVER/SPLEEN	Size, tenderness	☐ ☐
ENT	EARS & NOSE, EXTERNAL	Appearance	☐ ☐		HERNIA EVAL	Inspection, palpation	☐ ☐
	OTOSCOPY	Canals, tymp membranes	☐ ☐		ANUS/RECTUM/PERIN	Appearance, palpation	☐ ☐
	HEARING	Response to sound	☐ ☐		STOOL, HEMACULT	Eval for blood	☐ ☐
	INTERNAL NOSE	Septum, mucosa, turbs	☐ ☐	**LYMPH**	NECK/AXILLAE/GROIN/OTHER	Adenopathy	☐ ☐
	LIPS,TEETH, & GUMS	Mucosa, dentition	☐ ☐		(circle areas examined; requires exam in 2 or more regions)		
	OROPHARYNX	Mucosa, tonsils, palate	☐ ☐	**MSKEL**	GAIT & STATION	Stability & smoothness	☐ ☐
NECK	MASSES & TRACHEA	Symmetry, masses	☐ ☐	(partial)	DIGITS & NAILS	Color & appearance	☐ ☐
	THYROID	Size, nodules	☐ ☐	**SKIN/**	INSPECTION	Head, trunk, RUE	☐ ☐
RESP	RESPIRATORY EFFORT	Inspiratory-expiratory	☐ ☐	**SUBCU**		LUE, RLE, LLE	☐ ☐
	CHEST PALPATION	Movement	☐ ☐		PALPATION	Head, trunk, RUE	☐ ☐
	CHEST PERCUSSION	Sound	☐ ☐			LUE, RLE, LLE	☐ ☐
	AUSCULTATION	Lung sounds	☐ ☐	**NEURO**	CRANIAL NERVES	II - XII	☐ ☐
CVS	HEART PALPATION	Rhythm	☐ ☐		DEEP TENDON REFLEXES	Knee, ankle, Babinski	☐ ☐
	HEART AUSCULTATION	Sounds	☐ ☐		SENSATION	Light touch	☐ ☐
	CAROTID ARTIERIES	Pulsation	☐ ☐	**PSYCH**	JUDGEMENT & INSIGHT	Subjectively	☐ ☐
	ABDOMINAL AORTA	Pulsation	☐ ☐		ORIENTATION	Person, place, time	☐ ☐
	FEMORAL ARTERIES	Pulsation	☐ ☐		MEMORY	Recent & remote	☐ ☐
	PEDAL PULSES	Pulsation	☐ ☐		MOOD & AFFECT	Comments	☐ ☐
	EDEMA,VARICES, LE	Appearance	☐ ☐	☐ Continued on supplemental page		☐ See attached dictation	

1. Problem focused = 1-5 elements (level 1) 2. Expanded = 6-11 elements (level 2)   3. Detailed = 12 or more elements [in 2 or more systems] (level 3)
4. Comprehensive = document two (or more) elements in each of nine (or more) systems (level 4 or 5)   *Optional

This permits the physician to exclude documentation for up to five of the body areas listed on the general multisystem template, while still having sufficient organ systems present in the check-box section to document level 4 and level 5 care. Any body area that the physician would never include as an appropriate part of the physical examination of his or her patients may be entirely excluded from his or her customized template. For example, a female genitourinary examination, which requires pelvic examination, would not be part of a typical physical examination conducted by a rheumatologist or many other physicians. Any organ systems that might be examined in only some cases should, of course, be included on the physician's customized form. Elimination of some of the organ systems from an examination template is an option available solely for the general multisystem examination; the single-specialty examinations may not be edited in this fashion.

Comparing Documentation Requirements for Different Examinations

For *problem-focused*, *expanded problem-focused* and *detailed* levels of care, the documentation requirements for a general multisystem physical exam are comparable to those for most of the single-organ-system exams. The requirements do differ for comprehensive examinations. The multisystem examination allows documentation of as few as two elements in each of the multiple different organ systems, while the single-specialty examinations require in-depth assessment of a smaller number of organ systems.

Customization 2: Adding Elements to the Basic Template

After selecting the appropriate examination template, the physician's second step in customization is to assess whether the existing elements on the form encompass all of the examination areas he or she commonly documents. Each physician should supplement the basic template by incorporating additional examination areas that he or she frequently includes when caring for patients.

For example, most otolaryngologists would find the template labeled "Ear, Nose, Mouth, and Throat Examination" to be highly appropriate for their practices. However, an individual specialist might frequently perform several additional exam elements that are not included on the standard template, such as clinical tests of balance function. Adding these elements to the graphic interface portion of the examination template, with the check-box designation for "normal/abnormal," facilitates documentation efficiency.

We suggest that the listings for these additional exam elements should be accompanied by an asterisk (*). This will serve as a reminder to the physician (or to a potential auditor) that these elements are not part of the standard template defined by the 1997 *Documentation Guidelines*, and therefore checking one of these boxes marked with an asterisk does not count for the purpose of supporting a selected level of care (E/M code). Similarly, failure to document one or more of these asterisked elements does not have a negative impact on satisfying the comprehensive examination requirement for documenting all elements in a given anatomic area. Figure 15.5 includes the following examples of elements added to the standard form and marked:

- *after decongestion (a subheading under the internal nose examination, which allows the physician to indicate the appearance after spraying a decongestant in the nose to shrink the membranes)
- *Romberg, *tandem Romberg, and *past-pointing (three balance tests in the neurological/psychological section of the examination)

Customization 3: Adding Brief Descriptions of Normal Findings

The physician should add brief descriptions of normal findings to each of the examination elements included in the check-box graphic interface section that is used to indicate whether findings are normal or abnormal. This is not a component of the standardized exam templates. Practical E/M adds these descriptions to the IMR templates to fulfill the requirement for documenting "relevant negative findings of the affected or symptomatic body area."[2] For these portions of the examination, simply reporting "normal" does not satisfy the *Documentation Guidelines* requirements, and the additional brief descriptions improve quality by conveying a more complete picture of the features that the physician actually examined.

SYNOPSIS AND ANALYSIS OF THE PHYSICAL EXAMINATION SECTION

Table 15.1 summarizes the structure selected for the physical examination section.

TABLE 15.1

Synopsis of IMR for Physical Examination

Component of Physical Exam	Interface	Data Entry Options	Format Options	Comments
Normal/ Abnormal	Graphic (with check boxes)	• Physician • Physician assistant/ nurse practitioner	Writing on paper	Check each area examined Rapid documentation of normal versus abnormal findings
Details of Abnormal Findings	Narrative	Physician	Writing or dictation	Most efficient method for documenting individualized details of examination findings

The IMR's documentation prompts ensure compliance for the physical examination section of every visit, based on the amount of care warranted by the nature of presenting problem (NPP). Starting from this foundation, the physician selects the exam elements to perform on the basis of the patient's clinical indications. Each of the two documentation sections is optimally suited for its task. The check-box interface gives the physician the ability to document all normal and abnormal exam findings rapidly. The narrative section allows the physician to indicate the unique details of each abnormal finding. The detailed description from the narrative assists subsequent care by facilitating the clinician's ability to monitor progress of an illness under treatment.

USING THE PHYSICAL EXAMINATION SECTION OF THE IMR

After assessing the NPP and determining the appropriate level of care, the physician performs the physical examination indicated for the patient's medical problems. The

IMR provides the examination template that the physician selected according to his or her medical specialty, and that the physician has further customized to accommodate his or her personal preferences. This should have an appearance similar to the templates illustrated in Figures 15.4 and 15.5. The physician documents on the check-box interface portion of the form whether each element examined appears normal or abnormal.

Also, while performing the examination, the physician should refer to the documentation prompt at the bottom of the template to ensure that he or she is performing and documenting an amount of care equal to or exceeding the level of care warranted by the severity of the NPP. For example, for an initial visit, if the patient's NPP were moderate and warranted level 3 care, the documentation prompt advises that 12 or more elements of the examination should be performed and documented. By performing and documenting these elements of care, the physician not only guarantees compliant documentation and coding but also ensures that he or she provides an amount of care that is consistent with the nature of the patient's medical problem.

The Extent of the Physical Examination and the Pole Vault Metaphor

As in the pole vault metaphor discussed in Chapter 6, the documentation prompts guide the physician with respect to the *minimum* amount of care needed to clear the height of the bar; ie, provide and document compliant levels of care. The physician may choose to jump higher than this minimum height and to provide and document whatever additional components of the physical examination his or her clinical judgment indicates are warranted to achieve the optimal quality of care for that particular patient. This increased care relates to quality, but it does not impact the level of care (E/M code).

The only exception to this analysis occurs when there are exam findings that compel the physician to reconsider the severity of the NPP (and metaphorically reset the height of the bar, either higher or lower). For example, an abdominal examination revealing absence of tenderness could eliminate several potential diagnoses that would have required immediate surgery, and this might reduce the level of the NPP (and therefore the level of care warranted). Conversely, a finding of significant abdominal tenderness could easily increase an original NPP assessment (and appropriate level of care) that had suggested only a mild flu syndrome.

The final task for the physician in the physical examination section is to document all abnormal findings, with appropriate detail, in the narrative section of the template. In some circumstances, the physician may also want to provide a more detailed description of pertinent normal findings in this narrative section, to further enhance the quality of care. For example, if a patient presents with pulmonary symptoms, and auscultation reveals normal lung sounds, it would be important to document this finding in a more detailed narrative, rather than to simply check the box for "normal breath sounds." It would be relevant, for example, to add "no rales or rhonchi; inspiratory and expiratory breath sounds symmetrical." This would be meaningful to the physician (or an associate) in monitoring the patient's clinical course through subsequent visits.

Added Elements of the Exam

As noted earlier in this chapter, all physical examination elements marked with an asterisk have been added to one of the standard exam templates for the physician's own practice preferences, independent of coding and documentation compliance

continued

requirements. Therefore, checking a box that has an exam element marked with an asterisk does *not* "count" toward the total number of exam elements required to meet the coding requirements. Similarly, leaving such an "asterisk" box unchecked does *not* interfere with the coding requirement for a comprehensive single-organ-system examination of having "every box checked in the unshaded areas."

Figure 15.5 illustrates a completed physical examination for a hypothetical patient with chronic sinusitis, to demonstrate how the IMR design facilitates efficient documentation.

FIGURE 15.5

Sample Completed ENT Examination Template, Initial Patient Visit, With E/M Documentation Prompts. Note that, in accordance with the documentation prompt for level 4 initial visit care, the physician has (examined and) documented each required (nonasterisk) element in the nonshaded areas and at least one element in each of the shaded areas.

PHYSICAL EXAMINATION:					Ear, Nose, & Throat				
GENERAL	(at least 3 measurements of vital signs)				HT _5_ ft _9_ in		WT ___163___ lbs		
	BP sitting-standing ____/____ mm Hg				BP supine____/____ mm Hg				
	PULSE _76_ /min regular - irregular				RESP ____/min		TEMP _____ ° (F-C)		
			Normal/AB					**Normal/AB**	
	GENERAL APPEARANCE	Stature, nutrition	☒	☐	NECK	MASSES & TRACHEA	Symmetry, masses	☒	☐
	COMMUNICATION & VOICE	Pitch, clarity	☒	☐		THYROID	Size, nodules	☒	☐
HEAD/	INSPECTION	Lesions, masses	☒	☐	EYES	OCULAR MOTILITY & GAZE	EOMs, nystagmus	☒	☐
FACE	PALPATION / PERCUSSION	Skeleton, sinuses	☒	☐	RESP __/min	RESPIRATORY EFFORT	Inspiratory-expiratory	☒	☐
	SALIVARY GLANDS	Masses, tenderness	☒	☐		AUSCULTATION	Lung sounds	☐	☐
	FACIAL STRENGTH	Symmetry	☒	☐	CVS	HEART AUSCULTATION	Rhythm, heart sounds	☐	☐
ENT	PNEUMO-OTOSCOPY	EACs; TMs mobile	☒	☐		PERIPH VASC SYSTEM	Edema, color	☒	☐
	HEARING ASSESSMENT	Gross; Weber/Rinne	☒	☐	LYMPH	NECK/AXILLAE/GROIN/ETC	Adenopathy	☒	☐
	EXTERNAL EAR & NOSE	Appearance	☒	☐	NEURO/	CRANIAL NERVES	II - XII	☒	☐
	INTERNAL NOSE	Mucosa, turbinates	☐	☒	PSYCH.	ORIENTATION	Person, place, time	☐	☐
	*AFTER DECONGESTANT	Septum, OMCs	☐	☒		MOOD & AFFECT	Comments	☒	☐
	LIPS, TEETH & GUMS	Mucosa, dentition	☒	☐		*ROMBERG		☐	☐
	ORAL CAVITY, OROPHARYNX	Mucosa, tonsils, palate	☒	☐		*TANDEM ROMBERG		☐	☐
	HYPOPHARYNX	Mucosa, pyriforms	☒	☐		*PAST POINTING		☐	☐
	LARYNX (mirror: adults)	Anatomy, vocal cord mobility	☒	☐					
	NASOPHAR (mirror: adults)	Mucosa, choanae	☒	☐				☐ See attached dictation	

Nose: Bilateral nasal congestion. Bilateral polyps

Following spray: Mild posterior septal spur interior to right, without

impaction or significant obstruction

Moderate polyps right middle meatus with mild obstruction

Extensive polyps left middle meatus with severe obstruction

1. Problem focused = 1-5 elements (level 1)   2. Expanded = 6-11 elements (level 2)   3. Detailed = 12 or more elements (level 3)
4. Comprehensive = document every element in basic areas AND at least 1 element in each optional area (level 4 or 5)   *Optional

For the purposes of this example, we assume that the NPP is moderate to high and warrants level 4 care. A comprehensive examination has been documented in the check-box portion of the exam template. For this type of service, the comprehensive examination satisfies the CPT coding requirement for supporting either level 4 or level 5 E/M codes, as indicated by the documentation prompt. The actual documentation of the check-box interface was completed rapidly, and only a small amount of writing was required in the narrative section to describe the abnormal findings in detail. For someone reading this record, it is easy to visually scan the check boxes and identify normal and abnormal physical examination findings. In addition, the written narrative section paints a picture of the abnormal findings that is both thorough and precise. The IMR's detail and accuracy provide a reliable baseline for comparison during subsequent examinations, whether the patient is receiving care from the same physician or an associate.

SUMMARY

The physical examination section of the IMR uses templates built on the standards of the 1997 edition of the *Documentation Guidelines*. This ensures compliant documentation when based on the patient's NPP and when used in conjunction with the documentation prompt that is included in the template.

The design of the IMR physical exam template guides physicians on the type and extent of care required by the guidelines, while also allowing physicians to add custom features to facilitate efficient documentation of exam elements they feel are important to providing quality care to their patients. It allows rapid documentation of both normal and abnormal findings, and it provides for detailed and precise narrative description of all abnormal and pertinent normal findings, which will aid the ongoing care of the patient.

References

1.   Health Care Financing Administration. *Documentation Guidelines for Evaluation and Management Services*. Chicago, IL: American Medical Association; 1995.

2.   Health Care Financing Administration. *Documentation Guidelines for Evaluation and Management Services*. Chicago, IL: American Medical Association; 1997.

3.   American Medical Association. *Current Procedural Terminology CPT® 2008*. Chicago, IL: American Medical Association; 2007.

Documenting Medical Decision Making

This chapter looks first at the challenges of dealing with medical decision making in the traditional evaluation and management (E/M) coding protocol. This enables us to understand the problems that must be addressed, and it helps us to appreciate the functionality provided by Practical E/M's approach to this component of the E/M system.

GOALS FOR DESIGN

Medical decision making (MDM), which is the third "key component" of the E/M coding system (along with the history and the physical examination), has created the greatest conceptual challenge for physicians attempting to accomplish compliant coding and documentation.

To fulfill Practical E/M's goal of achieving compliance as an integral part of providing quality medical care, we need to analyze and address the three hurdles that make documenting and coding this component of the medical record so challenging:

- Nontraditional documentation categories
- Current Procedural Terminology (CPT®) categories calling for quantitative assessment but having only qualitative descriptors
- Complex coding calculations

The documentation and coding difficulties resulting from these three problems have led most physicians to make a "best guess" about the level of complexity of MDM, or to ignore identifying levels of complexity of MDM completely. Both of these choices have contributed to physicians' failure to meet the standards required for E/M coding compliance.

Design for Compliance Requirements

Practical E/M employs a comprehensive combination of compliant template designs, documentation prompts, and reasonable assumptions to address these three compliance challenges.

Problem 1: Nontraditional Elements of the Medical Record
There are several elements of MDM that are included in the CPT coding guidelines but that are not traditionally taught to medical students when they learn to perform and document a history and physical (H&P). These include:

- the complexity of data reviewed,
- the complexity of data ordered,

■ the risk of presenting problem(s),

■ the risk of diagnostic procedures ordered, and the

■ risk of management options selected.

The concept of documenting these additional elements in the medical record is also generally not presented as part of coding courses for practicing physicians and administrators. As a result, the vast majority of physicians do not document these elements, regardless of whether their documentation is written, dictated, or entered into an electronic health record. Physicians' failure to document these categories in traditional medical records creates a significant compliance issue when their charts are audited. It allows (and requires) reviewers and auditors to determine the complexity of these elements subjectively, potentially resulting in their misinterpretation of the complexity of MDM, which may lead to an incorrect determination of the level of E/M care.

Solution to Problem 1 The Intelligent Medical Record (IMR) design provides selection list templates for ease of documentation of each of these nontraditional MDM elements, to ensure both compliance and audit protection.

When physicians accurately document these additional categories (particularly the three levels of risk) in the IMR at the time of patient care, their coding is supported and cannot be misinterpreted or disputed.

Problem 2: Quantification of Subjective Elements of MDM

As discussed in Chapter 5, MDM includes four elements that assess the "amount" or "number" of items physicians have documented. These elements are:

■ the *amount* of data reviewed,

■ the *amount* of data ordered,

■ the *number* of diagnoses, and

■ the *number* of management options.

The CPT coding system provides only descriptive assessments, without numerical values, for these four items. The amount of data is described by four subjective levels: minimal or none, limited, moderate, and extensive. Similarly, the number of diagnoses and/or management options is also described by using subjective terminology: minimal, limited, multiple, and extensive. The *Documentation Guidelines*[1] reiterates these descriptions but, unlike the numerical values it supplies for the levels of the medical history and the physical examination, it does not provide objective measures for any of these MDM terms. This leaves physicians and auditors without precise quantitative standards of measure to evaluate these elements.

Solution to Problem 2 Clearly, the terms *amount* and *number* indicate the need for quantitative values to assist physicians in compliant documentation and coding and to set objective standards for auditors. Using assumptions developed from extensive discussions with physicians, Medicare medical directors, insurance company medical directors, auditors, physician consultants, plus a dash of common sense, we can suggest reasonable quantitative values for these *qualitative* elements. These recommendations are listed in Table 16.1.

TABLE 16.1

Recommended Numerical Values for the Number of Diagnoses and Management Options and for the Amount of Data Ordered or Reviewed

CPT Description of Amount or Number	Practical E/M's Numerical Value
Minimal	1
Limited	2
Multiple or Moderate	3
Extensive	4 or more

During the development of the IMR, discussions of these proposed quantitative values with multiple reviewers (including those at the Centers for Medicare and Medicaid Services [CMS]), resulted in general agreement that it is reasonable to assign these numerical values to the CPT coding system's qualitative descriptions of *amount* and *number*. Therefore, we have incorporated these values into the IMR documentation prompts as guidelines for these elements of MDM (even though they have not been formally sanctioned in the CPT coding system or by CMS). Figures 16.1 and 16.2 demonstrate the application of these quantitative definitions in the documentation prompts for the amount of data reviewed and ordered and for the number of diagnoses and management options. Because all of the descriptors in the CPT coding system for levels of MDM are identical for outpatient initial visits, outpatient consultations, and established patient visits, the IMR uses the same quantitative definitions in the MDM documentation prompts for each of these types of service.

FIGURE 16.1

Documentation Prompt for Amount of Data (Ordered or Reviewed)*

<u>1.</u> Minimal (level 2)   <u>2.</u> Limited (level 3)   <u>3.</u> Moderate (level 4)   <u>4.</u> Extensive (level 5)

*The numerical values are underlined, as these are the pertinent guidelines for the amount of data.

FIGURE 16.2

Documentation Prompt for Number of Diagnoses or Management Options*

<u>1.</u> Minimal (level 2)   <u>2.</u> Limited (level 3)   <u>3.</u> Multiple (level 4)   <u>4.</u> Extensive (level 5)

* The numerical values are underlined, as these are the pertinent guidelines for number of diagnoses or number of management options.

Making a Judgment About the "Either/Or" Number Problem

The use of "and/or" relative to the number of diagnoses *and/or* management options in the CPT codebook introduces still another variable that was not addressed by the *Documentation Guidelines*. Although this description could be interpreted as providing an option to *add* the number of diagnoses and management options to reach a quantitative or a qualitative value, Practical E/M accepts the alternative option of giving credit for whichever of the two values is higher.

This conclusion appears to be appropriate and logical from a clinical perspective. It seems reasonable to assume that CPT codes would provide credit for an "extensive" number in the circumstance where the physician documents active consideration of four or more diagnoses even if documenting only one management option. It seems equally reasonable to assume that CPT codes would provide credit for an "extensive" number in the circumstance

continued

where the physician documents active consideration of four or more management options (eg, surgery, radiation therapy, chemotherapy, various sequences or combinations of therapy, or no treatment), even if documenting only one diagnosis (eg, colon cancer).

Problem 3: MDM's Complex E/M Coding Calculations

The CPT coding system's description of the MDM component of E/M coding contains three "elements,"[2] and each element is further subdivided into two or more parts that we will call "categories." The greatest challenge of the MDM component when using the traditional "document first and then calculate the E/M code" approach has been that the complexity of the relationships among these different elements and categories has required physicians to carry out an intricate series of calculations to determine the level of complexity of MDM.

The CPT coding system describes the three elements of MDM and their subcategories as follows:

- The first element, "diagnoses and management options,"[2] has two categories:
    - the number of possible diagnoses, and/or
    - the number of management options.
- The second element, "risks,"[2] has three categories:
    - the level of risk associated with the patient's presenting problem(s),
    - the level of risk associated with the diagnostic procedures ordered, and
    - the level of risk associated with the documented possible management options.
- The third element has four categories related to data:
    - the amount of data reviewed,
    - the amount of data to be obtained,
    - the complexity of data reviewed, and
    - the complexity of data to be obtained.[2]

The traditional method of determining the level of MDM, as explained in the CPT codebook and illustrated in Figure 16.3, has proven to be too complicated and too time consuming for physicians to accomplish while devoting their attention to their patients and providing thorough medical care. Figure 16.3 summarizes the conventional instructions for determining the level of complexity of MDM.

F I G U R E 16.3

Traditional Steps in Calculating the Complexity of MDM. This sequence shows the considerations conventionally required for determining the level of MDM.

1. Evaluate the number of diagnoses and/or management options
    a. Determine whether the *number of diagnoses* is "minimal, limited, multiple, or extensive"
    b. Determine whether the *number of management options* is "minimal, limited, multiple, or extensive"
    c. Select the higher value between these two categories
2. Evaluate the risk of complications and/or morbidity or mortality
    a. Determine whether the *risk of the presenting problem(s)* is "minimal, low, moderate, or high"
    b. Determine whether the *risk of the diagnostic procedures* ordered is "minimal, low, moderate, or high"
    c. Determine whether the *risk of the management options* is "minimal, low, moderate, or high"
    d. Select the highest value among these three categories

continued

3. Evaluate the amount and/or complexity of data ordered and/or reviewed
   a. Determine whether the *amount of data reviewed* is "minimal, low, moderate, or high"
   b. Determine whether the *complexity of data reviewed* is "minimal, low, moderate, or high"
   c. Determine whether the *amount of data ordered* is "minimal, low, moderate, or high"
   d. Determine whether the *complexity of data ordered* is "minimal, low, moderate, or high"
   e. Select the highest value among these four categories
4. Calculate the type of MDM
   a. Eliminate the lowest value among the three final values determined for steps 1, 2, and 3
   b. Eliminate the highest value among the remaining two values determined for steps 1, 2, and 3
   c. The final remaining value determines the complexity of MDM, selecting among "straightforward, low complexity, moderate complexity, and high complexity"

Source: American Medical Association. *Current Procedural Terminology CPT® 2008*. Chicago,IL: American Medical Association 2007.

Solution to Problem 3 Practical E/M eliminates the need for complex calculations. It substitutes the use of documentation prompts that guide compliant MDM documentation based on the level of care indicated by the nature of presenting problem (NPP). To eliminate the challenge of the "two out of three" elements calculation, we recommend always looking initially at the two elements of the MDM that are intrinsic to every visit: (1) levels of risk and (2) number of diagnoses or management options. Documenting these two elements according to the level of care indicated by the NPP ensures compliant documentation for MDM. For E/M coding purposes, omitting consideration of the amount and complexity of data eliminates all of the complex mathematical calculations. However, physicians still document the data reviewed and ordered, for the purpose of quality of care.

Documenting the Level of Risk

The CPT guidelines indicate that only one of the three risk categories needs to equal or exceed the severity of risk warranted by the NPP. Practical E/M further recommends that physicians should concentrate first on documenting the level of "risk of the patient's presenting problem(s),"[2] because the different levels of risk of the presenting problem correlate extremely well with the levels of severity of the NPP. This is a natural consequence of the fact that the description of the NPP relies significantly on *risk*. The CPT coding guidelines in fact define the severity of the NPP in terms of the "*risk* of morbidity, *risk* of mortality, and *risk* of prolonged functional impairment"[2] (italics added for emphasis). Therefore, when the physician refers to the documentation prompt for the section on risk, which is shown in Figure 16.4, in most cases the appropriate documentation of the level of risk of the presenting problem(s) should be at the same level as the NPP. Circling this indicated level of risk satisfies the first element of the two MDM documentation requirements.

FIGURE 16.4

Documentation Prompt for Levels of Risk*

1. <u>Minimal</u> (level 2)   2. <u>Low</u> (level 3)   3. <u>Moderate</u> (level 4)   4. <u>High</u> (level 5)

*The subjective descriptions for this documentation prompt are underlined, as these are the pertinent guidelines in the CPT coding system for level of risk.[2]

Example of Documenting the Level of Risk of Presenting Problems

For a patient whose NPP has been identified as "moderate," the CPT codebook definition of this degree of severity includes "risk of morbidity without treatment is moderate, there is moderate risk of mortality without treatment; uncertain prognosis OR increased probability of prolonged functional impairment."[2] This description of the NPP fits best with the descriptions of "moderate" risk of presenting problems found in the Table of Risk.[1] This correlation warrants the physician circling moderate severity for this level of risk.

This approach of relating risk of the presenting problem(s) to severity of the NPP will meet or exceed E/M compliance requirements for most visits.

Documenting the Number of Diagnoses or Management Options

Fulfilling the second element of the MDM documentation requirement should be addressed in the section of the form designated for "number of diagnoses or management options." The IMR documentation prompt (shown in Figure 16.2) for all outpatient office visit services reveals that the documented *number* of diagnoses or management options needed to satisfy the level of care warranted by the NPP is always one less than the level of that code.

For example, when the NPP warrants level 5 care, CPT guidelines indicate that this calls for an "extensive" number of diagnoses or management options, and our quantitative interpretation of "extensive" is at least four diagnoses or management options (ie, one number less than the indicated level of care). This relationship continues for the other levels of care as well, as shown in Figure 16.5.

FIGURE 16.5

Correlation Between Level of Care (E/M Code Level) and Number of Diagnoses or Management Options

Level of E/M Care	Indicated Number of Diagnoses or Number of Management Options
5	4 (extensive)
4	3 (multiple)
3	2 (limited)
2	1 (minimal)
1	1 (minimal)

Design for Efficiency and Quality Care

The IMR organizes the structure of the MDM template so that it follows the normal flow of patient care, starting with a section for the data reviewed and following this with a second section for impressions (ie, "diagnoses"), management plans, and data ordered. The IMR's appearance for these two sections is similar to that of traditional medical records, with the exception that it separates management plans from data ordered. The third section of the MDM form is dedicated to the assessment and documentation of the nontraditional categories of MDM, each of which is designed with a selection-list graphic interface for rapid documentation.

Figure 16.6 illustrates the appearance of the entire MDM section, before any customization. The following discussion will examine the three sections of the MDM portion of the IMR in greater detail, with consideration of some of the options that physicians can incorporate into a customized IMR.

F IGURE 16.6

Appearance of Entire Medical Decision-Making Section
The check boxes in the data sections and the numbering in the impression and management
option sections are optional customizations.

Date____/____/____

Patient Name:_____   Account No._____   DOB:____/____/____

Outpatient Initial Visit Form (p. 4):

| MEDICAL DECISION MAKING | 2 of the 3 sections (a vs a', b vs b' vs b", c vs c' vs c") must meet or exceed indicated level of care |
| DATA REVIEWED (c): | 1. Minimal (level 2)   2. Limited (level 3)   3. Moderate (level 4)   4. Extensive (level 5) |

☐ X-ray/CT scan   ☐ See attached dictation

☐ MRI

☐ Lab/blood work

IMPRESSIONS/DIFFERENTIAL DIAGNOSES (a):   PLANS/MANAGEMENT OPTIONS (a')

1. Minimal (level 2)   2. Limited (level 3)   3. Multiple (level 4)   4. Extensive (level 5)

1) _____   1) _____ ☐ See attached dictation

2) _____   2) _____

3) _____   3) _____

4) _____   4) _____

5) _____   5) _____

DATA ORDERED (c'):   1. Minimal or none (level 2)   2. Limited (level 3)   3. Moderate (level 4)   4. Extensive (level 5)

☐   ☐   ☐   ☐   ☐

                                                                                                   ☐ See attached dictation

Information Sheets Given:

COMPLEXITY OF DATA REVIEWED OR ORDERED (c")

1. Minimal (level 2)   2. Limited (level 3)   3. Moderate (level 4)   4. Extensive (level 5)

| | | 1. min | 2. limited | 3. mod | 4. extensive |

RISK OF COMPLICATIONS &/OR MORBIDITY OR MORTALITY (see examples in Table of Risk)

1. Minimal (level 2)   2. Low (level 3)   3. Moderate (level 4)   4. High (level 5)

	1. min	2. low	3. mod	4. high
risk of presenting problem(s) (b):	1. min	2. low	3. mod	4. high
risk of diagnostic procedure(s) (b'):	1. min	2. low	3. mod	4. high
risk of management option(s) selected (b"):	1. min	2. low	3. mod	4. high

First Section of the MDM Template: Data Reviewed
The "data reviewed" section appears in the beginning of the MDM template because physicians must consider this information before finalizing their impressions and selecting management options. The structure of this section, before any customization, consists of a series of blank lines for the physician to enter short descriptions of test findings, reports, and chart reviews of outside medical records. As shown in Figure 16.6, this subsection includes two documentation prompts:

- a general documentation prompt for the entire MDM section, based on CPT guidelines. This prompt identifies the traditional two out of three coding paradigm (the prompt for a versus a' versus a", b versus b", c versus c' versus c" refers to the labeled categories of number of diagnoses/management options the three levels of risk, and amount and complexity of data reviewed and ordered); and
- The specific "data reviewed" documentation prompt from Figure 16.1, with the number underlined, to indicate the amount of data reviewed that is required to support each code level.

Documentation efficiency can be increased by customization with pre-loaded descriptions (with or without check boxes) for data commonly reviewed in a physician's practice. For example, the "data reviewed" section of a cardiology template can be as sophisticated as the form shown in Figure 16.7.

F I G U R E 16.7

Sample MDM Data Reviewed Template for Cardiology Specialty

Physicians save a significant amount of time by using this type of graphic interface to streamline the process of documenting laboratory data in the patient's chart. It is inefficient to write the names of commonly reviewed tests freehand time after time, and these can easily be preprinted in the custom IMR. This section also includes a check box stating "see attached dictation," for physicians who prefer dictation to writing. It is important to note, however, that the process of dictation does add additional time.

Second Section of the MDM Template: Number of Diagnoses and/or Management Options
Audits demonstrate that the documentation in this section of medical records commonly falls short of the physician's actual cognitive work product. That is, physicians commonly do the intellectual work of considering a significant number of possible diagnoses and considering a significant number of possible management options,

but they do not take the time to adequately document the lists of these possibilities in the chart. Most often, they document only the most probable diagnosis and the primary treatment. This limited documentation is one of the primary sources of failure in E/M audits. In contrast, the IMR documentation prompt for this section (shown in Figure 16.2) guides the physician to appropriately document his or her intellectual effort. This additional documentation serves two purposes. First, it fulfills the requirement for compliant E/M documentation. In addition, as described below, when physicians document their thought process for considering possible diagnoses and management options, it often promotes more comprehensive care during each visit, and it frequently facilitates providing optimal care during future visits.

Diagnoses and management options appear side by side on the IMR template. In customizing their templates, physicians have the option of preprinting a number on each line for clarity (as shown in Figure 16.6), and identifying the managements associated with each diagnosis. The short description design is both efficient and highly flexible for this section, giving physicians the option to enter more extended narrative information. This narrative option allows physicians to elaborate on their thought processes, using additional descriptions that can help guide subsequent care. For example, they might indicate their impression of the severity and/or probability of various differential diagnoses, as well as a blue print for therapeutic steps they will take next, including potential responses to results of pending laboratory and radiology tests, or what to do if a particular treatment is unsuccessful. Figure 16.8 illustrates a sample template, including the option of preprinted numbers for the impressions and management options. It also includes a separate section for the "data ordered" category, which is described below.

FIGURE 16.8

Sample MDM Diagnoses and Management Options Template, Including "Data Ordered" (for an ENT physician)

IMPRESSIONS/DIFFERENTIAL DX (b):	PLANS/MANAGEMENT OPTIONS (b')
1. Minimal (level 2) 2. Limited (level 3) 3. Multiple (level 4) 4. Extensive (level 5)	
1.	1. ☐ See attached dictation
2.	2.
3.	3.
4.	4.
5.	5.
DATA ORDERED: 1. Minimal (level 2) 2. Limited (level 3) 3. Moderate (level 4) 4. Extensive (level 5)	
☐ Audiogram ☐ ENG ☐ ABR ☐ Allergy Evaluation ☐ CT Scan Sinuses ☐ MRI of IACs, with Gadolinium	

Second Section of the MDM Template: Data Ordered

Physicians customarily list both diagnostic tests ordered and managements recommended in the same section of the medical record. This section is conventionally labeled "plans" or "recommendations." However, to comply with the CPT coding guidelines for MDM, the IMR separates the "data ordered" section from the "plans/management options" section and includes its own documentation prompt. Physicians should document diagnostic procedures and treatment options in the "plans/management options" subsection. They should use the "data ordered" subsection to document requests for laboratory tests, radiology tests, physiologic tests, and medical records from other physicians.

When customizing their own IMR, physicians have the option of prelisting their commonly ordered tests on the form. This may be done by using check boxes, as shown in Figure 16.8, or by listing the tests so that the physician can circle the ones he or she wishes to order. This feature has no effect on compliance; rather, it can be incorporated to increase the efficiency of documentation. The number of preprinted tests a physician may include on the form is limited only by the space available.

Personal Experience With "Number of Diagnoses/Plans" Subsection

In my own medical practice, I used this portion of the medical record to increase my recall, insight, and efficiency during follow-up visits (or when responding to telephone calls from a patient). The extended documentation reminded me of my previous analysis of the patient's condition and clearly defined my "game plan" for future care. This helped not only me, but also anyone else who might refer to the medical record.

For example, continuing from the physical examination of a patient with probable chronic sinusitis shown in Figure 15.5 in Chapter 15, I might document this section of the MDM as shown in Figure 16.9. Adding the brief narrative comments allows physicians to describe a roadmap for care that is easy for any member of the health care team (including themselves) to follow. It also helps physicians to consider the possible protocols available for the care of each patient. While this amount of documentation requires a small amount of additional time, the positive impact on the quality of patient care clearly justifies the effort.

F I G U R E   16.9

Sample MDM Diagnoses and Management Options Template, Including "Data Ordered"

IMPRESSIONS/DIFFERENTIAL DX (b):	PLANS/MANAGEMENT OPTIONS (b')
<u>1.</u> Minimal (level 2) <u>2.</u> Limited (level 3) <u>3.</u> Multiple (level 4) <u>4.</u> Extensive (level 5)	
1. Bilat nasal polyps, L>R	1. Nasacort AQ bid ☐ See attached dictation
2. Probable chronic sinusitis	2. Ampx 500 tid x 2 wks; then Vantin,
3.	3. Then Levaquin if Sx not resolved
4. Chronic irritative rhinitis 2° smoke	4. D/C smoke; disc Nicoderm and Zyban
5. Probable allergic component	5. Re-eval. in 2 wks;

DATA ORDERED: (a"):   <u>1.</u> Minimal (level 2)   <u>2.</u> Limited (level 3)   <u>3.</u> Moderate (level 4)   <u>4.</u> Extensive (level 5)

☐ Audiogram   ☐ ENG   ☐ ABR   ☒ Allergy Evaluation   ☒ CT Scan Sinuses   ☐ MRI of IACs, with Gadolinium

1. Nasal endoscopy 4 wks	☐ See attached dictation
2. CT after 6-8 wks medication	
3. Possible future allergy eval and Rx	

Third Section of the MDM Template: Complexity of Data Reviewed or Ordered

Because the "complexity of data reviewed or ordered" category of MDM does not appear in conventional medical records, the IMR includes it in the text box that contains all the categories of the medical record that are not usually found in physicians' records. It provides physicians with the ability to document the "complexity" portion of the CPT coding system category titled "amount and/or complexity of data to be reviewed."[2] Because "amount" is quantitative and "complexity" is qualitative, it is certainly logical and reasonable to document these two features separately. The amount of data reviewed was documented in the first section of the MDM form, and the amount of data ordered was documented in the second subsection.

To allow rapid documentation of the level of complexity, the IMR uses a simple selection-list graphic interface, showing the four levels of complexity and allowing the physician to circle the level most appropriate for the data reviewed (and/or ordered). The documentation prompt for this component emphasizes (by underlining) the subjective descriptions that measure the complexity of data. An example of this section of the IMR template is shown in Figure 16.10.

As described in the CPT coding system guidelines, data reviewed and/or ordered may include "medical records, diagnostic tests, and/or other information that must be obtained, reviewed, and analyzed."[2] (The medical records discussed are from external sources, not from the practice's own records.)

FIGURE 16.10

Complexity of Data Ordered and/or Reviewed Selection List Template*

COMPLEXITY OF DATA REVIEWED OR ORDERED (c")	1. Minimal (level 2)	2. Limited (level 3)	3. Moderate (level 4)	4. Extensive (level 5)
	1. min	2. limited	3. mod	4. extensive

*The subjective descriptions for this documentation prompt are underlined, as these are the pertinent guidelines for complexity of data.

As shown in Figure 16.10, the qualitative CPT descriptors for complexity of data are "minimal, limited, moderate, and extensive."[2] Although neither CPT nor the *Documentation Guidelines* provides any quantifiable parameters for these descriptors, some reasonable examples have emerged from discussions with consultants and auditors. Generally, they consider the review of printed laboratory or radiology reports to qualify as minimal or limited complexity. The review of outside medical records, an electrocardiogram rhythm strip, a pulmonary function test, x-rays, or other tasks that involve interpretation are reasonably categorized as tasks requiring moderate complexity. The actual review and interpretation of more complex tests, such as computed tomographic scans, magnetic resonance images, or stress tests, usually qualify as tasks of extensive complexity. However, these examples are offered only as reasonable guidelines. The critical factor is that the physician must document his or her assessment of the complexity involved in reviewing data in order to achieve compliance and audit protection.

Third Section of the MDM Template: Risk of Complications and/or Morbidity and/or Mortality

The Table of Risk, published in the *Documentation Guidelines*,[1] provides examples of health problems within each of the three categories of risk:

- risk of the presenting problem(s),
- risk of diagnostic procedures(s) ordered, and
- risk of management options selected.

The physician's task is to identify and document the appropriate level of each of these risks, based on the descriptions provided in the Table of Risk.[1] The philosophy of Practical E/M is that the physician should use his or her judgment to document these choices about levels of risk, so that a reviewer cannot impose his or her judgment on this essential element of MDM. The IMR employs a selection-list graphic interface, similar to the one used for complexity of data. It lists the three categories of risk, each with four levels of severity, and instructs the physician to circle the appropriate level of risk in one or more of these three categories.

The *Documentation Guidelines* rule for the risk element of MDM is that "the highest level of risk in any one category (presenting problem[s], diagnostic procedure[s], or management options) determines the overall risk."[1] While documentation of the risk for only one of these three categories is necessary for the purposes of compliance and audit protection, it is advisable to document the risk of the presenting problem(s) in all cases, since this level of risk correlates so well with the NPP. Documentation of the other two categories of risk is also appropriate, particularly if the risk level for one or both of these categories is higher than that of the presenting problem(s). In addition to the audit protection benefits, documenting information in this section helps to convey the severity of risk for illness and treatment options for other physicians who may review the patient's medical record at a later date. It could also provide added protection in the event of a liability review. Figure 16.11 illustrates a sample selection list type of graphic interface for this section of the MDM form.

Figure 16.11

Sample MDM Risk Template

RISK OF COMPLICATIONS &/OR MORBIDITY OR MORTALITY (see examples in Table of Risk)				
	1. Minimal (level 2)	2. Low (level 3)	3. Moderate (level 4)	4. High (level 5)
risk of presenting problem(s) (b):	1. min	2. low	3. mod	4. high
risk of diagnostic procedure(s) (b'):	1. min	2. low	3. mod	4. high
risk of management option(s) selected (b"):	1. min	2. low	3. mod	4. high

We advise physicians to keep a laminated copy of the Table of Risk in each examining room for reference. A copy of the Table of Risk is shown in Table 16.2.

T A B L E   16.2

Table of Risk from the *Documentation Guidelines*[1]

Level of Risk	Presenting Problem(s)	Diagnostic Procedure(s) Ordered/ Reviewed	Management Options Selected
Minimal	One self-limited or minor problem (eg, cold, insect bite, tinea corporis)	Laboratory tests requiring venipuncture Chest x-rays EKG/EEG Urinalysis Ultrasound; eg, echocardiography KOH prep	Rest, gargles, elastic bandages, superficial dressings
Low	Two or more self-limited or minor problems One stable chronic illness (eg, well-controlled hypertension or non–insulin-dependent diabetes, cataract, benign prostatic hypertrophy) Acute uncomplicated illness or injury (eg, cystitis, allergic rhinitis, simple sprain)	Physiologic tests not under stress (eg, pulmonary function tests) Noncardiovascular imaging studies with contrast (eg, barium enema) Superficial needle biopsies Clinical laboratory tests requiring arterial puncture Skin biopsies	Over-the-counter drugs Minor surgery with no identified risk factors Physical therapy Occupational therapy IV fluids without additives

continued

TABLE 16.2

Table of Risk From the *Documentation Guidelines,* cont'd.

Level of Risk	Presenting Problem(s)	Diagnostic Procedure(s) Ordered/ Reviewed	Management Options Selected
Moderate	One or more chronic illnesses with mild exacerbation, progression, or side effects of treatment Two or more stable chronic illnesses Undiagnosed new problem with uncertain prognosis (eg, lump in breast) Acute illness with systemic symptoms (eg, pyelonephritis, pneumonitis, colitis) Acute complicated injury (eg, head injury with brief loss of consciousness)	Physiologic tests under stress (eg, cardiac stress test, fetal contraction stress test) Diagnostic endoscopies with no identified risk factors Deep needle or incisional biopsy Cardiovascular imaging studies with contrast and no identified risk factors (eg, arteriogram, cardiac catheterization) Obtain fluid from body cavity (eg, lumbar puncture, thoracentesis, culdocentesis)	Minor surgery with identified risk factors Elective major surgery (open, percutaneous, or endoscopic) with no identified risk factors Prescription drug management Therapeutic nuclear medicine IV fluids with additives Closed treatment of fracture or dislocation without manipulation
High	One or more chronic illnesses with severe exacerbation, progression, or side effects of treatment Acute or chronic illnesses or injuries that pose a threat to life or bodily function (eg, multiple trauma, acute myocardial infarction, progressive severe rheumatoid arthritis, psychiatric illness with potential threat to self or others) Abrupt change in neurologic status (eg, seizure, TIA, weakness, sensory loss)	Cardiovascular imaging studies with contrast with identified risk factors Cardiac electrophysiologic tests Diagnostic endoscopies with identified risk factors Discography	Elective major surgery (open, percutaneous, or endoscopic) with identified risk factors Emergency major surgery (open, percutaneous, or endoscopic) Parenteral controlled substances Drug therapy requiring intensive monitoring for toxicity Decision not to resuscitate or to de-escalate care because of poor prognosis

EEG, electroencephalogram; EKG, electrocardiogram; IV, intravenous; KOH, potassium hydroxide; TIA, transient ischemic attack.

Source: Health Care Financing Administration. *Documentation Guidelines for Evaluation and Management Services*. Chicago, Ill: American Medical Association; 1997.

We encourage physicians to become familiar with the examples presented in the Table of Risk. While the examples do not actually quantify risk, they present reasonable guidelines that physicians can apply during patient care. For example, in the category concerning the risk of management options documented, there are two clinical situations that frequently come into consideration. First, any management of prescription drugs qualifies as *moderate risk*. For surgeons, any consideration of elective surgery without identified risk factors also qualifies as *moderate risk*. Per CPT guidelines (and as shown in the documentation prompt), documentation of a moderate level of risk is appropriate to support levels 1, 2, 3, or 4 E/M codes for most types of service, including either initial or established patient visits.

Considering Surgery With "Identified Risk Factors"

According to the Table of Risk, "elective surgery with identified risk factors" qualifies as "high risk."[1] Although a definition of what qualifies as a surgical "risk factor" is not specified in the *Documentation Guidelines*, it is reasonable to assume that this phrase refers to risks *extrinsic* to the actual surgery (since all operations have identified *intrinsic* risk factors). We interpret these risk factors to be those local or systemic abnormalities that would increase the anesthesia and/or surgical risk above the normal levels for a given operation and/or postoperative recovery. Examples might include significant scarring from previous surgery, diabetes, congestive heart failure, chronic obstructive pulmonary disease, coagulation problems, and coronary artery disease. The important consideration for this category is that the physician must identify and document these *extrinsic* risks, as well as documenting on the IMR template that the risk of the procedure is high.

SYNOPSIS AND ANALYSIS OF MDM

Table 16.3 summarizes the designs selected for the MDM section of the medical record.

TABLE 16.3

Synopsis of IMR for MDM

Category of MDM	Interface	Data Entry Options	Format Options	Comments
Data reviewed	Graphic (with check boxes and short answer)	Physician	Writing or dictation	Check boxes save some time
Number of diagnoses/ treatment options	Short answer/ brief narrative	Physician	Writing or dictation	Narrative provides rich descriptive detail
Data ordered	Graphic (with check boxes and short answer)	Physician	Writing or dictation	Check boxes save some time
Complexity of data ordered	Graphic (selection list, circle descriptors)	Physician	Writing	Minimal time required
Risks	Graphic (selection list, circle descriptors)	Physician	Writing	Minimal time required

The Practical E/M approach to MDM facilitates increased efficiency for documenting some of the categories and adds some time in other categories. The brief additional time required to document one or more levels of risk and the complexity of data is generally offset by the increased efficiency resulting from the use of graphic interface documentation tools for the sections of the form for data reviewed and data ordered. Quality of care is enhanced by incorporating the documentation of ancillary and "rule out" diagnoses and the listing of alternative management options to describe a blueprint for future care. The inclusion of documentation of risks helps to reinforce compliance and audit protection. For similar reasons, the overall degree of MDM documentation in the IMR design increases protection in the event of a medicolegal investigation.

USING THE MDM SECTION OF THE IMR

After completing the physical examination and documenting the data reviewed in the first section of the MDM template, the physician should have refined his or her initial clinical impressions and mentally made any suitable adjustments to the differential diagnosis, the NPP, and the appropriate level of care. The physician should now complete the remaining sections of the MDM by documenting care at (or above) the level of complexity warranted by the NPP.

For E/M compliance purposes in the MDM section, Practical E/M recommends that physicians should focus their attention on the level of risk and the number of diagnoses and management options. Proper documentation of these two components should satisfy the E/M compliance requirements in almost every case. This saves time and effort by eliminating complex calculations introduced by also weighing the amount and complexity of data.

First MDM Section: Data Reviewed

In the "data reviewed" template, illustrated in Figures 16.6 and 16.7, the physician documents any laboratory tests, radiology studies, outside medical records, or other medical information that has been reviewed as part of this visit. In some cases a large amount of data may be documented, and in other cases there may be none.

Reviewing Medical Records

When the CPT coding guidelines consider "the amount and/or complexity of medical records . . . that must be obtained, reviewed, and analyzed,"[2] it is referring to medical records obtained from outside sources. Reviewing the practice's own records of a patient is considered to be part of the process of taking the patient's medical history. It is treated as a routine component of every established patient visit. Therefore, the physician should not document or claim additional credit in the "data reviewed" section of MDM for reviewing the patient's existing records in the physician's own practice.

Second MDM Section: Impressions, Plans, and Data Ordered

A sample IMR template of the second portion of the MDM (impressions, plans, and data ordered) was shown in Figure 16.8. In traditional medical records, the physician first documents the list of his or her clinical impressions of the patient's illnesses, and then lists recommendations for both diagnostic evaluations and management options. On the basis of descriptions in the CPT coding system for MDM, the IMR template separates the management plans and the diagnostic tests ordered into two separate sections on the form.

When documenting this section of the MDM form, the physician should refer to the documentation prompt to ensure that he or she is documenting an amount of decision making actually performed, and that equals or exceeds the level warranted by the severity of the NPP. For example, if the patient's NPP were moderate and warranted level 3 care, the documentation prompt indicates that at least two diagnoses or two management options should be actively considered and documented to support a claim for this level of care.

The basic principle supporting this approach is that documentation of *all* the clinically relevant diagnoses and management options is indicated for quality care, as well as for medicolegal protection. Although this amount of information often exceeds the number called for as a threshold by the CPT coding guidelines shown in the documentation prompt, the listing of additional diagnoses and management options does not change either the NPP or the associated medically indicated level of care.

Subsection for Impressions/Diagnoses

The description of the "clinical impressions" section in the *Documentation Guidelines* indicates that compliant documentation of the "number of diagnoses" can be accomplished in several ways[1]:

- by documenting a number of separate diagnoses,
- by documenting a differential diagnosis, or
- by a combination of these approaches.

In addition, the *Documentation Guidelines* advises that physicians may also document their subjective impressions about the relative probabilities of each potential diagnosis listed, stating that, "for a presenting problem without an established diagnosis, the assessment or clinical impression may be stated in the form of differential diagnoses or as a 'possible,' 'probable,' or 'rule out' (R/O) diagnosis."[1] These added descriptors assist physicians during subsequent care by reminding them of their reasoning and the implications of their assessments. An example of this type of listing could read:

> Acute tracheobronchitis
> Probable pneumonia
> Possible underlying reflux (doubt)

Examples of Documenting Impressions/Diagnoses

Assuming an example where 99204 is the level of care indicated by the NPP, the documentation prompt calls for documenting three or more identified diagnoses. Possible options for satisfying this requirement include:

1. Three (or more) unrelated diagnoses, if appropriate. For example:
   - Chest pain, probable costochondritis
   - Chronic obstructive pulmonary disease
   - Asthma, likely related to allergic sensitivity
   - Hypertension (controlled with medication)
2. One symptom with three possible differential diagnoses. For example:
   - Chest pain, probable coronary disease
   - Rule out reflux esophagitis
   - Rule out costochondritis (unlikely)

continued

3. Combination of differential and unrelated diagnoses. For example:

- Chest pain; probable coronary disease
- Rule out reflux esophagitis
- Hypertension (controlled with medication)

According to the criterion of medical necessity, to be considered as one of the number of documented diagnoses for coding compliance purposes, an illness must be actively related to the problems of the day's visit. Any problems, listed for reasons of quality or completeness, that are otherwise inactive or unrelated to the day's visit should not be included in the total number of diagnoses counted for E/M compliance purposes. (For example, if the internist of one of the above patients added to the list of diagnoses, for completeness, "status post left knee replacement surgery," this would not be considered an active diagnosis unless the patient had a complaint about the knee that the physician had evaluated.)

Subsection for Management Options
Similarly, indicating the "number of management options" appropriate for the level of care can be achieved in one of several possible ways:

- by documenting the treatments matched to each of a number of separate diagnoses,
- by documenting multiple treatments employed for a single diagnosis,
- by documenting a list of possible alternative treatment options, or
- by a combination of these approaches.

In addition, Practical E/M encourages physicians to consider and document potential alternative treatments that might be considered if a primary treatment proves unsuccessful. It is also recommended that documentation of a request for a consultation by another physician be most appropriately listed in the "management options" section, since the requesting physician is seeking help for the patient in managing a specific medical problem.

Doing Nothing Is a Treatment Option

It is appropriate to add that one management option may include discussing with the patient the alternative of "doing nothing." Surgeons commonly include discussion of this possibility when conferring with their patients about the possibility of performing surgery. Therefore, for patients who are considering a surgical option, there is commonly a minimum of three management options available: surgery, continued medical therapy, and no intervention at all. Although this option is not typically presented to nonsurgical patients, it is reasonable to discuss (and document) the option of "doing nothing" with patients undergoing medical treatments. Before discussing the potential risks and complications associated with a particular medication, it is helpful to advise a patient of the potential risks of the illness if it is left untreated. It is noteworthy that discussing and documenting this information also fulfills one of the requirements of the medicolegal doctrine of "informed consent." This principle specifically calls for physicians to discuss the option of "doing nothing" with their patients, as well as informing them about the potential consequences of that choice.

Subsection for Data Ordered
"Data ordered" is the final subsection of the second section of the MDM form. The IMR form provides blank lines, and customized templates may also include lists of commonly ordered tests and documents, with or without check boxes. For completeness, the physician should also circle the appropriate subjective level of

complexity of data (the highest level for data reviewed or data ordered) at the beginning of the third MDM Section.

Third MDM Section: Levels of Risk

The final section of the MDM template, which is illustrated in Figure 16.11, enables the physician to document his or her subjective assessment of the levels of risk for three categories of care:

- the risk of the patient's presenting problem(s),
- the risk of the diagnostic tests ordered, and
- the risk of the management options recommended.

For assistance in judging the appropriate levels of risk, the physician should refer to the Table of Risk (from the *Documentation Guidelines*). As noted earlier, we suggest keeping a laminated copy of this document in each patient examination room.

The physician should also refer to the risk section's documentation prompt, shown in Figures 16.4 and 16.11, to ensure that the documented level of risk, for at least one of the three categories, equals or exceeds the level warranted by the severity of the NPP. We can again consider the example of an initial patient visit where the NPP is determined to be "moderate," and therefore warrants level 3 care according to the descriptors in the CPT guidelines. The documentation prompt indicates that one of the documented levels of risk should be at least "low" to establish appropriate risk severity for this NPP and level of care.

EXCEPTIONS TO THE MDM PARADIGM

To make E/M documentation and coding as user-friendly as possible for physicians, Practical E/M recommends the use of a simplified paradigm for documentation of MDM. As previously noted, this approach concentrates on only two of the three categories of MDM: risk and number of diagnoses or management options. Using this approach promotes good medical care and enables physicians to efficiently achieve E/M compliance for the vast majority of E/M visits.

Situations do, however, arise when it may be necessary to expand this approach. This can occur when (A) there are insufficient diagnoses and management options to meet the level of care appropriate for the NPP, (B) the risks seem too low to meet the level of care appropriate for the NPP, or (C) the risks seem inordinately high when compared to the level of care warranted by the NPP.

Exception A: The risk is at or above the indicated level, but the physician cannot reasonably document the number of diagnoses or management options warranted by the NPP.

In this scenario, the E/M code submitted must be lowered to the level indicated by the documentation prompt (Figure 16.2). In our example, which calls for level 3 care, if the physician can reasonably document only one diagnosis and one management option, then the E/M code to be submitted would be reduced to level 2 (ie, 99202), on the basis of these two elements alone.

However, in this circumstance, the physician should consider the third element that the CPT coding guidelines include in MDM. As shown in the documentation prompts for the data categories, if the amount or complexity of data ordered and reviewed is documented as "low" (or higher), the MDM would still have "low" complexity, which would support the level 3 care indicated by the NPP.

Exception B: The number of diagnoses or management options is at or above the indicated level, but the physician cannot reasonably document the level of risk warranted by the NPP, for any of the three categories of risk.

This situation should occur only rarely, because the CPT coding guidelines define both the "severity of the NPP" and the "risk of the presenting problem(s)" in terms of the severity and risks of the patient's illnesses. A comparison of the examples for the level of risk of the presenting problem(s), which appear in the Table of Risk,[1] with the CPT coding system's definitions for the types of NPP demonstrates that these two factors should be interpreted at the same level in almost every case.

If a situation arises in which the physician does conclude (and document) that the *risk* of the presenting problem is less than the *severity* of the NPP, then the physician's determination of the severity of the NPP should be reevaluated as a "compliance check." Under this circumstance, the physician has several options related to the coding and documentation:

- Reduce the NPP, with a concomitant reduction in the indicated level of care (and E/M code to be submitted).
- If the severity of the NPP still seems appropriate, then the indicated E/M code level may be submitted only if either the risk of diagnostic procedures or the risk of management options is high enough to meet the level indicated by this NPP. In our example, which calls for level 3 care, one of the risk elements must be documented at the level of "low" or higher.
- If the physician cannot reasonably document one of the three risk categories at the level indicated by the NPP, then the E/M code to be submitted must be reduced to the level permitted by the CPT coding guidelines, as indicated by the documentation prompt (Figure 16.4). In the example in which the NPP calls for level 3 care, if all three risk categories are "minimal," then the highest level of E/M code that may be submitted would be level 2, on the basis of these two elements alone.

This is another circumstance where the physician would then consider the amount and complexity of data ordered and reviewed. If this is documented as "low" (or higher), the MDM would still have "low" complexity, which would support the level 3 care indicated by the NPP.

Exception C: The physician determines that the risk of the presenting problem(s) is higher than the severity of the NPP.

If a situation arises in which the physician concludes (and documents) that the *risk* of the presenting problem is greater than the *severity* of the NPP, then the physician's determination of the severity of the NPP should be reevaluated as a "compliance check." The severity of the NPP may need to be increased, with a concomitant increase in the indicated level of care. If the physician concludes that the original determination of the severity of NPP remains valid, then no change in coding or documentation is necessary.

When One or More Levels of Risk Is Higher Than the Severity of the NPP

Occasionally, one or more of the categories of risk has a level of risk that is higher than the severity of the NPP. This situation is particularly relevant when we can consider a patient whose severity of NPP is moderate to high, which would warrant either level 4 or level 5 care. If the physician judges (and documents) the level of risk to be "high" in one or more of the three risk categories, the physician could reasonably submit a level 5 E/M code, but only if the number of documented diagnoses or management options (or the level of data) is also sufficient for level 5 care.

SUMMARY

This MDM compliance and care discussion concentrates on a functional approach to compliant documentation for this section of the medical record. Instead of complicated mathematical calculations, Practical E/M provides guidance through the use of documentation prompts. These prompts inform the physician of CPT coding guidelines for MDM, enabling him or her to confirm that the documented level of risk, and the documented number of diagnoses or management options considered, are both sufficient to support the level of care associated with the patient's NPP on the day of the visit.

By using the NPP as the reference standard, not only does the physician guarantee that the amount of care provided is consistent with the nature of the patient's medical problem, he or she also confirms that this section of the medical record provides sufficient documentation to effectively describe that care and support compliant E/M coding.

References

1.   Health Care Financing Administration. *Documentation Guidelines for Evaluation and Management Services*. Chicago, IL: American Medical Association; 1997.

2.   American Medical Association. *Current Procedural Terminology CPT® 2008*. Chicago, IL: American Medical Association; 2007.

Documenting Time, Counseling, and Coordination of Care

The *Current Procedural Terminology* (CPT®) codebook provides a list of average times required for most evaluation and management (E/M) services. It states that these times are included specifically "to assist physicians in selecting the most appropriate level of E/M services,"[1] even though time is generally not included in E/M code calculations under most circumstances.

The CPT coding system further qualifies that the time guideline applies only to face-to-face time that the physician spends with the patient during office and other outpatient visits, including office consultations.[1] On the other hand, for hospital services and nursing facility services, the CPT coding system defines time as "unit/floor time, which includes the time that the physician is present on the patient's hospital unit and at the bedside rendering services for that patient. This includes the time in which the physician establishes and/or reviews the patient's chart, examines the patient, writes notes, and communicates with other professionals and the patient's family."[1]

GOALS FOR DESIGN

Design for Compliance Requirements

Although time is not taken into account as a factor for determining the level of E/M care during most patient visits, the CPT codebook and the *Documentation Guidelines for Evaluation and Management Services* report a special circumstance under which the E/M coding system permits time to be considered as the sole *determining factor* in E/M code selection. This provides that when counseling and/or coordination of care comprise more than 50% of the time spent during an encounter (face-to-face time or unit/floor time, depending on the type of service), then "time is considered the key or controlling factor to qualify for a particular level of E/M service."[1,2] This means that the amount of time spent is permitted to become the sole determining factor of the level of the E/M code regardless of whether the physician performed an extensive history or no history at all. This is true of the exam and medical decision making (MDM) components of the visit as well. There is also no consideration of the nature of presenting problem (NPP) in this circumstance.

How Time Factors Are Determined

The CPT coding system and the *Documentation Guidelines* do not indicate a specific amount of time associated with each E/M code level. Instead, consultants, auditors, and medical directors conventionally refer to the times that are listed in the CPT codebook as "average times" associated with each CPT code. These are then treated as if they are

---

continued

threshold times for the selection of the proper code. For example, the CPT coding system description of E/M service 99214 includes the statement "physicians typically spend 25 minutes face-to-face with the patient and/or family."[1] Even though this is presented in the CPT codebook as an average time, it is generally interpreted to mean that 25 minutes or more supports code 99214, but less than 25 minutes does not. This analysis is not written in the *Documentation Guidelines*; it is simply my observation of how "time" and code levels are consistently related by those who review E/M medical records.

The *Documentation Guidelines* further directs that the physician must document the total length of time of the encounter plus a description of the counseling and/or activities involved in coordinating care.[3] The physician must also *document* the fact that more than 50% of the encounter was involved with counseling and/or coordination of care. (An alternative design could provide for the physician to document the time devoted to counseling in addition to the total time of the visit).

Design for Efficiency and Quality Care

Figure 17.1 illustrates an intelligent medical record (IMR) graphic format that facilitates rapid documentation of the three elements needed to fulfill CPT coding system compliance requirements in situations in which time becomes the controlling factor. The documentation prompt reminds the physician that this section should be considered only when the ">50% of the visit" test is met.

For an office visit in which the duration of counseling and coordination of care meets the ">50% of the visit" test, the physician simply (1) fills in the total time of the encounter (not just the time devoted to counseling and coordinating care), (2) checks the box to indicate that more than 50% of the encounter involved counseling and coordination, and (3) enters a brief narrative description of these services. As an example of a brief narrative, documentation of a patient visit to discuss options for breast cancer treatment might read:

> Discussed diagnosis, natural course of the disease if left untreated, and treatment options including chemotherapy, radiation, lumpectomy, mastectomy. Also reviewed rehab, reconstruction, support groups, and meeting with treated patients.

FIGURE 17.1

Sample Documentation Template for Time, Including Documentation Prompt

Complete this section only if documented below > 50% of visit time involved counseling and/or coordinating care.	
TIME: _____ minutes	☐ > 50% of visit time involved counseling and/or coordination of care
	Clinician's signature:

When a physician devotes more than 50% of visit time to counseling and coordinating care, the E/M code can be determined by the "typical" time values listed in the descriptions in the CPT codebook for each type of E/M service and each level of care.[1] For outpatient office visits, Practical E/M provides a set of documentation prompts on a separate information sheet, which is shown in Figure 17.2. These prompts list the total amount of face-to-face time that must be spent during a visit to qualify for each level of E/M code. We recommend that physicians keep a copy of this information in each patient examination room. Generally, it is most convenient to print this information on the reverse side of the laminated Table of Risk.

For other types of service in which time may be considered as a factor, the physician should refer to the descriptors for each type of service in the E/M section of the CPT codebook to obtain the amounts of time that correlate with different levels of care (E/M codes).

FIGURE 17.2

E/M Codes and Time for Counseling/Coordination of Care (Outpatient Visits)

A. Initial Patient Visit

> 50% of visit devoted to counseling or coordination of care

Face-to-face time with patient*	20 MIN	30 MIN	45 MIN	60 MIN
E/M Code	99202	99203	99204	99205

* This is the total time of the visit, with > 50% of that time devoted to counseling.

B. Established Patient Visit

> 50% of visit devoted to counseling or coordination of care

Face-to-face time with patient*	10 MIN	15 MIN	25 MIN	40 MIN
E/M Code	99212	99213	99214	99215

* This is the total time of the visit, with > 50% of that time devoted to counseling.

C. Outpatient Consultation

> 50% of visit devoted to counseling or coordination of care

Face-to-face time with patient*	30 MIN	40 MIN	60 MIN	80 MIN
E/M Code	99242	99243	99244	99245

* This is the total time of the visit, with > 50% of that time devoted to counseling.

SYNOPSIS AND ANALYSIS OF THE TIME, COUNSELING, AND COORDINATION OF CARE SECTION OF THE IMR

This brief documentation section on the last page of each IMR form is a highly efficient template for documenting counseling and coordination of care services. The graphic interfaces make it extremely quick and easy to document the total amount of time spent and the confirmation that more than 50% of the visit was involved with counseling and/or coordination of care. The brief narrative section is also the most efficient option for describing the details of those activities. Table 17.1 summarizes the structure selected for the Time section of the medical record. Submitting codes based on time can lead to enhanced productivity in those particular instances when the level of care determined by the amount of time spent in counseling and coordinating care exceeds the level of care that would otherwise be appropriate on the basis of the three key components plus NPP.

TABLE 17.1

Synopsis of IMR for Time When >50% of Visit Is Devoted to Counseling and Coordination of Care

Section of Record	Interface	Data Entry Options	Format Options	Comments
Time	Graphic (check box), plus short answer (for amount of time), plus brief narrative	Physician	Writing, with option for dictating narrative section	This section of the form is not used unless time is considered the controlling factor. The code based on time is then compared with code based on key components and NPP.

USING THE TIME, COUNSELING, AND COORDINATION OF CARE SECTION OF THE IMR

The time, counseling, and coordination of care section of the IMR is straightforward and easy to use. If more than half the time of a visit is spent on counseling and/or coordination of care, the physician should fill in the total amount of time of the visit, following the criteria above that explain the different ways to measure time for outpatient and inpatient services. Next, he or she should check the box that confirms that the 50% of visit requirement has been met. The final step is for the physician to describe briefly the counseling and coordination topics involved in the visit.

As a practical matter, in cases where more than 50% of the time of the visit involves counseling and coordination of care, the physician should remember to compare the E/M code level for the visit based on the time factor with the code level indicated by the NPP and the three key components (as if time were not considered as a factor). The physician certainly has the option to select whichever of these two codes results in the highest level of E/M care, and therefore the highest level of reimbursement.

Example of Comparing E/M Code Levels

If a patient's initial outpatient visit involves 35 minutes of face-to-face physician time, and 20 minutes of the visit involves counseling, the time guideline indicates the submission of CPT code 99203 (see Figure 17.2). However, if the NPP is moderate to high (warranting level 4 care), and the physician performs and documents a comprehensive history, comprehensive examination, and MDM of moderate complexity, then the time factor should be bypassed in favor of submitting code 99204 determined by the NPP and the three key components.

COUNSELING VISITS

Because the CPT coding system allows physicians to submit E/M codes for medical care based solely on time involved with counseling and coordination of care services, physicians have the option of scheduling "counseling visits." Scheduling a counseling visit can be appropriate for patients whose complex medical problems require the physician to spend significant time to provide their E/M care, and who additionally require lengthy explanations and/or discussion of their problems. In a regularly scheduled visit, it is often not practical to add sufficient additional time to counsel the patient in detail about his or her medical conditions and treatment options. Furthermore, prolonging the patient's scheduled appointment may cause unreasonable delays for other patients who are waiting, and this can lead to significant patient dissatisfaction.

When faced with this situation, physicians may find it particularly helpful to consider delaying the in-depth discussion for a "counseling visit." After completing the detailed medical evaluation, the physician would provide the patient with a concise overview of the medical problem and treatment plan, initiate treatment when appropriate, provide a pamphlet or information sheet (as discussed in the next chapter), and advise that he or she is going to schedule a "special appointment to discuss the problem in detail" with the patient (and his or her family, if desired). The patient is advised to read the pamphlet or information sheet and write down any questions he or she has "so we can be sure to answer them at the next visit." This approach, combined with scheduling the counseling visit in a reasonable time frame (usually within a week), is highly acceptable to most patients.

The use of scheduled counseling visits in appropriate circumstances is beneficial to both physicians and patients. This practice certainly improves office *efficiency*, by keeping the physician on schedule, and reducing pressure on both the physician and his or her waiting patients. In addition, patients usually consider on-time appointments to be one of the most important criteria for satisfaction with their physician's care. Counseling visits also have a positive effect on office *productivity*, by providing payment for the time (and skills) involved in counseling, which would often otherwise not be reimbursed when provided as part of a high-level E/M visit.

Counseling Visits and Productivity

To illustrate the positive economic impact of counseling visits, we can consider the example of an initial visit for a patient with a progressive neurological deficit, who the physician determines has a moderate to high NPP that warrants level 4 E/M care. The physician provides and documents a level 4 initial E/M visit (ie, CPT code 99204, which includes comprehensive history, comprehensive examination, and moderate-complexity MDM), which requires 25 minutes of time. If the physician now spends an additional 30 minutes discussing the diagnosis, treatment, and prognosis, there is no additional payment for this counseling time. Since more than 50% of this total care involves counseling, the visit is eligible to be considered for time-based coding. However, the total time of the visit is 55 minutes, so the time-based coding approach still supports CPT code 99204 (see Figure 17.2), which is the same code as the conventional level of care documented after the first 25 minutes of the visit. The bottom line is that the physician receives no additional reimbursement for the last 30 minutes of this visit.

If instead, after 25 minutes, the physician elects to schedule a counseling visit one week later, then the initial visit is still appropriately submitted with code 99204 for the E/M services. The second visit may involve only counseling, without any documentation of history, physical examination, or MDM. The 30-minute established patient counseling visit can be submitted as CPT code 99214 (see Figure 17.2), and the physician can be appropriately reimbursed for his or her additional time and expertise.

The most interesting advantage of a counseling visit is the positive impact it may have on the quality of patient care. As we have all been told, when physicians try to squeeze too much information into one visit, patients often forget much of what they are told, and they may feel rushed, confused, or dissatisfied with the care they received. In contrast, the "counseling visit" alternative of providing complex information to the patient during two visits, particularly with printed information to help support the verbal explanation, almost always results in much higher levels of understanding and patient satisfaction.

SUMMARY

The CPT coding system and the *Documentation Guidelines* provide for consideration of coding and reimbursement when physicians spend an unusual amount of time counseling the patient about their illness and/or coordinating their medical care. This follows CPT coding guidelines of the typical times of visits, independent of the NPP and of the level of history, examination, and MDM documented.

Used properly, consideration of E/M care related to counseling and coordination of care provides benefits to both physicians and patients.

References

1.   American Medical Association. *Current Procedural Terminology CPT® 2008*. Chicago, IL: American Medical Association; 2007.

2.   Health Care Financing Administration. *Documentation Guidelines for Evaluation and Management Services*. Chicago, IL: American Medical Association; 1995.

3.   Health Care Financing Administration. *Documentation Guidelines for Evaluation and Management Services*. Chicago, IL: American Medical Association; 1997.

Documenting Optional Features

To boost the quality of patient care and increase efficiency, some physicians provide their patients with written materials that give brief and effective explanations of their illnesses, management protocols, and instructions regarding surgical care (including both preoperative and postoperative care). In addition to giving out documents they created for their own practices, some physicians also distribute helpful brochures published by commercial medical information companies. The design of the intelligent medical record (IMR) provides physicians with the option of including a section that enables rapid documentation of the materials they give to their patients during the visit.

Option of Separate Forms for Diagrams

Many physicians also like to add diagrams to their medical records so that they can draw the location of abnormalities they find during an examination. Practical E/M recommends placing diagrams on their own individual sheet(s) of paper. This allows the diagrams to be significantly larger and easier to use than if they had to be squeezed into a section of the IMR form, where they would take up significant space even for visits where they are not needed. They can be added to a patient chart whenever the physician finds it beneficial to use them.

GOALS FOR DESIGN

Although evaluation and management (E/M) compliance does not require that physicians document the informational materials they distribute to their patients, it is helpful for them to have a record of the materials their patients have received. Documentation of this information may also be helpful in the event of a liability investigation. It not only records the detailed information shared with the patient, but also demonstrates the physician's caring and concern.

Design for Efficiency and Quality Care

The highly efficient selection list interface is an effective means of documenting the distribution of informational materials. Another reasonable option would be to use a check-box interface. Figure 18.1 illustrates a sample information sheet/booklet section for an otolaryngologist. The published booklets are listed in all capital letters for easy recognition. Of course, each physician who chooses to include this optional section will customize it for his or her own needs. The IMR places this portion of the chart on the final page, where it can be located either after the "data ordered" section or after the section documenting the nature of presenting problem (NPP).

F IGURE 18.1

Sample of a Completed Template for Information Sheets and Booklets

| **Information Sheets Given:** Ear Care | Hearing | Balance | Vestibular exercises |
| Epistaxis   Nose & sinus   Nose care | URI info | Childhood airway obstruct | GERD |

PATIENT AND PHYSICIAN BENEFITS OF INFORMATION SHEETS

In my own practice, we had a long history of distributing preoperative instruction sheets of our own design related to helping patients prepare for common surgical procedures. These described the conditions calling for surgery, briefly outlined the operation, gave a preliminary overview of risks and treatment alternatives, and provided patients with an in-depth discussion of preoperative preparation and postoperative care and expectations. These forms enabled us to "inform before you perform," helping to alleviate patient anxieties and eliminate most postoperative telephone calls addressing questions about common postoperative symptoms. For example, many postoperative tonsillectomy patients experience referred pain in one or both ears. Having this common symptom described on the "tonsil information sheet" essentially eliminated the occurrence of telephone calls about this symptom during the two weeks after surgery.

Because the operative instruction sheets were in the practice's repertoire when I joined the group in 1976, I took their benefits for granted. It was not until many years later that it occurred to me that similar "information sheets" might also prove helpful in giving patients information about everyday medical problems we frequently discussed during their visits. My first effort was a one-page summary of "ear care." This simply presented my standard discussion of how to prevent earwax buildup, ear itch, and ear irritation, a topic we discussed with patients very frequently. With our addition of the new information form, life changed overnight. It saved me 2 to 3 minutes per patient with ear concerns, and the patients came away with written information to take home, which reinforced the message about proper maintenance and preventive care. We had the patients review the information in the office, and my nurse checked with them to answer the few questions they occasionally had. We're always told that patients forget 85% of what we tell them verbally, but their take-home sheets forget nothing. And both patients and physicians benefit when physicians have an extra 3 minutes in their schedules, 5 to 10 times a day. This additional time for physicians translates into more quality time with each patient and/or two or three added patients per day.

The ear care discovery led to our creating multiple information sheets discussing care of frequent ear, nose, and throat concerns. These included dizziness, nasal and sinus concerns, hearing loss and tinnitus, throat and voice abnormalities, and tips to help with smoking cessation. We also found two helpful booklets that contained more extensive discussion about obstructive sleep apnea and the cause and treatment of laryngopharyngeal reflux.

With all these new tools, the 3 extra minutes of time saved easily expanded to benefit 15 to 25 patients per day. Some of these sheets also assisted with our patient care. For example, a patient with chronic sinus problems goes through an established standardized medical protocol over a period of several months. Describing this on the information sheet not only saved time on the initial visit, but also gave the patient a template to take home, discuss with family, and record questions for the next visit. Finally, giving a brief introduction to the information sheet conveyed to patients the fact that we cared enough to give them information in a usable form that would contribute to long-term health. The bottom line was that these straight-forward forms not only saved time but also improved quality of care, enhanced patient relations, and increased my own satisfaction that good information was "getting through."

SUMMARY

Some physicians provide information sheets and/or booklets to their patients as a means of informing them about aspects of their medical and/or surgical care and as a means of increasing both quality and efficiency of care. The IMR offers physicians the option of efficiently recording the distribution of these information sheets in the medical record.

PART 4

Other Types of E/M Services

This part of the book provides details of additional types of services beyond outpatient office visits. Readers concentrating on outpatient services may choose to move on to Part 5 and return to this section when they need to research other types of care. For others, selected reading for an abridged overview of Practical E/M and the effective use of intelligent medical records (IMR) in these types of services includes:

Chapter 19
- *Introduction*
- *The Challenges Presented by Other Types of E/M Service*
- *Summary*

Chapter 20
- *Introduction*
- *Summary*

Chapter 21
- *Introduction*
- *Summary*

Additional Types of Service Based on the Three Key Components and the NPP

For the majority of physicians, the three office outpatient visits (initial visit, established patient visit, and consultation) are the most commonly performed evaluation and management (E/M) services. Therefore, this familiar context has provided the optimal setting for presenting the concepts of Practical E/M methodology and the rationale underlying intelligent medical record (IMR) tools. However, there are many other E/M services whose quality care and compliance features also rely on applying the E/M paradigm of the Current Procedural Terminology (CPT®) codebook[1] for assessing the severity of the nature of the presenting problem (NPP), identifying the medically indicated level of care, and then providing and documenting the appropriate levels of medical history, physical examination, and medical decision making (MDM) to meet the requirements for such care.

Another common setting for E/M services is care delivered in a hospital. This includes both inpatient services (initial admission, subsequent care, and inpatient consultation) and outpatient services (emergency department care and hospital observation services). In addition to the fact that many physicians with office-based practices will need to use these codes under appropriate circumstances, inpatient services comprise the predominant E/M care provided by a number of hospital-based physicians, including hospitalists, intensivists, and most academic physicians, as well as medical students, resident physicians, and fellows. Emergency medicine specialists are the principal users of the Emergency Department (ED) and observation codes. Finally, the CPT codebook provides additional E/M codes for services physicians provide in nursing facilities and domiciliary (eg, assisted living) settings. Table 19.1 lists the various types of service that follow the typical E/M paradigm, along with their associated code ranges.

Table 19.1

Additional E/M Services That Rely on the Typical E/M Paradigm for Key Components and NPP, as Previously Illustrated for Outpatient Office Services

Category	Type of Service	Code Range
Hospital Inpatient	Admission	99221–99223
	Subsequent Care	99231–99233
	Discharge Day Care	99238–99239
	Inpatient Consultation	99251–99255
Emergency Department	Emergency Dept Care	99281–99285
Hospital Observation	Observation Care	99217–99220

continued

Table 19.1

Additional E/M Services That Rely on the Typical E/M Paradigm for Key Components and NPP, as Previously Illustrated for Outpatient Office Services, cont'd.

Category	Type of Service	Code Range
Same Day Admission and Discharge	Inpatient admission and discharge Observation admission and discharge	99234–99236
Nursing Facility	Admission Subsequent Care	99304–99306 99307–99310
Domiciliary; Assisted	Initial Visit Care Subsequent Care	99324–99328 99334–99337

THE CHALLENGES PRESENTED BY OTHER TYPES OF E/M SERVICE

Although physicians providing these different paradigm-based E/M services need to use the same approach to providing and documenting their care, the significant challenge of these other types of service has been that the CPT requirements for most of these services differ significantly from those of outpatient office services. Depending on the specific type of service, these differences range from the total number of levels of care available for a service (eg, initial and subsequent hospital care have only three levels of care) to variations in the level of care appropriate for each level of severity of NPP (eg, ED care requires high-severity NPP to warrant level 4 care) to entirely different descriptors of the severity of the NPP (eg, subsequent hospital care descriptors are based on patients' clinical status rather than levels of NPP severity).

As noted previously, it is neither reasonable nor appropriate to require physicians to memorize the specific documentation and coding guidelines for each of the many types of E/M service. Similarly, it is inappropriate to require physicians to search through reference books or coding pamphlets while they provide care to their patients. However, just as described for the outpatient services presented in previous chapters, the solution to overcoming these challenges is to incorporate all the specific rules for each type of service into IMR tools that allow physicians to focus on providing quality care while the tools easily guide compliant documentation and coding.

The two barriers that physicians must overcome in applying these tools in hospital or nursing home settings are their own inertia and facility administrative barriers. Physicians are accustomed to using only blank sheets of paper or blank dictation tapes that most facilities provide for them to document their care. However, the use of such unstructured records for providing and documenting care has been just as unsatisfactory in achieving compliance, efficiency, and appropriate levels of care in these locations as they have been in the outpatient setting. The second problem is that many institutions require a challenging and often prolonged process to obtain approval for acceptance of forms in their facilities.

In response to these two challenges, physicians who become accustomed to the use of sophisticated and successful forms in the outpatient setting will readily adapt to correctly designed facility forms with documentation prompts appropriately modified to match CPT descriptors for each type of service. In dealing with potential facility concerns, it is reasonable to anticipate acceptance of IMR forms after pointing out that they are based on CPT compliance and that documenting all the appropriate History and Physical (H&P) information is necessary to meet recognized standards of care.

> **Recognizing IMR Benefits in the Inpatient Setting**
>
> My first use of IMR forms for inpatient care was in providing consultations. As soon as I appreciated the quality and efficiency benefits of using IMR forms in the office setting, it was obvious that they would bring the same advantages when caring for hospital patients. I brought outpatient initial visit forms from the office, since these forms and their documentation prompts coincidentally match the descriptors for inpatient consultations. I recorded my care on the four-page forms and inserted them into the hospital charts immediately behind the normal blank sheet request form, on which I wrote "see attached consultation form." Taking a photocopy back to the patient's medical record in my office completed the documentation requirements. Using the forms increased the speed of documenting medical information, ensured compliance, and guided the appropriate levels of care for each patient. Interestingly, the hospital administration made no comments about the forms.

The IMR forms for these various types of service generally look almost identical to those for the common outpatient office services presented in previous chapters and illustrated in Appendix D, and physicians will be able to use the same effective methodology during patient care. The most significant differences for each type of service relate primarily to the descriptors and/or level of care associated with the severity of the NPP. The subsections in the remainder of this chapter will discuss the different types of E/M service that use the normal paradigm of key components and NPP, first identifying distinguishing features of that service and the correlation of NPP descriptors with levels of care. It will also present examples from the CPT codebook's Appendix C (Clinical Examples) to illustrate the degree of illness severity associated with each level of care. The sections will conclude with presentation of IMR designs for optimal efficiency in the clinical setting for each type of service. For reference, examples of complete IMR forms for most of these types of service are included in the CD-ROM that accompanies this edition.

INPATIENT E/M SERVICES

Initial Hospital Care (CPT Codes 99221–99223)

When compared with the E/M requirements for an initial outpatient office visit, the most obvious distinguishing feature of the care and coding of an inpatient initial visit is that there are only three possible levels of service rather than five. The appropriate logic behind this difference appears to relate to the fact that only patients with clinically significant health problems should be admitted to the hospital, and such patients warrant higher levels of care. Therefore, there should be no need for codes that report minimal and low levels of care for patients being admitted to the hospital. The CPT descriptors confirm this impression, since the lowest level of inpatient initial care requires at least a detailed history, a detailed physical examination, and low-complexity MDM.

Design for Compliance and Quality Care

Even though many patients admitted to the hospital are "established patients" in the admitting physician's practice, the compliance requirements of the *Documentation Guidelines for Evaluation and Management Services*[2] call for care and documentation that is essentially identical to that provided for outpatient initial visits. This particularly means that physicians must reassess and completely document the past, family, and social history (PFSH) and review of systems (ROS) rather than obtaining and recording an update from the last patient encounter. Therefore, the design of the first two pages of the IMR forms for an admission can be identical to the first two pages of the physician's office initial outpatient visit form. Since Practical E/M methodology recommends a complete PFSH and ROS for this care, no documentation prompts are required.

Similarly, the design of pages 3 and 4 of the admission form can also be identical to the physician's office initial visit forms. The only significant differences will be in the levels of care associated with the descriptors in the NPP section and the corresponding changes for levels of care in the documentation prompts for the physical examination and MDM. The documentation prompt for the history of present illness (HPI) also reports the CPT minimum requirement for detailed level of history as comprising a chronological description plus at least four elements of the HPI; this requirement for an "extended" HPI has already been a constant recommendation in Practical E/M methodology.

The NPP and Levels of Care for Inpatient Admission

The correlation between severity of NPP and levels of E/M care for this type of service are shown in Table 19.2.

TABLE 19.2

Level of Inpatient Admission Care Warranted by Severity of NPP*

Severity of NPP	Level of Care
Low	99221
(Low to moderate)	(99221)
Moderate	99222
(Moderate to high)	(99222)
High	99223

*The levels of NPP that the CPT codebook indicates as being associated, in most cases, with each of the three levels of care are indicated without parentheses. The intermediate severities of NPP are included in parentheses for clarity.

The CPT descriptors indicate that for 99221, "the nature of the presenting problem is usually low,"[1(pp 12-13)] while for 99222 the NPP is usually moderate and for 99223 the NPP is usually high. In today's medical environment, it is interesting to consider whether, and under what circumstances, any patient whose illness has a low risk of morbidity and mortality without intervention would be a candidate for hospitalization. Therefore, it appears that most patients who are sufficiently ill to demonstrate medical necessity for hospital admission will warrant level 2 or level 3 care.

Why Does the CPT Codebook Include an Admission Code for Patients With a Low NPP?

The NPP descriptor for code 99221 does not seem to match the conventional medical necessity benchmarks of 2008. It is, on the other hand, a reminder of the health care environment that existed in 1990 and 1991, when the E/M system itself and Appendix C's clinical examples were created.

The CPT codebook's descriptors for both 99222 and 99223 require a comprehensive history and a comprehensive physical examination. Figure 19.1 illustrates a physical examination documentation prompt that guides physicians to perform and document this level of care. The distinction in the amount of documentation of key components between these two higher levels of care is based on MDM, which requires moderate complexity to support level 2 care and high complexity to support level 3.[1(pp 12-13)]

Figure 19.1

Sample Documentation Prompt for the Physical Examination This prompt is specific for the general multisystem examination of an inpatient admission.

---

3. detailed = 12 or more elements [level 1] *(NOTE: < 12 elements documented is insufficient for initial hospital care)*
4. comprehensive = document 2 (or more) elements in each of 9 (or more) systems [level 2 or 3]

The CPT Codebook's Clinical Examples for Inpatient Admissions

Appendix C of *CPT 2008* provides several pages of clinical examples of patients with diseases whose severity (ie, NPP) warrants each of the three levels of care for this type of service. The following are representative cases from that section:

- 99221: "Initial hospital visit following admission for a 42-year-old male for observation following an uncomplicated mandible fracture."[1(p 480)]

- 99222: "Initial hospital visit for a 15-year-old male, with acute status asthmaticus, unresponsive to outpatient therapy."[1(p 481)]

- 99223: "Initial hospital visit for a 50-year-old man with acute chest pain and diagnostic electrocardiographic changes of an acute anterior myocardial infarction."[1(p 481)]

Design for Efficiency

The customary approach for most physicians documenting an inpatient admission is to dictate the entire H&P. However, this technology lacks the capability of assessing medical necessity and leaves physicians without guidance to meet compliance criteria and without tools for patients to assist with documentation of medical history. Physicians using these inefficient and incomplete tools often fail to provide and document a comprehensive history and/or examination, and they almost never document the risk elements of MDM or the NPP.

Because the IMR form blends graphic interface and narrative interface elements in appropriate locations for maximum documentation efficiency, these forms can optimize speed of documentation while maintaining compliance and recording of meaningful data. Physicians can further increase their own efficiency by having patients or their staff complete the check-box sections of the PFSH and ROS as long as they review these responses, supplement any positive responses with detailed information, and sign each section to attest to performing a thorough review. Those who prefer to dictate the narrative components of the record will have significantly reduced time for this effort, and the hospital can combine the written and narrative sections in the patient's chart.

Admission and Discharge on the Same Date

The CPT codebook provides three different E/M codes (99234, 99235, and 99236) that apply when patients are admitted to the hospital or observation status and discharged on the same date. The descriptors of the key components and NPP for these codes correlate precisely with those for inpatient admission codes 99221, 99222, and 99223, with the exception that the three same-day codes do not provide a value for the typical time spent for these visits. Therefore, it is equally appropriate to use the initial hospital care forms for care and documentation of an admission that subsequently results in a discharge on the same date.

Subsequent Hospital Care (CPT Codes 99231–99233)

Most hospital charts supply only blank sheets of paper for physicians to document subsequent care visits for their hospitalized patients. These provide no structure or guidance for determining each patient's indicated levels of E/M care and medical documentation. As a result, most physicians create an unstructured note that documents a summary of the status of the present illness, pertinent examination findings, laboratory reports, any modifications to treatment, and perhaps a review of the current diagnoses. Other physicians employ the structure of a SOAP note (subjective, objective, assessment, and plan), which, as discussed in Chapter 3, is commonly used in a manner that tends to guide physicians to provide and document problem focused care. Using either of these two approaches therefore frequently fails to encourage documentation capable of meeting CPT requirements for level 2 or level 3 subsequent hospital care.

Design for Compliance and Quality Care

In contrast to the initial hospital care services discussed above, the three levels of care described for subsequent hospital visits do not require a comprehensive history or physical examination. In addition, the most dramatic feature of this type of service is that the descriptions of the NPP replace the common measures of severity (ie, "low," "moderate," "high," etc) with descriptions of patients' clinical status during each day of their stay. As with all types of established patient visits, compliance requires documentation of only two of the three key components at the indicated levels of care.

Similar to the approach for established patients in the outpatient setting, for the medical history component, it is permissible to review and update the information previously recorded in the hospital chart.[2(p 6)] In addition, the *Documentation Guidelines* advises that "it is not necessary to record information about the PFSH"[2(p 9)] for this type of service. This exclusion appears reasonable and logical, since subsequent hospital care visits generally occur on a daily basis, and it would be extremely unlikely that a patient's past medical history, family history, or social history would change from one day to the next. However, the *Documentation Guidelines* provides no such waiver of the requirement for performing and documenting an update of the patient's ROS. Importantly, updating this information can provide valuable insights from early identification of the development of new symptoms, unrelated to the patients' primary problems, since the previous day. Figure 19.2 shows an example of the ROS update section of an IMR form. In addition to providing a free-text narrative section for any general changes, it also allows for check boxes for rapid documentation of a number of questions that a physician might consider sufficiently important to ask on a daily basis. In the sample illustration, these check boxes help the physician confirm that the patient has not experienced chest pain, shortness of breath, or calf tenderness (which could indicate possible development of deep vein thrombosis).

The physical examination and MDM sections for this type of service duplicate the familiar sections from other IMR forms, with appropriate changes to the documentation prompts for levels of care. These prompts are illustrated in the subsequent inpatient care charts located on Practical E/M CD-ROM.

Figure 19.2

Sample Medical History Section for Inpatient Subsequent Care This IMR template illustrates the medical history section. This includes the update of the ROS, with check boxes for rapid documentation of commonly asked update questions. It also shows the HPI section with appropriate documentation prompts for this type of service. No update of the PFSH is required.

Date: ____/____/____	Time:_____AM / PM	ROS: no change since last visit date: ____/____/____
☐ No chest pain	☐ No shortness of breath	☐ No calf pain or tenderness
Except: _____		

PRESENT ILLNESS   Chronology with: 1. one to three elements [level 1 or 2] 2. four to eight elements; OR status of 3 chronic or inactive conditions [level 3]
    (1) duration   (2) timing   (3) severity;   (4) location   (5) quality   (6) context   (7) modifying factors   (8) assoc. signs & symptoms

☐ See attached dictation

The NPP and Levels of Care for Inpatient Subsequent Care Visits

The most distinguishing E/M compliance feature of this type of service is the significant change in the descriptors for the NPP. The CPT codebook replaces the customary subjective severity scale (minor, low, low to moderate, moderate, etc) with descriptions of the clinical status of hospitalized patients. Figure 19.3 shows a documentation prompt for the NPP. This includes the complete CPT definitions and the level of care associated with each described clinical status. It conveys the CPT descriptors, which state that patients who are stable, recovering, or improving have medical necessity that is appropriate for only level 1 care; for this type of service, level 1 care requires only a problem-focused history, a problem-focused examination, and/or straightforward MDM. Those patients with an inadequate response to treatment or who have developed a minor complication warrant level 2 care, which calls for an expanded problem-focused history and examination, with documentation of moderate-complexity MDM. For the patient who is unstable or has developed a significant complication or significant new problem and warrants level 3 care, the CPT codebook's history and examination requirements are only for detailed history and examination, but the MDM component requires documentation of high-complexity decision making. For this type of service, two of the three key components must be documented at the indicated levels to support those levels of care.

Figure 19.3

Sample NPP Documentation Prompt for Inpatient Subsequent Care This prompt is brief because there are only three levels of care associated with this service, and because the CPT descriptors for level of NPP are relatively succinct when compared with the definitions for other types of service.

NATURE OF PRESENTING PROBLEM(S)		
1. Stable:	(level 1)	Usually, the patient is stable, recovering, or improving
2. Inadequate response:	(level 2)	Usually, the patient is responding inadequately to therapy or has developed a minor complication
3. Unstable:	(level 3)	Usually, the patient is unstable or has developed a significant complication or a significant new problem

In the current health care environment, most patients are discharged soon after they become stable. Therefore, it is unlikely that many patients will be candidates for level 1 care for longer than one day before they are discharged. As a consequence, the status of most hospitalized patients will likely correspond to the category of having not yet responded adequately to therapy, warranting level 2 care (99232). Documenting this clinical status in the NPP section will also confirm the medical necessity of continued hospitalization. Level 3 services are reserved for unstable patients with threatening health concerns.

The CPT Codebook's Clinical Examples for Inpatient Subsequent Care Visits
Representative clinical examples in Appendix C of *CPT 2008* describing patients whose disease severity (ie, NPP) is appropriate for each of the three levels of care for this type of service include:

- 99231: "Subsequent hospital visit for a 10-year-old male admitted for lobar pneumonia with vomiting and dehydration, is becoming afebrile and tolerating oral fluids."[1(p 483)]

- 99232: "Subsequent hospital care for a 62-year-old female with congestive heart failure, who remains dyspneic and febrile."[1(p 484)]

- 99323: "Subsequent hospital visit for a 60-year-old female, four days post uncomplicated inferior myocardial infarction who has developed severe chest pain, dyspnea, diaphoresis and nausea."[1(p 485)]

Design for Efficiency
When combined with an appropriate HPI, obtaining and documenting an update of the ROS during each day's subsequent care visit ensures sufficient medical history to support either level 2 or level 3 care. More important for the physician, this information confirms that the patient has not developed other significant medical problems in the last 24 hours. Including check boxes for commonly asked questions in this section facilitates rapid documentation, while details related to any positive responses can be recorded in the accompanying free-text area. As noted in the documentation prompt in Figure 19.2, an extended HPI is mandated only if the patient is unstable or has a significant new problem (ie, level 3 care).

In many such encounters, physicians confine their physical examination to the affected body areas. Even if the examination is problem focused, the compliance requirements for this type of service allow consideration of only two of the three key components, so that requirements can be met by appropriate documentation of history and MDM. Design for the MDM section is identical to IMR forms for outpatient services. It includes designated areas for recording data reviewed and data ordered, relatively large sections for documenting an extended problem list (impressions) and treatment list, and the usual IMR check boxes for rapid documentation of the three levels of risk. Thorough documentation of the MDM section is important in all hospital patients, because it allows physicians to keep an accurate record of all aspects of each patient's care. The NPP documentation section shown in Figure 19.3 is in its customary location at the end of the MDM section.

Inpatient Consultations

Requests for inpatient consultations are usually most appropriate for patients who have associated medical problems with NPPs of moderate, moderate to high, or high severity, and therefore require attention while the patient is in the hospital. These illnesses therefore usually warrant higher levels of care, which call for a detailed or comprehensive history and examination as well as documentation of MDM that is of at least low complexity. However, because most hospitals provide physicians with only an unstructured blank consultation request form or a blank dictation tape, audits of inpatient consultation records commonly reveal documentation of problem-focused levels of history and/or examination, as well as documentation of straightforward MDM (eg, one documented diagnosis, one documented treatment option, and no documentation of the levels of risk). This limited amount of care and documentation commonly supports only level 1 or level 2 care, even though most of these patients' problems have severity calling for significantly higher levels of care.

The CPT descriptors for the inpatient consultation service duplicate those for an outpatient consultation. Additionally, the CPT criteria for coding outpatient consultation services, which were described in Chapter 9, also apply to inpatient consultations. This type of service also includes five levels of care, in contrast to the three levels for inpatient initial visits and subsequent care visits. The critical factor for optimizing efficiency for this type of care while maintaining compliance and quality is the ability of physicians to incorporate medical history information that has already been documented in the patient's medical record by other physicians during the hospitalization.

Design for Compliance and Quality Care

The IMR design for inpatient consultation care is almost identical, including the documentation prompts, to forms for an outpatient initial visit and consultation, as illustrated in Appendix D of this book. Additional documentation elements can be added to the first two pages to accommodate instructions in the *Documentation Guidelines* that permit abbreviated documentation of the PFSH and ROS through confirming review of the existing records. Specifically, the *Documentation Guidelines* advises, "[a] ROS and/or a PFSH obtained during an earlier encounter does not need to be re-recorded if there is evidence that the physician reviewed and updated the previous information. This may occur. . .in an institutional setting or group practice where many physicians use a common record."[2(p 6)]

When building on previous history information that has been obtained by others, it is important for physicians to realize that if the documented medical history information contained in the admitting record is less thorough than required for a "complete" PFSH and ROS, then simply confirming review and update will achieve only a similarly reduced level of care (ie, "problem pertinent" or "extended"). This would result in a low level of history and consequently a low level of E/M care. For this reason, it is beneficial to have complete graphic interface components available for these sections in addition to the ability to document an update. Many examples of this type of IMR form for inpatient consultations are available in the accompanying CD-ROM. Figure 19.4 illustrates the upper portions of the PFSH and ROS sections that provide physicians with the ability to document which of several methods they use to obtain and document a complete PFSH and ROS.

F i g u r e 19.4

Header for PFSH and ROS Sections of Inpatient Consultation. This form illustrates sample informational sections from the top of the PFSH and ROS pages of an inpatient consultation. The complete templates are included in the accompanying CD-ROM. Physicians can use the check boxes to indicate whether the medical history information was obtained from the existing medical record, as permitted by the *Documentation Guidelines*, and/or directly from the patient or family. Regardless of the source of this data, all significant medical history responses should be documented in the usual PFSH and ROS sections of these IMR forms.

PFSH

Date: ___/___/___ Age:	❏ PFSH from review of H&P by Dr._____ on ___/___/__
Reason for consultation:	❏ H&P documentation included a <u>complete</u> PFSH
	❏ Additional history obtained from patient / family member
	❏ Patient unable to communicate

Significant medical issues from these sources and any changes since that visit (indicated by an asterisk) listed below:

ROS

❏ ROS from review of H&P by Dr._____ on ___/___/__   ❏ H&P documentation included a <u>complete</u> ROS

❏ Additional history obtained from patient / family member   ❏ Patient unable to communicate

Significant medical issues from these sources and any changes since that visit (indicated by an asterisk) listed below:

In summary, these forms give physicians several possible ways to obtain and document the PFSH and ROS for a hospital consultation:

1. If the admission H&P contains a complete PFSH and a complete ROS, the physician may check the boxes that indicate the name of the physician who recorded that care and the date of that visit, and that attest to its being complete. The physician should then provide details of significant positive elements on the check box and narrative sections of the form.

2. If the admission H&P does not contain a complete PFSH and/or a complete ROS, the physician may copy all the material from that chart onto this record and check the box indicating the name and date of that documentation (but leaving blank the box indicating a complete PFSH and ROS). The physician would then finish documenting this information by either interviewing the patient or family, or having them complete the check boxes themselves, after which the physician would inquire about details of all positive responses and document these details in the narrative section. Under these circumstances, the physician would also check the box indicating that the patient contributed to the information.

3. The physician can ignore the previous chart and simply obtain all information from the patient in the conventional manner.

The important consideration for quality care and compliance is that the physician who refers to preexisting documentation in the medical record must review all of this documented material so that it can be analyzed and incorporated into the clinical aspects of the consultation. This goal can best be accomplished by using these two pages to completely document all of the significant responses from the existing records plus any information obtained from the patient. For example, if the patient has a history of diabetes recorded in the chart, the physician can indicate this information by checking the corresponding box on page 1 and adding narrative details when appropriate. Similar documentation of positive signs and symptoms should be documented on page 2. The physician also has the option of using an asterisk (*) to designate any new diagnoses or symptoms that have developed since the admission to the hospital.

The designs for all of the remaining portions of the inpatient consultation form (ie, the present illness, physical examination, decision making, and NPP) can be identical to those on the physician's outpatient initial visit forms. Therefore, pages 3 and 4 of the forms are unchanged from those of the outpatient initial visit forms.

The NPP and Levels of Care for Inpatient Consultations

The descriptors for severity of the NPP for both outpatient and inpatient consultations are identical to those for outpatient initial visits with the exception that the NPP associated with level 2 initial visits is described as "low to moderate," while for both types of consultations the presenting problems for level 2 visits are described as usually being of "low severity." The documentation prompt therefore has an identical appearance to the one illustrated on the initial visit template in Appendix D of this book with this single exception. This template therefore includes a footnote to document this minor discrepancy so that the form can be used accurately for documenting inpatient (and outpatient) consultations.

The CPT Codebook's Clinical Examples for Inpatient Consultations

In the current health care environment, it is unlikely that the minor and low levels of NPP associated with level 1 and level 2 care would warrant a request for inpatient consultation. It is more common that evaluation for such problems would be provided on an outpatient basis after hospital discharge. Representative clinical examples in Appendix C of *CPT 2008* of patients whose disease severity (ie, NPP) is appropriate for each of the five levels of care for this type of service include:

- 99251: "Initial hospital consultation for a 27-year-old female with fractured incisor post-intubation."[1(p 487)]
- 99252: "Initial hospital consultation for a 35-year-old dialysis patient with episodic oral ulcerations."[1(p 487)]
- 99253: "Initial hospital consultation for a 42-year-old non-diabetic patient, post-op cholecystectomy, now with an acute urinary tract infection."[1(p 488)]
- 99254: "Initial hospital consultation for a 72-year-old male with emergency admission for possible bowel obstruction."[1(p 488)]
- 99255: "Initial hospital consultation for a 75-year-old female, admitted to intensive care with acute respiratory distress syndrome, who is hypersensitive, has a moderate metabolic acidosis, and a rising serum creatinine."[1(p 488)]

Design for Efficiency

The inpatient consultation form incorporates all the documentation efficiency elements of outpatient IMR forms. The options for obtaining past history, social history, family history, and ROS may present challenges that require added time if the documentation in the current record is insufficient to contribute to a comprehensive medical history. Physicians can use this form to obtain and document information from the patient or have the patient fill out the form to complete the documentation. However, when there is effective documentation already in the record, it will likely be most efficient to document review of that information (by checking the appropriate boxes shown in Figure 19.4) and summarize the pertinent history information on the record.

Discharge Day Management

The CPT codebook provides two different codes, 99238 and 99239, for E/M care provided on the day of hospital discharge. These codes are not related to either the patient's clinical status (which is obviously improved) or to documentation of the three key components. Rather, these codes are "used to report the total duration of time spent by a physician for final hospital discharge of a patient. The codes include, as appropriate, final examination of the patient, discussion of the hospital stay,. . .instructions for continuing care to all relevant caregivers, and preparation of discharge records, prescriptions and referral forms."[1(p 14)] Code 99238 is used when the total time for discharge care is 30 minutes or less; code 99239 is appropriate when the total time is more than 30 minutes. The actual amount of time required should be documented in the progress note recorded on the date of service. The physician should provide a simple narrative note describing assessment and care on the date of discharge and then dictate an official discharge summary of the patient's complete hospitalization.

The IMR and Hospital Coding Responsibilities for Medicare Severity Diagnosis Related Groups

It is reasonable to ask how and when effective structured medical records will make their way into medical institutions such as hospitals, EDs, and nursing homes. In the absence of external political and economic forces, it seems likely that such an initiative would have to begin with individual physicians who recognize the quality and efficiency benefits of introducing their own customized forms, similar to the ones they use in their offices, to these facilities. Eventually, the institutions themselves might begin to recognize the quality care and compliance benefits of properly structured records and begin to develop beneficial structured forms for their medical staffs.

However, there are now significant external economic forces, initiated by the Centers for Medicare and Medicaid Services (CMS), that are accelerating the need for compliant documentation and coding for inpatient services, and these should awaken hospital administrators to the imperative for structured records to meet their facilities' compliance requirements for receiving optimal payments. It is also reasonable to assume that CMS will implement similar rules and regulations that will have a corresponding impact on documentation requirements for correct payment of emergency department and nursing facility services.

On October 1, 2007, CMS initiated a significant change in the hospital inpatient reimbursement system with the introduction of payments based on the new Medicare Severity Diagnosis Related Groups (MS-DRGs).[3] In theory, this approach is intended to refine the existing DRG system through consideration of the costs related to the relative severity of each patient's illnesses. The restructuring mechanisms for achieving this goal include CMS's defining 745 severity-based DRGs, which replace the long-standing system that included 538 DRGs. This complexity is compounded by subdividing each DRG into three subgroups, labeled as having:

- major comorbidity and complication (MCC),
- comorbidity and complication (CC), or
- absence of comorbidity and complication (non-CC).

There are extensive lists of CCs and MCCs that apply individually and specifically to each of the 745 MS-DRGs. The CMS also imposed further documentation requirements for accurate hospital payments by reducing payments for conditions that develop during a hospitalization, ie, for conditions that are not *present on admission* (POA).

While the combination of all of these new CMS requirements may or may not provide "a new opportunity for appropriate reimbursement, *subject to precise physician documentation and accurate coding* [italics added],"[3] it certainly presents an increased requirement for compliant documentation and coding of inpatient services.

While the burden of accurate coding under these complex rules must fall to each hospital's health information management (HIM) specialist, their challenge will be to encourage and, hopefully, facilitate precise physician documentation to determine accurate coding. In her 2008 article reviewing MS-DRGs and the impact on hospitals, attorney Cherlyn Murer concludes, "Therefore, now more than ever, it is imperative for physicians to ensure accurate and detailed documentation in patient charts. The bottom line is that hospitals must implement clinical documentation improvement programs that engage both medical and coding staff to cooperatively document and report illness severity using ICD-9-CM terminology."[3]

How to Get From Here to There

A hospital's chief financial officer recently invited me to present a review of the MS-DRG requirements for increased documentation precision to the hospital's medical staff. This followed thorough presentations by the hospital's own HIM staff on the details of the MS-DRG system, including the financial imperatives of documenting all diagnoses and conditions present on admission and documenting every morbidity and complication that develops during hospitalizations. The lack of enthusiasm from the physician staff led the administration to request that I present this information again, feeling that a fellow MD could more effectively motivate their enthusiasm.

During our discussion of how I could help the administrators and HIM staff promote improved physician documentation, I pointed out that, regardless of who made this presentation, physicians would likely recognize this significantly increased documentation burden as being an unfunded administrative mandate. Further, I suggested that most physicians are presently in no mood for more unfunded mandates, especially in the context of realizing that the current CMS conversion factor pays for E/M services at a rate of approximately 25% to 30% of the true resource-based value of those services.[4(p 42)] I then suggested that the solution to this challenge is not to require physicians to work harder, it is to provide them with structured medical record tools that help them work better. Physicians can achieve the required documentation without extra work by having structured records that incorporate the MS-DRG documentation requirements as a normal element of providing quality care.

How can hospitals implement clinical documentation improvement programs to empower sophisticated and complex coding for MS-DRGs when their current approved medical record documentation system for physicians consists of blank pages of paper and blank dictation tapes? In the absence of structured records, it has proven to be impossible for physicians to achieve E/M compliance. Yet physicians must start with, and build upon, a foundation of E/M-compliant high-quality documentation if they are to succeed in meeting these complex new MS-DRG requirements to help hospitals meet their increased coding burden. A reasonable solution would involve implementing IMR forms and training physicians to use them properly. This will benefit physicians by providing a system they can use in their offices as well as in the hospital, thereby improving their efficiency and productivity along with compliance and quality records. With this solid foundation, which includes documentation of a comprehensive medical history and a thorough differential diagnosis for every encounter, it should be possible for physicians to address the documentation requirements for MS-DRGs without disrupting their patient care schedules. Meeting these additional requirements calls for making several minor modifications in the structure of the IMR forms for initial and subsequent care:

1. Initial hospital care form
    a) On page 1, the "Past Medical History" section would be renamed to read "Past Medical History (Present on Admission)"

b) On page 2, the "Review of Systems" section would be renamed to read "Review of Systems (Present on Admission)"

c) On page 4, the "Impressions/Differential Diagnoses" section would be renamed to read "Impressions/Differential Diagnoses (Present on Admission)"

2. Subsequent hospital care form

a) On page 2, the "Impressions/Differential Diagnoses" section would be renamed to read "Impressions/Differential Diagnoses (Postadmission problems identified by +)"

With these tools available, physicians would be instructed regarding the need to list a thorough numbered problem list, including a comprehensive differential diagnosis, in the "Impressions" section of the initial hospital care form. The numbering system would be carried forward for documentation during subsequent care visits, so that each problem would be identifiable as having been present on admission. Any new problems arising after the initial evaluation would be designated with a plus sign (+), to indicate that they were not present on admission.

With physicians providing this degree of medical documentation, the work of the HIM staff in accomplishing their coding tasks should be greatly streamlined and highly accurate. This result should reduce the need for significant expansion of the HIM workforce. As a final benefit, when these hospitals begin to consider implementation of electronic health records (which are introduced in Chapter 23), they will appreciate the importance of requiring intelligent designs for the data entry screens of the H&P component of these systems to continue to facilitate the accurate and precise physician documentation needed for hospital-based coding compliance.

Hospital HIM Cost Savings Through the Use of Structured Records

During a recent conversation about the coding requirements for MS-DRGs, an administrator for a large hospital system shared the results of a consultant's recent assessment of increased workforce needs to meet the coding and documentation requirements of this initiative. The consultant recommended hiring one new HIM specialist for every 14 beds in one of their hospitals. The administrator agreed with my recommendation that implementing IMR forms for this hospital would sufficiently improve physician documentation and thereby significantly decrease the number of additional HIM specialists that would be needed. She concluded that the cost savings would provide a powerful incentive for the hospital system to implement IMR structure forms in either paper forms or electronic record screens.

EMERGENCY DEPARTMENT SERVICES

Emergency department care is considered to be an outpatient service that is provided in "an organized hospital-based facility for the provision of unscheduled episodic services to patients who present for immediate medical attention. The facility must be available 24 hours a day."[1(p 17)] The salient E/M compliance features of this service include the following:

■ The same five codes and descriptors are used for both new and established patients.

■ There is a significantly higher severity of NPP associated with level 4 and level 5 care than for the three lower levels of care. This separation is far greater than for other types of service that have five levels of care.

- No clear-cut compliance policy has been established on whether it is permissible to update prior documentation of the PFSH and ROS for patients who have previously been evaluated in the ED. However, since this care occurs in an institutional setting where physicians use a common record, this service appears to meet all of the *Documentation Guidelines* requirements for the option of *updating* the PFSH and ROS of patients who have been seen in the facility within the previous 3 years, rather than asking a complete survey of questions.

- If an ED physician initially evaluates a patient in the ED and subsequently admits that patient to "observation status" in the hospital, only the appropriate initial observation care code should be reported; ie, the ED care should not be separately reported

Design for Compliance and Quality Care

The IMR template for ED visits, which is illustrated in the accompanying CD-ROM, is constructed on the framework of an initial visit form, and it requires appropriate levels of medical necessity plus provision and documentation of all three key components for every level of care. The form's documentation prompts account for the distinct requirements for this type of service, making it easy for physicians to apply Practical E/M methodology to facilitate their care and ensure compliance. As with outpatient E/M services, the foundation for effective E/M is performance of a comprehensive medical history, which allows physicians to make an assessment of the overall picture of each patient's health, a meaningful differential diagnoses, and a preliminary determination of the NPP(s) at the time of the visit. However, in most facilities, the responsibility of obtaining and documenting all of the PFSH and ROS information has been assigned to the physicians themselves. The time physicians require to perform these tasks has proven excessively burdensome under the time constraints necessitated by the volume and illness severity of patients in these facilities. As a consequence, review of ED documentation commonly reveals problem focused medical histories that concentrate almost exclusively on the HPI.

Intelligent medical records address this challenge with tools that permit patients and/or staff to provide the initial documentation of the PFSH and ROS portions of the medical history. In a minimal amount of time, ED physicians can rapidly review and complete these sections, allowing them to meet their quality and compliance requirements for a comprehensive medical history while working under these stressful conditions.

Patients having their first visit to an ED, as well as those who have not received care in the facility in a significant period of time, are required to complete a full PFSH and ROS survey, just as they would during an initial outpatient visit in a physician's office. The physicians staffing the department should also establish a policy concerning whether, and under what circumstances, it will be permissible to use an update of the PFSH and ROS. Use of this approach follows the same documentation method and tools discussed for hospital inpatient consultations and illustrated in Figure 19.4. It would be appropriate for patients who have recently received care in the facility and whose charts contain compliant documentation of a *complete* PFSH and a complete ROS. The physician should *document* whether the information is partially or completely obtained from review of the existing record and that the existing record contains a complete PFSH and ROS. The physician (or ED staff) should also record significant positive responses on the form to assist assessment during the encounter, including the use of an asterisk to distinguish new diagnoses and/or symptoms from those that had been reported during previous encounters.

Finally, since there has not been an established policy to address the principle of obtaining an update in the ED setting, it is further suggested that the administration of the department obtain a written opinion on this topic from the Medicare medical director who is responsible for its location.

The NPP and Levels of Care for ED Services

The descriptors for the NPP reflect the fact that a number of patients seen in the ED present with severe or life-threatening conditions. They demonstrate a significant leap in the level of illness severity between level 3 and level 4. While most other types of E/M service increase the level of NPP from "moderate" for level 3 to "moderate to high" for levels 4 and 5, for this type of service the level of NPP increases all the way to "high" severity for level 4 problems. For level 5, CPT identifies even greater severity, stating, "Usually the presenting problems are of high severity and pose an immediate significant threat to life or physiologic function."[1(p 17)] The documentation prompts for the NPP incorporate this guidance in the forms shown for this type of service in the CD and illustrated in Figure 19.5.

Figure 19.5

Documentation Prompt of NPP for ED Services

NATURE OF PRESENTING PROBLEM(S)		
1. minor	(level 1)	Problem runs definite and prescribed course, is transient in nature, and is not likely to permanently alter health status; OR, has a good prognosis with management and compliance.
2. low	(level 1)	Problem where the risk of morbidity without treatment is low; there is little to no risk of mortality without treatment; full recovery without functional impairment is expected.
3. low - mod	(level 2)	Problem where the risk of morbidity without treatment is low to moderate; there is low to moderate risk of mortality without treatment; full recovery without functional impairment is expected in most cases, with low probability of prolonged functional impairment.
4. moderate	(level 3)	Problem where the risk of morbidity without treatment is moderate; there is moderate risk of mortality without treatment; prognosis is uncertain, or there is an increased probability of prolonged functional impairment.
5. mod - high	(level 3)	Problem where the risk of morbidity without treatment is moderate to high; there is moderate risk of mortality without treatment; uncertain prognosis or increased probability of prolonged functional impairment.
6. high	(level 4)	Problem where the risk of morbidity without treatment is high to extreme; there is moderate to high risk of mortality without treatment, or high probability of severe prolonged functional impairment.
7. high with immed threat to life or fct	(level 5)	Problem where the risk of morbidity without treatment is high to extreme; there is moderate to high risk of mortality without treatment, or high probability of severe prolonged functional impairment. There is an immediate threat to life or physiologic function.

The CPT Codebook's Clinical Examples for ED Services

Representative clinical examples in Appendix C of *CPT 2008* of patients whose disease severity (ie, NPP) is appropriate for each of the five levels of care for this type of service include:

- 99281: "Emergency department visit for a patient with several uncomplicated insect bites."[1(p 489)]

- 99282: "Emergency department visit for a patient presenting with a rash on both legs after exposure to poison ivy."[1(p 489)]

- 99283: "Emergency department visit for a well-appearing 8-year-old who has a fever, diarrhea, and abdominal cramps, is tolerating oral fluids and is not vomiting."[1(p 489)]

- 99284: "Emergency department visit for a 4-year-old who fell off a bike sustaining a head injury with brief loss of consciousness."[1(p 490)]
- 99285: "Emergency department visit for a patient who presents with a sudden onset of the 'worst headache of her life,' and complains of a stiff neck, nausea, and inability to concentrate."[1(p 490)]

Design for Efficiency

The IMR designs provide maximal documentation efficiency for all components of the E/M service. The greatest time savings available to ED physicians is providing a design that allows patients, their families, or the facility's ancillary staff to provide preliminary documentation of the PFSH and ROS sections of the medical record while they are in the waiting room, before being evaluated. Similarly, for patients seen previously in the facility, a staff member can transfer the previous positive PFSH and ROS significant findings to the current form and then ask the patient whether any significant changes have occurred since the date of that visit. Physicians can then have a similar experience to the one described for outpatient visits in Chapter 7, where a quick scan of the two pages completed by the patient (or staff) provides a detailed overview of the patient's general health. Although the physician will need to provide supplemental documentation for any positive patient responses by writing or dictating appropriate details, the amount of time required is relatively small, and the information acquired is invaluable for providing excellent care as well as for achieving compliant documentation.

HOSPITAL OBSERVATION (CPT CODES 99217–99220)

The CPT codebook provides a separate set of E/M codes to deal with patients who are designated as "observation status," which is classified as an outpatient service in the hospital setting and includes "supervision of the care plan for observation and performance of periodic reassessments."[1(p 11)] There are also specific rules governing the relationship of this category of care to other E/M services provided on the same date:

- As reported above for ED services, other E/M services on the same date (eg, an office outpatient visit or an ED visit) by the same physician initiating observation status should not be reported separately. The observation level of service should include those E/M services provided in other sites along with any additional care required for admission to observation status.
- When a patient who was initially admitted to observation status is subsequently admitted to the hospital on the same date by another physician, the hospital admission is additionally reported with the appropriate initial hospital care code. Under this circumstance, the physician providing observation services should not additionally report an observation discharge service (code 99217).
- For a patient admitted to observation status and discharged on the same date, the appropriate codes to employ are 99234-99236, as described in the section above related to inpatient admission and discharge on the same date of service.

Design for Compliance and Quality Care

The three codes utilized for initial observation care (when a patient is not discharged on the same date) are 99218-99220. The descriptors for the three key components and for the NPP for these three levels of care are identical to the three levels of care for initial hospital care (codes 99221–99223). Therefore, physicians should utilize the IMR form for initial hospital care to admit patients to observation status, recognizing that when a documentation prompt on those forms states "level 1" it will refer to code 99218, "level 2" will refer to code 99219, and "level 3" will refer to code 99220.

The NPP and Levels of Care for Initial Observation Care

The CPT codebook indicates that the problems associated with code 99218 are usually of low severity, problems appropriate for 99219 are of moderate severity, and problems warranting 99220 are of high severity. Appendix C in *CPT 2008* provides no clinical examples for this type of service. However, logic suggests that most patients whose NPP is of low severity would likely not be sufficiently ill to require admission to observation status, while most patients whose NPP is of high severity would likely be candidates for hospital admission rather than observation. Therefore, it can be anticipated that the majority of patients appropriate for this type of service will likely warrant care at the level of 99219, which calls for performance and documentation of a comprehensive history, a comprehensive examination, and MDM of moderate complexity.

NURSING FACILITY E/M SERVICES

The CPT codebook describes the set of nursing facility codes as being appropriate for reporting E/M care provided in nursing facilities and psychiatric residential treatment centers. There are only two categories of nursing facility services: initial nursing facility care and subsequent nursing facility care. Both of these categories are applicable for patients who are either new or established in a physician's practice. Physicians providing consultations in these locations should use the inpatient consultation codes (99251–99255). There are additional time-based codes for services on the date of a discharge from a nursing facility (codes 99315 and 99316).

Initial Nursing Facility Care (CPT Codes 99304–99306)

These three codes apply to an admission to a nursing facility. The CPT codebook also describes appropriate coding when a physician performs other E/M services on the same date. In circumstances involving admission to a nursing facility in the course of E/M care rendered in another location, such as a physician's office or an ED, all E/M services by the same physician on the same date are included in the code for initial nursing facility care. However, hospital discharge services or observation status discharge services performed on the same date may be reported in addition to the initial nursing facility care.

Design for Compliance and Quality Care
The descriptors for the three key components and the NPP for the three codes included in this type of service correlate exactly with the levels of care and disease severity the CPT codebook describes for initial hospital care. The only *discernible* difference is in the amount of time CPT assigns as being "typical" for providing these services. Therefore, as illustrated in the accompanying CD-ROM, IMR forms for initial nursing facility care look identical to the forms for initial hospital care, with the documentation prompts correlating levels of care with code levels 4, 5, and 6 instead of levels 1, 2, and 3.

The NPP and Levels of Care for Initial Nursing Facility Care
The CPT codebook indicates that usually the problems associated with code 99304 are of low severity, problems appropriate for 99305 are of moderate severity, and problems

warranting 99306 are of high severity. As with other types of service, determining the severity of the NPP guides a physician's medically indicated level of care and the code to be submitted, so it is critical to document this measure on the medical record. Appendix C of *CPT 2008* provides no clinical examples for this type of service.

Subsequent Nursing Facility Care (CPT Codes 99307–99310)

The CPT codebook provides four levels of subsequent nursing facility care. The distinguishing feature of this type of service is that the descriptors for the NPP relate to a patient's clinical status on the date of care and have wording similar to that used for subsequent inpatient care. For this service, the highest severity of NPP indicates that a patient is either "unstable or may have developed a significant new problem requiring immediate physician attention."[1(24)]

The NPP and Levels of Care for Subsequent Nursing Facility Care

Figure 19.6 shows an IMR documentation prompt for the NPP for this type of service. Its content is similar to that in the prompt shown for inpatient subsequent care in Figure 19.3, with the additional fourth level of severity that is appropriate for this setting.

F i g u r e 19.6

Sample Documentation Prompt for Subsequent Nursing Facility Care This succinct prompt includes descriptors associated with the four levels of care for this service.

NATURE OF PRESENTING PROBLEM(S)		
1. Stable:	(level 7)	Usually, the patient is stable, recovering, or improving.
2. Inadequate response:	(level 8)	Usually, the patient is responding inadequately to therapy or has developed a minor complication.
3. Signif new problem:	(level 9)	Usually, the patient has developed a significant complication or a significant new problem.
4. Immediate attention	(level 10)	The patient may be unstable or may have developed a significant new problem requiring immediate physician attention.

Appendix C in *CPT 2008* provides no clinical examples for this type of service.

DOMICILIARY, REST HOME, OR CUSTODIAL CARE E/M SERVICES

The CPT codebook describes this category as being appropriate for facilities whose services do not include a medical component. It recommends using these codes to report E/M services "in a facility which provides room, board and other personal assistance services, generally on a long-term basis. They are also used to report evaluation and management services in an assisted living facility."[1(p 24)] There are two categories of domiciliary facility services: new patients and established patients. Physicians providing consultations in these locations should use the outpatient consultation codes (99241–99245).

New Patient Domiciliary E/M Services (CPT Codes 99324–99328)

This type of service includes five levels of care, and the descriptors in the CPT codebook for the three key components are similar, but not identical, to those of an initial outpatient visit. The variations are found in the levels of MDM and the NPP.

Design for Compliance and Quality Care

The IMR forms for this type of service have an identical framework to those for initial outpatient visits, but the documentation prompts reflects the changes in the CPT codebook's descriptors. For this reason, physicians who regularly care for patients residing in assisted living facilities or other domiciliary-type locations should have specific forms for this type of service. These permit the use of the usual Practical E/M approach, with the prompts guiding selection of the appropriate levels of service and provision of the indicated levels of care.

The NPP and Levels of Care for New Patient Domiciliary Services

The CPT descriptors for the severity of the NPP for domiciliary services are notably higher than described for the various levels of care for initial outpatient visits. Table 19.3 displays the severity of NPP associated with each level of care for this type of service.

Table 19.3

Severity of NPP Associated With Each Level of Care for Domiciliary New Patient Services

E/M Code	Severity of the NPP
99324	Low severity
99325	Moderate severity
99326	Moderate to high severity
99327	High severity
99328	Usually the patient is unstable or has developed a significant new problem requiring immediate physician attention.

Established Patient Domiciliary E/M Services (CPT Codes 99324–99327)

This type of service includes four levels of care, requiring appropriate documentation of at least two of the three key components. The descriptors for the three key components and the NPP for these four levels of care correspond exactly to those used by CPT for the established outpatient visit codes 99212-99215. The forms are identical with the minor modification that the documentation prompts refer to levels 4-7 (corresponding to codes 99324–99327) rather than levels 2-5.

The NPP and Levels of Care for Established Patient Domiciliary Services

Table 19.4 displays the severity of NPP associated with each level of care for this type of service.

Table 19.4

Severity of NPP Associated With Each Level of Care for Domiciliary Established Patient Services

E/M Code	Severity of the NPP
99334	Self-limited or minor severity
99335	Low to moderate severity
99336	Moderate to high severity
99237	Moderate to high severity (and "the patient may be unstable or may have developed a significant new problem requiring immediate physician attention"[1](p 26))

SUMMARY

While physicians have made an active effort to incorporate guidelines for compliant documentation into their office medical records, there has not been a significant parallel effort in other locations for patient care. In most hospitals, EDs, and nursing care facilities, physicians are provided with only a blank sheet of paper or a blank documentation tape to document their patient care. However, in these locations physicians face the same needs as they do in their own offices for documentation approaches and tools that ensure compliance, optimize efficiency, promote quality care, and record meaningful clinical information that accurately reports the care they provide.

These nonoffice locations also confront physicians with an additional compliance challenge. Even though almost all of the E/M services in these facilities rely on consideration of the three key components plus the NPP, the CPT descriptors for each type of service have distinctive variations for determining the levels of care. Whether these variations are minor or major, physicians cannot memorize all the possible combinations, and it is unreasonable to require them to look the descriptors up and do extensive coding calculations in the midst of patient care. Once again, these challenges call for an IMR solution to incorporate the rules of compliance into the tools physicians use for recording their services, thereby making the task of achieving compliance an integral and positive component of providing quality care.

References

1. American Medical Association. *Current Procedural Terminology (CPT®) 2008, Professional Edition.* Chicago, IL: American Medical Association; 2007.

2. American Medical Association & Health Care Financing Administration. *Documentation Guidelines for Evaluation and Management Services.* Chicago, IL: American Medical Association; 1997.

3. Murer C. CMS implements severity-based DRG system for 2008. *Rehab Management.* January 2008. http://www.rehabpub.com.issues/articles/2008-01_09.asp Accessed April 18, 2008.

4. Levinson S. *Practical EHR: Electronic Record Solutions for Compliance and Quality Care.* Chicago, IL: American Medical Association; 2008:42.

Other E/M Services, Not Based on the Key Components

In its "Evaluation and Management (E/M) Services Guidelines" section, the *Current Procedural Terminology* (CPT®) codebook describes a wide range of patient care services that are not defined by the coding paradigm of the seven components of E/M care that have been the focus of Practical E/M to this point. All of these additional services and their CPT codes are listed in Table 20.1.

Even though correctly coding the appropriate levels of care for each of these services does not require documentation prompts to eliminate complex calculations of the key components and the nature of presenting problem (NPP), introducing well-designed forms that incorporate the care requirements for these nonparadigm services can help physicians select correct codes, ensure sufficient documentation to meet compliance requirements, and significantly increase documentation efficiency. This chapter examines prototype intelligent medical record (IMR) tools that physicians could use or modify to assist with two of the most common and important nonparadigm E/M services provided by certain groups of physicians: (1) preventive medicine services in the outpatient setting and (2) critical care services in the hospital setting.

Table 20.1

E/M Services That Do Not Use the Typical E/M Paradigm These services are not based on the seven components of E/M care, and code levels are not determined by the three key components and NPP. The types of service described in detail in this chapter are shown in boldface type.

Category	Type of Service	Code Range
Hospital Emergency Department or Critical Care Department	Physician-directed advanced life support	99288
Interfacility Transport	Pediatric critical care patient transport	99466-99467
Critical Care	**Critical care services**	**99291–99292**
Inpatient Neonatal and Pediatric Critical Care and Intensive Services	Inpatient pediatric critical care	99471-99476
	Inpatient neonatal critical care	99468-99469
	Inpatient subsequent intensive care for infants 5000 grams or less	99478-99480
	Initial hospital care per day for neonate who requires intensive observation and care	99477
Prolonged Services	With face-to-face patient contact	99354–99357
	Without face-to-face patient contact	99358–99359

continued

T a b l e   20.1

E/M Services That Do Not Use the Typical E/M Paradigm, cont'd.

Category	Type of Service	Code Range
Physician Standby	Physician standby services	99360
Case Management	Anticoagulant management	99363–99364
	Medical team conferences with direct (face-to-face) contact with patient and/or family	99366
	Medical team conferences without direct (face-to-face) contact with patient and/or family	99367-99368
Care Plan Oversight	Physician supervision of home health agency patient (patient in home, domiciliary, etc)	99374–99375
	Physician supervision of hospice patient	99377–99378
	Physician supervision of nursing facility patient	99379–99380
Preventive Medicine	**New patient**	**99381–99387**
	Established patient	**99391–99397**
Counseling Risk Factor Reduction/Behavior Change Intervention	Preventive medicine, individual counseling	99401–99404
	Behavior change interventions, individual	99406–99409
	Preventive medicine, group counseling	99411–99412
	Other preventive medicine services	99420–99429
Newborn Care	Services to newborns in different settings	99460-99464
	Newborn resuscitation	99465
Non–Face-to-Face Physician Services	Telephone services	99441–99443
	Online medical evaluation	99444
Special Evaluation and Management Services	Basic life and/or disability evaluation	99450
	Work-related or medical disability evaluation services	99455–99456

*At the time of this printing, this chart was updated to reflect information that will be presented in the 2009 CPT codebook.

PREVENTIVE MEDICINE SERVICES

Preventive medicine services are used to report medical evaluation and management provided on a scheduled basis for recommended health assessment and maintenance. The CPT code designations are based solely on each patient's age and whether the visit is an initial comprehensive preventive medicine visit or a periodic reevaluation preventive visit. There are seven age-related codes in each of these two categories, beginning with infants (less than 1 year of age) and extending to senior patients who are age 65 and older.

Overview of Preventive Medicine Services

The CPT guidelines for physicians providing preventive services are fairly general, specifying that preventive medicine includes "an age and gender appropriate history, examination, counseling/anticipatory guidance/risk factor reduction interventions, and the ordering of appropriate immunization(s), laboratory/diagnostic procedures."[1] More detailed guidelines specifying care that is age- and gender-appropriate have been established by a number of medical specialty societies, particularly the American Academy of Pediatrics[2] and the American Academy of Family Practice.[3]

It should be helpful for physicians using IMR forms for conventional office services to maintain a similar medical record architecture for preventive care templates. This should include maintaining the basic framework of history, physical examination, and medical decision making. The basic forms can be augmented with check boxes to indicate standardized examination and preventive testing elements and to facilitate efficient documentation of that care. Medical necessity is not included as a component of preventive care services, so the NPP section can be eliminated. The forms shown in this chapter for preventive care should be viewed as a possible starting point. Physicians should further customize them to meet their own preferences as well as those of their patients. Physicians who provide these services to patients in different age groups may also wish to custom design forms for each age group to maximize usability and efficiency of documentation.

Pediatric Preventive Care Services

The American Academy of Pediatrics recommends frequent preventive care services during the first year of life, including newborn, 3 to 5 days, 1 month, 2 months, 4 months, 6 months, and 9 months old. Visits are then recommended every 3 months until age one and a half, followed by every 6 months until age 3. After age 3, preventive visits are recommended on an annual basis through the 21st birthday.[2]

For all these preventive encounters, an appropriate initial or interval history and age-appropriate physical examination are recommended. Therefore, it would seem reasonable to use these sections of the initial and established patient visit forms already presented (and shown in Appendix D), with appropriate modifications of the questions to fit the pediatric age group. The medical decision making component of these forms can also be employed after elimination of the compliance-related sections for complexity of data and levels of risk. For young children, most of the recommended preventive care criteria relate to physical examination, laboratory testing, and immunizations. These measures can be easily integrated into these IMR forms, and it is recommended that they be identified with a double asterisk or color coding to indicate that they are preventive care services. Figure 20.1 suggests logical locations for these measures in modified IMR forms. For older children and adolescents, additional measures (body mass index), assessments (alcohol and drug use), and procedures (sexually transmitted infection screening and cervical dysplasia screening when indicated) would be added to appropriate sections of the forms.

Figure 20.1

Suggested Organization for Pediatric Preventive Health Care Measures The following table shows the common infancy and early childhood preventive care measures and suggested logical sections of modified IMR forms that would be appropriate for inserting these assessments. The use of double asterisks is suggested to identify these entries on the forms as preventive measures for purposes of compliance.

Major Section of IMR-Type Form	Preventive Care Measure	Subsection of IMR-Type Form
Medical history	Initial or interval history	Past history, family history, social history, review of systems, and HPI
Physical examination	Measurements: **Length, **height, **weight, **head circumference, **blood pressure	Vital signs section
	**Vision screening	Eyes section
	**Hearing screening, **oral health	ENT section
	**Developmental screening, **developmental surveillance	Neurology section
	**Autism screening, **psychosocial/ behavioral assessment	Psychiatry section
Medical decision making	**Immunizations (age appropriate)	Treatment options section
	**Newborn metabolic/hemoglobin screening	Data ordered section
	**Hematocrit or hemoglobin **Lead screening **Tuberculin test **Dyslipedemia screening	Data ordered section

Adult Preventive Care Services

Similar integration of age- and gender-appropriate screening examinations and diagnostic testing into physicians' existing E/M templates should be effective for adult services as well. For those physicians wishing to adapt to IMR forms, the sections on the last page of E/M forms that are usually devoted to levels of risk and NPP can be replaced on the preventive care forms by sections for immunizations given and for documenting counseling and risk factor reduction interventions.

Modifications to IMR Forms to Address Documentation for Preventive Care
Most physicians will want to maintain compatibility of their forms for preventive care with those they use for normal outpatient E/M services. For new patient initial visit preventive services, this approach allows retention of identical forms for the first two pages, which address the past, family, and social history and the review of

systems (ROS). The third page would be nearly identical, except for removal of the documentation prompts that relate extent of care to the NPP, since this factor is not relevant in the preventive services. Forms for established patient preventive medicine services can also be similar to a physician's usual outpatient established visit IMR forms for the medical history and examination sections, located on page 1, except for the removal of the unnecessary documentation prompts.

The significant changes on both the new patient and established patient forms appear on the last page, which should include portions of the standard medical decision making plus sections for immunizations and for counseling. Physicians should be encouraged to create check boxes for efficient documentation of the standard diagnostic procedures they order, the types of counseling they commonly provide, and the information sheets they distribute. Figure 20.2 shows a sample form for the final page appropriate for both new patient and established patient adult preventive care services. For illustration purposes, the sample form is preloaded with check boxes for tests (data ordered), immunizations, and counseling that are recommended by the American Academy of Family Practice (AAFP) for the "Welcome to Medicare" preventive care visits described below. Physicians can customize the lists of diagnostic tests, immunizations, and counseling topics to meet their personal preferences for each age group they care for.

The "Welcome to Medicare" Physical Exam

On January 1, 2005, the Centers for Medicare and Medicaid Services (CMS) introduced their own guidelines for a new covered preventive medicine service, the Medicare Part B "Welcome to Medicare" Physical Exam.[4] Although Medicare policy fails to provide coverage for all other preventive care E/M services, this new policy provides payment for patients to receive a one-time preventive care evaluation during the first months that they have Part B coverage. The CMS defines this service as including "a thorough review of your health, education and counseling about the preventive services you need, like certain screenings and shots, and referrals for other care."[4] It concludes by encouraging patients that this is "a great way. . .to talk with your doctor about your family history and how to stay healthy."[4]

The AAFP has described seven required elements of the Welcome to Medicare Exam:

1. Review of comprehensive medical and social history
2. Review of risk factors for depression
3. Review of functional ability and level of safety
4. A focused physical exam
5. Performance and interpretation of an electrocardiogram
6. Brief education, counseling, and referral to address any pertinent health issues identified during the first five elements of the exam
7. Brief education, counseling, and referral, with maintenance of a written plan (such as a checklist), regarding separate preventive care services covered by Medicare Part B[3]

Figure 20.2

Sample for Final Page of Preventive Care IMR-Type Form The top portion of this form is identical to IMR forms used for outpatient office services, although the documentation prompts have been removed. The lower portion of the form replaces documentation sections for complexity of data, levels of risk, and the NPP with preprinted sections for documentation of immunizations and counseling. The bottom of the page includes a section with coding guidance linking the preventive care E/M codes to the appropriate age group, and a shaded documentation prompt listing the CPT codebook's identified components of preventive care services.

Preventive Care New Patient (page 4)

Patient Name:	Account No.	DOB:

MEDICAL DECISION MAKING

DATA REVIEWED:

☐ Radiology   ☐ See attached dictation

☐ EKG

☐ Lab / blood work

IMPRESSIONS / DIFFERENTIAL DIAGNOSES:

1)
2)
3)
4)
5)

PLANS / MANAGEMENT OPTIONS   ☐ See attached dictation

1)
2)
3)
4)
5)

DATA ORDERED: ☐ See attached dictation

☐ Glaucoma screening   ☐ Screening mammogram   ☐ Pelvic & Pap screen   ☐ PSA screening

☐ Fecal Occult Blood Test   ☐ Flexible sigmoidoscopy   ☐ Screening Colonoscopy   ☐ Barium Enema

☐ Lipid panel with triglycerides   ☐ Fasting blood sugar   ☐ Glucose tolerance test

☐ Ultrasound screening for abdominal aortic aneurysm

IMMUNIZATIONS GIVEN / ORDERED:

☐ Pneumoccocal   ☐ Influenza   ☐ Hepatitis B   ☐

COUNSELING / ANTICIPATORY GUIDANCE / RISK FACTOR REDUCTION INTERVENTIONS: ☐ See attached dictation

☐ Diabetes outpatient self-management training   ☐ Medical nutritional therapy for patient with diabetes

☐ Diet counseling for obesity   ☐ Medical nutritional therapy for patient with renal disease

☐ Smoking cessation   ☐ Alcohol counseling   ☐ Exercise counseling

Information Sheets Given:

Periodic comprehensive preventive medicine service:

☐ 99291: Infant (age younger than 1 year)   ☐ 99295: Age 18 through 39 years

☐ 99292: Early childhood (age 1 through 4 years)   ☐ 99296: Age 40 through 64 years

☐ 99293: Late childhood (age 5 through 11 years)   ☐ 99297: Age 65 years and older

☐ 99294: Adolescent (age 12 through 17 years)

Age and gender appropriate   1) history   2) examination   3) counseling / anticipatoryguidance / risk factor reduction interventions

    4) Ordering of appropriate immunizations | Clinician's signature:

    5) Ordering of appropriate laboratory tests / diagnostic procedures

History Sections of the Welcome to Medicare Exam

It is appropriate to include a complete past history, family history, and social history exactly as shown in Appendix D on page 1 of an IMR form for initial patient visits (and replicated on page 1 of the new patient preventive medicine form in part 3 of the accompanying CD-ROM). A thorough ROS, as illustrated on page 2 of that form, would also be appropriate to meet Medicare's description of "a thorough review of your health." This component of the medical history can be designed to include, in the Psychiatry section, recommended mental status questions designed to identify risk factors for depression. Similarly, questions concerning the patient's level of safety can be incorporated into the Neurology section through inquiries about a patient's history of falling and ability to carry out the activities of daily living, including executive function.

Hearing Status and the Welcome to Medicare Exam

The ENT section of the ROS sample template includes an inquiry about hearing loss. However, even though a significant percentage of individuals begin to have compromised hearing as they enter their Medicare age, many of these patients are unaware that they have a problem, or they refuse to acknowledge it. Therefore, it is often wise to ask a family member whether the patient frequently asks for conversation to be repeated or has episodes of not hearing or of hearing incorrectly. Responses that indicate a possible hearing problem warrant an ear examination and hearing test, because loss of hearing can lead to challenges interacting with friends and family. Communication problems can also lead to subtle withdrawal, which can contribute to depression, and this is an important concern to be evaluated during the Welcome to Medicare Exam.

Physical Examination Section of the Welcome to Medicare Exam

The physical examination for this preventive care visit should, at a minimum, include vital signs and a screening test of visual acuity. Physicians are further advised to include any organ systems that would be relevant on the basis of significant findings in the medical history. The standard examination template used by the physician for conventional office visits allows effective documentation, and no prompts are required, as illustrated in the new and follow-up preventive care forms in part 3 of the accompanying CD-ROM.

Decision Making Section of the Welcome to Medicare Exam

The upper portions of the final page should include the customary sections for documentation of data reviewed, impressions, treatments (including continuation of current therapies), and data ordered. The lower sections include documentation for immunizations and counseling services. Physicians should use their judgment to order appropriate preventive care services, especially those now covered by Medicare. These include the following[1,5]:

- Vaccinations for influenza, pneumoccocus, and hepatitis B
- Ultrasound screening for abdominal aortic aneurysm
- Electrocardiogram
- Screening mammography
- Screening Pap test and pelvic exam
- Prostate screening by examination and prostate-specific antigen testing
- Colorectal cancer screening (eg, fecal occult blood test, flexible sigmoidoscopy, screening colonoscopy, and/or barium enema)
- Diabetes outpatient self-management training services
- Bone mass measurements
- Screening for glaucoma
- Medical nutritional therapy for individuals with diabetes or renal disease
- Cardiovascular disease screening (eg, lipid profile including triglycerides)
- Diabetes screening tests, including fasting blood glucose or glucose tolerance test
- Smoking cessation care

For ease of documentation, physicians can preprint these tests, as well as others they commonly order, on their preventive care forms for this Welcome to Medicare service and for other adults as well. A sample of the last page, including all the preventive care evaluations and interventions covered by Medicare, was illustrated in Figure 20.2

Care of Active Medical Problems on the Same Day as Preventive Medicine Services

Although preventive services are specifically oriented to assess patient risk factors and provide guidance to maximize health, a variety of issues can arise when a patient scheduled for a preventive medicine visit presents with an acute problem or when the physician addresses a new or preexisting problem during the course of this type of visit. The CPT codebook provides the following guidance concerning proper coding to address these circumstances:

- "An insignificant or trivial problem/abnormality that is encountered in the process of performing the preventive medicine evaluation and management service and which *does not require additional work* and the performance of the key components of a problem-oriented E/M service should not be reported"[1(p 32)]
- If the problem/abnormality is significant enough to require additional work to perform the key components of a *problem-oriented E/M service* [italics added], then the appropriate Office/Outpatient code 99201-99215 should also be additionally reported"[1(p 31)]

When both an outpatient E/M service and a preventive medicine service are reported on the same date, the CPT codebook further advises that the physician submit the conventional E/M code with an attached modifier -25 and also report the preventive medicine code.

The submission of codes for such "dual" E/M services has created a number of troublesome issues for insurers and medical practices alike. By their nature, the preventive services are not intended to address existing medical issues. Therefore, claims for associated medical care should occur infrequently. Additionally, some Medicare carriers and insurers have raised concern about a degree of redundancy because both outpatient and preventive E/M services include a medical history and an examination. Practices are advised to review specific carrier policies to confirm whether they support CPT guidelines for submitting claims for both E/M services on the same date, or if they create exceptions.

Additional Issues for Dual E/M Service Visits

Diagnosis codes alone are usually not adequate for an insurer's payment software to determine whether the problem being addressed with an outpatient E/M service is "insignificant or trivial" or of sufficient concern to warrant a "problem-oriented E/M service." In practice, insurers do not want to audit each record for claims submitted with two E/M services on the same date. As a result, the software used by many insurers is often programmed to override the -25 modifier attached to the outpatient E/M code and deny payment for the preventive medicine service. Although the medical practice may challenge this noncompliant practice and appeal a denial, the administrative cost for processing the appeal commonly exceeds the income recaptured. The result is unfair to physicians and to patients. Therefore, it is often wise to maintain separate visits that are devoted exclusively to preventive care, allowing additional care only for trivial problems that would not justify a separate E/M service.

Class Action Lawsuits and Claims for Dual E/M Services on the Same Date

Most of the major national insurers have signed settlement agreements in response to national class action lawsuits brought by physicians in 2002. Under the terms of these agreements, the insurers pledged to recognize the -25 modifier and not automatically bundle or deny payment for the second service. However, this condition did not preclude the insurers from requesting and reviewing documentation and then denying payment if the service had been coded improperly.

However, the first several of these four-year agreements were signed in 2003, and they have now expired. There are no further restraints on insurers at this time to prevent their once again deciding to automatically deny payment for a preventive care service when an outpatient E/M service is submitted on the same date, even when the outpatient care is properly submitted with a -25 modifier.

Medicare Patients and Other Preventive E/M Visits

Although Medicare introduced the Welcome to Medicare Exam as a covered preventive medicine service, all other preventive care E/M visits remain uncovered by Medicare Part B. Physicians are permitted to establish their own appropriate fees for uncovered services, and the patients are responsible for payment. Physicians are reasonably advised to confirm with their local Medicare carrier whether it is appropriate to obtain a signed Advanced Beneficiary Notice from patients receiving these services and then submit the appropriate preventive medicine service code with a GA modifier to indicate that it is likely Medicare will treat this care as an uncovered service. This permits medical practices to collect appropriate payment directly from the patient.

Practices should have a policy (in writing if possible) emphasizing to their patients the importance of preventive medicine services and explaining that these services are provided separately from visits to care for new or ongoing medical illnesses. It should also describe the fee for preventive care appointments, and remind patients that Medicare does not cover preventive medicine visits except for the Welcome to Medicare Exam.

Physicians should be aware that to avoid paying for these important services themselves, some Medicare patients might request that the physician submit a claim to Medicare, with a diagnosis code for an illness or symptom, as if the physician had provided an outpatient service rather than a preventive medicine service. Under such circumstances, the practice's business manager should gently explain to the patient that Medicare rules prohibit submission of claims that do not accurately report the care provided, and that doing so could be considered fraud against the federal government.

CRITICAL CARE SERVICES

With regard to the severity of a patient's condition at the time of care, critical care services are the polar opposite of the preventive services discussed above. Nevertheless, physicians gain similar benefits from using medical record forms that incorporate the CPT system's coding criteria and increase documentation efficiency by matching the normal workflow for this type of care.

Overview of Critical Care Services

The CPT codebook specifies that "providing medical care to a critically ill, injured, or post-operative patient qualifies as a critical care service only if both the illness or injury and the treatment being provided meet requirements,"[1(p 19)] including the total amount of time that critical care is provided on the date of service. For compliance and audit protection, incorporating these criteria into a medical record template specific for critical care not only informs physicians how to confirm that a service qualifies as critical care, it also facilitates effective and efficient documentation of that care.

The CPT coding system subdivides critical care services into three categories, which are distinguished on the basis of patient age. These classifications are listed in Table 20.2. This analysis will focus solely on design for forms for critical care services provided to patients older than 24 months (CPT codes 99291 and 99292), though physicians can apply similar principles to creating forms for the critical care of young pediatric patients and neonates.

Location

Critical care services can be provided in any location, including a medical office, though they are usually performed in one of the critical care areas of a hospital, "such as the coronary care unit, intensive care unit, pediatric intensive care unit, respiratory care unit, or the emergency care facility."[1(p 19)] Conversely, not all patients who receive care in a critical care area are critically ill; for those who are not critically ill or whose care does not meet all the criteria required for submitting critical care codes, physicians should report their services by using the appropriate E/M code (eg, hospital inpatient codes for admission, subsequent care, or consultation).

T a b l e   20.2

Types of Critical Care Services The CPT coding system defines three types of critical care services, based on the age of the patient. The types of service shown in boldface type are described in detail in this chapter.

Category	Type of Service	Code Range
Critical Care	**Critical care of the critically ill or critically injured patient; first 30–74 minutes**	**99291**
	Critical care of the critically ill or critically injured patient; each additional 30 minutes	**99292**
Inpatient Pediatric Critical Care	**Initial inpatient pediatric critical care,** per day, for the evaluation and management of a critically ill infant or young child, 29 days through 24 months of age	99471
	Subsequent inpatient pediatric critical care, per day, for the evaluation and management of a critically ill infant or young child, 29 days through 24 months of age	99472
	Initial inpatient pediatric critical care, per day, for the evaluation and management of a critically ill infant or young child, 2 through 5 years of age	99475
	Subsequent inpatient pediatric critical care, per day, for the evaluation and management of a critically ill infant or young child, 2 through 5 years of age	99476
Inpatient Neonatal Critical Care	**Initial inpatient neonatal critical care,** per day, for the evaluation and management of a critically ill neonate, 28 days of age or less	99468
	Subsequent inpatient neonatal critical care, per day, for the evaluation and management of a critically ill neonate, 28 days of age or less	99469

*At the time of this printing, this chart was updated to reflect information that will be presented in the 2009 CPT codebook.

Critical Care Criteria

The three criteria that must be met for reporting this type of E/M service are (1) the severity of illness, (2) the intensity of services required to treat the illness, and (3) the time spent in providing the care. The CPT codebook defines the first criterion of critical care, the severity of a critical illness or injury, by the fact that it "acutely impairs one or more vital organ systems such that there is a high probability of imminent or one or more vital organ systems such that there is a high probability of imminent or life threatening deterioration in the patient's condition."[1(p 19)] Examples of vital organ system failure are described to include, but not be limited to, the following:

- Central nervous system failure
- Circulatory system failure
- Shock
- Renal system failure
- Hepatic failure
- Metabolic failure
- Respiratory failure

The second criterion defines critical care as involving "high complexity decision making to assess, manipulate, and support vital system function(s) to treat single or multiple vital organ system failure and/or to prevent further life threatening deterioration of the patient's condition."[1(p 19)] Additional elements that are commonly associated with critical care services, such as interpretation of multiple physiologic parameters or use of advanced technology, are not mandatory for reporting this type of care.

The final factor that must be fulfilled to report critical care is that the physician (or his or her associates) must spend a total of at least 30 minutes providing critical care on a particular date of service. The CPT codebook further specifies that critical care time is counted only when the physician is paying full attention to the patient in question, without providing any services to other patients during the same time frame.

Guidelines for Critical Care Services

The codes for critical care include the interpretation of tests (cardiac output measurements, chest x-rays, pulse oximetry, blood gases, and computerized laboratory and test results) and the performance of certain specified procedures, which should therefore not be separately reported:

- Gastric intubation
- Temporary transcutaneous pacing
- Ventilatory management
- Vascular access procedures (venipuncture, collection of blood from an implanted venous access device, arterial puncture for diagnostic blood testing)

However, physicians should separately report performance of any other procedures. Physicians should refer to the Critical Care guidelines in the CPT codebook for the specific procedure codes that are associated with these component services of critical care. According to Medicare guidelines, when submitting a code for a procedure that has a zero or 10-day global period (eg, insertion of a subclavian catheter, code 36556) on the same date as performing a critical care service, physicians should also attach a -25 modifier to the critical care E/M code (99291).

It is unreasonable for physicians to be required to memorize all the criteria for severity of illness, complexity of decision making, and time involved to determine when they can validly report critical care services, and it is inappropriate for them to research these definitions every time they provide care to critically ill patients. It is far more effective to incorporate these guidelines into an IMR-type critical care form, page 1 of which is illustrated in Figure 20.3. The upper portion of this form includes all the CPT critical care criteria and includes check boxes to allow rapid documentation that the criteria have been met. It also provides for documentation of the total time involved providing critical care and a documentation prompt that advises how this factors into correct coding. The remaining portions of page 1 and all of page 2, which is illustrated in Figure 20.4, provide for conventional documentation of information related to medical history, physical examination, description of care performed, and medical decision making.

Details of Time Parameters

The third requirement for submitting a claim for critical care services is that the physician must spend at least 30 minutes performing critical care services directly for the patient. If a physician spends less than 30 minutes of critical care time on a

Figure 20.3

Sample Documentation Form for Critical Care Services (> Age 2), Page 1 The upper portion of this first page includes check boxes to confirm that the care meets CPT criteria for *severity of illness* and *complexity of care* required for critical care services. As noted in the shaded documentation prompts, if these criteria or the time criteria are not met, physicians should employ an appropriate E/M form for subsequent inpatient care or other appropriate service. The lower portion of the form provides documentation for descriptions of medical history, examination findings, and care performed

Patient Name: Account No.   DOB:____/____/____

Critical Care Form

Critical Care Criteria:

Please check the "Yes" or "No" box to indicate whether circumstances are appropriate for critical care;
ALL THREE "YES" BOXES MUST BE CONFIRMED TO MEET THE CRITERIA FOR "CRITICAL CARE"

Critically ill or critically injured patient with all of the following: Yes   No

Acutely impairs one or more vital organ systems   ☐   ☐

    Affected System(s):   ☐ Cardiovascular   ☐ Hepatic

                               ☐ Respiratory   ☐ Renal

                               ☐ CNS   ☐ Metabolic

                               ☐ Shock   ☐ Other

High probability of imminent or life threatening detioration   ☐   ☐

High complexity decision making   ☐   ☐

   ☐ To assess, manipulate, & support vital system function in order to treat vital organ system failure

   ☐ To prevent life threatening deterioration of the patient's condition

Provided in: ☐ Critical care area   ☐ Non-Critical care area

   Total time for CRITICAL CARE of patient: _____minutes (includes all time related to direct care of patient)

   Note: Critical care includes interpretation of the following procedures, which are not separately coded

      ☐ cardiac output measurements   ☐ chest X-rays   ☐ pulse oximetry   ☐ blood gases   ☐ lab and test results

   Critical care also includes performance of the following procedures

      ☐ gastric intubation   ☐ temporary transcutaneous pacing   ☐ ventilator management ☐ vascular access procedures

1. First 30 - 74 minutes (99291)   2. Each additional 30 minutes; listed in addition to 99291 (99292)
(Note: Use usual inpatient codes for critical care less than 30 minutes on a given day, regardless of intensity of care)
(Note: Time to perform procedures that are coded separately is not counted as critical care time)

Current History: ☐ See attached dictation

Significant examination findings: ☐ See attached dictation

Description of Care: ☐ See attached dictation

☐ See attached dictation   Reviewed by:

F i g u r e 20.4

Sample Documentation Form for Critical Care Services, page 2 This second portion of the critical care form provides for meaningful and efficient documentation of the medical decision making components of the care provided. Physicians may customize these forms by pre-entering the names of diagnostic tests they commonly order to the boxes available in the Data Reviewed and Data Ordered sections of the form.

Patient Name:_____   Account No._____   DOB:____/____/____

MEDICAL DECISION MAKING
DATA REVIEWED (c):

☐   ☐ **See attached dictation**

☐

☐

IMPRESSIONS / DIFFERENTIAL DIAGNOSES (a):   **PLANS / MANAGEMENT OPTIONS (a')**

1) _____   1) _____ ☐ **See attached dictation**

2) _____   2) _____

3) _____   3) _____

4) _____   4) _____

5) _____   5) _____

DATA ORDERED (c'):

☐   ☐   ☐   ☐   ☐

                                             ☐ **See attached dictation**

particular day, then, regardless of the severity of patient illness and complexity of decision making and treatment, an appropriate code for E/M care must be submitted based on the location and type of service (codes for inpatient care, emergency department care, outpatient care, etc). The CPT codebook further clarifies that time cannot be counted as contributing to the critical care provided under the following circumstances:

- Time spent when the physician is not immediately available to the patient; ie, activities outside of the unit or off the floor where the patient is located
- Time spent in activities that are not directly involved with evaluation or treatment of the patient, even if in the same location as the patient; eg, meetings or calls to discuss other patients
- Time spent with the patient performing separately reportable procedures or services; eg, the insertion of a subclavian catheter, as described above

For compliance purposes, it is important for physicians to accurately document the total time during a day that they provide critical care to the patient, whether or not the care is continuous. The upper portion of the form shown in Figure 20.3 provides a preprinted location for recording this time value. When this amount of time equals or exceeds 30 minutes, the physician can submit code 99291 to report critical care services of between 30 and 74 minutes in total duration. In circumstances where greater than 74 minutes of critical care is provided, the physician should report an additional code, 99292. One unit of this code is used to report each additional 30 minutes of time. For example, when 75 to 104 minutes of critical care is being reported, the physician should submit codes 99291 and 99292; when 105 to 134 minutes of critical care is being reported, the physician should submit codes 99291 and 99292 × 2.

SUMMARY

Even though accurate code determination for the most frequently used E/M services relies on consideration of the seven components of E/M care, there are many additional E/M services that are defined by different criteria, including the nature of the encounter, the patient's age, the severity of illness, the patient's location, and/or the amount of time involved. Determining the care, documentation, and coding required for submitting claims for these services does not involve complex relationships among medical history, physical examination, medical decision making, and the NPP. However, as illustrated by the important preventive care and critical care services, the coding and documentation rules for these nonparadigm services are sufficiently complex that physicians gain significant benefits for ensuring compliance and increasing efficiency by incorporating the CPT guidelines into the design of the medical records they use to record this care.

References

1. American Medical Association. *Current Procedural Terminology (CPT®) 2008, Professional Edition*. Chicago, IL: American Medical Association; 2007.

2. Pediatric Common Practice and Ambulatory Medicine and Bright Futures Steering Committee. Recommendations for preventive pediatric health care. *Pediatrics*. 2007;120(6):1376. http://pediatrics.aappublications.org/cgi/data/120/6/1376/DC1/1. Accessed April 20, 2008.

3. Card RO. How to conduct a "Welcome to Medicare" visit. *Fam Pract Manage*. 2005;27. http://www.aafp.org/fpm/20050400/27howt.html. Accessed April 20, 2008.

4.   Centers for Medicare and Medicaid Services. Preventive Services: One-time "Welcome to Medicare" Physical Exam. http://www.medicare.gov/health/physicalexam.asp. Accessed April 20, 2008.

5.   Centers for Medicare and Medicaid Services. Prevention—general information. http://www.cms.hhs.gov/PrevntionGenInfo/. Accessed April 23, 2008.

Supplemental IMR Forms

Under certain defined circumstances, physicians may submit claims for services performed when working cooperatively with other clinicians who are providing a portion or all of their evaluation and management (E/M) services to patients. This potential occurs for physicians at teaching hospitals, who are supervising care provided by resident physicians, and for physicians working in the outpatient setting with nurse practitioners (NPs) and physician assistants (PAs) who are providing care "incident to" the physician's supervision.

While the underlying E/M definitions and criteria of the Current Procedural Terminology (CPT®) coding system and the *Documentation Guidelines for Evaluation and Management Services* continue to apply for physicians providing and supervising these services, the circumstances involved in these situations are also governed by additional care and documentation rules cited by the Centers for Medicare and Medicaid Services (CMS). These rules must also be addressed to ensure compliant coding. Just as with the fundamental E/M services themselves, the various sets of documentation and coding rules governing care under these special circumstances are too complex for physicians to memorize and too inconvenient for them to carry volumes of coding rules for reference in the process of providing patient care. Instead, a Practical E/M approach of incorporating the documentation rules into intelligent medical record (IMR) tools allows physicians and their clinical colleagues to integrate documentation and coding compliance seamlessly into their provision of patient care.

"PHYSICIAN PRESENCE" DOCUMENTATION FOR PHYSICIANS AT TEACHING HOSPITALS

The 1995 audit of physicians at the University of Pennsylvania discussed in Chapter 2 paved the way for a series of reviews by the Office of Inspector General (OIG) that were known as "PATH audits," PATH being an acronym for "physicians at teaching hospitals." These audits, which were performed at a significant number of major medical centers, concentrated on the two prime areas of noncompliance identified by the OIG's chief health care auditor in the original audit as:

1. "The billing of Medicare by some attending physicians for a higher level of services than they actually performed"[1]

2. "[B]illings for services performed by residents. Payments for these services are normally made to hospitals through special allowances for graduate medical education, under Part A of Medicare"[1]

The first of these issues refers to the submission of codes for E/M services at levels higher than supported by the documented level of care for the three key components (medical history, physical examination, and medical decision making). In conventional E/M audits, this is commonly described as "overcoding," which will be discussed further in Chapters 25 and 26. This problem is eliminated through the use of Practical E/M methodology and IMR documentation tools.

The second issue deals with a concept that has been labeled as "physician presence"—the billing for services by teaching physicians when there was no documentation in the medical record that they had provided those services or that they had been present in the patient's room when resident physicians provided the services under their supervision. The underlying cause of this problem is that for many years it had been common practice for teaching physicians to just sign the medical record documentation created by the residents who were assisting with the care of their hospitalized patients. Yet when they submitted claims for these E/M services, the only documentation in the medical record was of care provided by the residents, with no further documentation of the physicians' personal involvement. During these compliance audits, the teaching physicians' signatures on the charts were interpreted to document only that they had reviewed the resident's notes, not that they had provided actual E/M services.

However, Medicare does not pay twice for the same service. Medicare Part A had already made payments for the care of these patients, because it provides increased hospitalization payments to teaching hospitals for the purpose of paying for the care given by residents. Therefore, the OIG determined that it was inappropriate for the teaching physicians to be charging for the same care that had been provided and documented by their residents.

CMS Supporting Documents

In 1995, the OIG referred to the longstanding Intermediary Letter 372 Guidelines (IL-372) from the Health Care Financing Administration (HCFA; now CMS) that specified the requirements for billing by teaching physicians when their care also involved residents. Subsequent to the first teaching hospital audit after the University of Pennsylvania settlement, HCFA responded to complaints that the IL-372 criteria were imprecise by issuing a new "Final Rule for Teaching Physicians" in section 15016 of its *Medicare Carriers Manual*.[2] This rule provides teaching physicians with several circumstances under which they may submit claims for E/M services provided to a patient for whom a resident also provides care. In 2002, CMS augmented section 15016 by adding a number of clarifications and examples to the existing text, though without substantially altering this section's established principles and documentation requirements for teaching physicians to submit claims for E/M services.[3]

Compliance Options for Teaching Physicians Providing E/M Services

Physicians have a variety of alternatives for coding or not coding these E/M services. The first alternative, which is not recommended, would follow the old model of simply signing the resident's note, except that under this circumstance the physician should not submit a claim for E/M care. However, since teaching physicians do, in fact, evaluate their patients each day, this option is inappropriate not only economically, but on quality care grounds; it is important for physicians to accurately document the care they provide for quality care and liability protection purposes, and they should receive appropriate payment for that care.

Under the criteria of section 15016, teaching physicians have three reasonable options available that will allow them to submit claims for E/M services for care they provide when residents are sharing responsibility for those patients:

1. The teaching physician may obtain and document a complete E/M service on the same basis as if a resident were not involved in the patient care. In this situation, correct E/M coding is determined solely by the care the physician provides and documents.[2(p 3)]

2. The resident performs all elements of the E/M care "in the presence of, or jointly with, the teaching physician," and the resident documents that care.

3. The resident provides and documents his or her care of the patient, and the teaching physician independently "repeats key elements of the examination."[2(p 3)] In addition, "the teaching physician's note must include summary comments that revise or confirm the findings of the resident's physical examination and discussion of the history and medical decision making. The combined entries must be adequate to substantiate the level of service required by the patient and billed."[2(p 3)] Under these circumstances, the teaching physician is also required to discuss the findings related to the three key components with the resident.[2(p 3)]

Matching Physician Presence Guidelines to Teaching Physicians' Normal Workflow

Although the CMS guidelines seem complex, they in fact match up well with appropriate patient care workflow for teaching physicians. In general, teaching physicians see their hospitalized patients on a daily basis; these visits may be in association with their residents, on "rounds," or they may occur independently, either before or after the residents examine these patients and enter their notes in the medical record. In addition, the teaching physicians will commonly focus on the patients' most significant problems and rely on their residents to research, evaluate, and document less critical aspects of care. These options align perfectly with the documentation alternatives provided in CMS *Medicare Carriers Manual* section 15016.

The first physician presence option provided by CMS would be appropriate if a resident was not involved in a patient's care on a particular date. Under that circumstance, the teaching physician provides the sole care and is responsible for complete documentation. Under these conditions, the physician would be advised to use one of the IMR forms discussed in Chapter 19 for inpatient initial or subsequent care visits.

The second of the three CMS options applies appropriately when the teaching physician is on rounds with the residents, so that all patient care is performed in the presence of the teaching physician. Although the resident will document this care and may also document the teaching physician's participation, the teaching physician is also required to document a portion of the care as well. The CMS instructs that "[t]he teaching physician's personal documentation may be limited; at a minimum, it must include a confirmation of each component of the resident's documentation and the teaching physician's presence during the service required by the patient."[2(p 3)]

The final CMS option is applicable when physicians see their patients independently of the residents, performing the key elements of care and documenting "summary comments that revise or confirm the findings of the resident's physical examination and discussion of the history and medical decision-making. The combined entries must be adequate to substantiate the level of service required by the patient and billed."[2(p 3)]

These last two CMS options both provide teaching physicians with reasonable documentation and coding alternatives that are compatible with the possible roles they and their residents play in team care. With proper documentation tools, these choices permit the teaching physician to perform and document *problem-focused care* while coding appropriately for higher levels of care by acknowledging and incorporating the residents' additional care and documentation. This benefit also recognizes the communication between attending physician and resident involved in good teaching. Specifically, the CMS rules governing these two circumstances provide that when

> [a] teaching physician documents his or her presence and participation in the E/M service, the level of service may be selected based on the extent of history and/or examination and/or the complexity of the medical decision making required by the patient and documented in his or her personal entry in the medical record which may include references to notes entered by the resident . . . the documentation of the teaching physician may be brief, summary comments that tie into the resident's entry and which confirm or revise the key elements defined for the purpose of this sections as:
>
> - relevant history of present illness and prior diagnostic tests;
> - major finding(s) of the physical examination;
> - assessment, clinical impression or diagnosis; and
> - plan of care[2(p 2)]

As with documentation for all inpatient services, the teaching physician's documentation must address all three key components for initial hospital care and consultations but only two of the three key components for subsequent inpatient care.

Design for Compliance, Usability, and Efficiency

Compliant documentation and coding for teaching physicians requires compliance by the residents as well. Their care and documentation should "reflect the level of care required by the patient," which is based on the nature of the presenting problem (NPP). Residents therefore need intelligent inpatient medical record forms so that teaching physicians can rely on their documentation and code determination. The teaching physicians require a different set of forms that incorporate all the CMS guidelines for correct documentation of the physician presence elements as well as the key components. These physician presence forms should be complete and easy to use, provide for efficient documentation of the care provided, and clearly coordinate the level of care with the documentation in the resident's record.

Figure 21.1 illustrates a sample form that fulfills these requirements. The form is in four sections. The upper portion lists the criteria that must be met for documentation by the teaching physician, advising that this requires either (1) presence and participation in or (2) repeat and confirmation of the key elements of each listed component of care. It also includes a documentation prompt reminding physicians of the number of key components required for each type of service. The second section guides the physician to document the name of the resident whose note is referenced and the date of that note. The third portion has subsections for each of the three key components. There are three identical check boxes with preloaded information about possible care options in each of these subsections. The first two check boxes allow the teaching physician to attest to either being physically present during the resident's care of the patient or personally repeating the key elements of that care; the physician must check one of these two boxes to submit a claim for E/M service under these rules. The physician must also check the third box, which confirms review of the resident's documentation and provides an introduction to the free-text comments the physician will document to summarize his or her own findings and offer any modifications to the resident's documentation. The fourth section of the form includes the option of documenting instances where counseling and/or coordination of care dominate more than 50% of the teaching physician's encounter with the patient, which then might supersede the level of care warranted by the NPP and supported by the combined documentation of the three key components.

F i g u r e 21.1

Sample Form for the Teaching Physicians to Document Care Provided Under the Rules of Physician Presence

Patient Name: _____ Record # _____ Date: ___/___/____

Physician Presence - <u>Attending Physician should indicate either presence and participation in, or repeat and confirmation of, key elements of each component below and, in either event, enter summary comments on review of resident's documentation and confirmation or revision of findings.</u>

A. 3/3 elements required for initial visit and consultation	*B. 2/3 elements required for subsequent care visit*

☐ **Please refer to resident medical record note by Dr.** _____ **dated** ___/___/___

HISTORY: ☐ Physically Present ☐ Personally Repeated (history of present illness and prior tests)
☐ Review of history confirms the resident's documentation, with the following modifications and/or summary comments:

_____

_____

_____

_____

EXAMINATION: ☐ Physically Present ☐ Personally Repeated (major exam findings)
☐ Review of physical exam confirms the resident's documentation, with the following modifications &/or summary comments:

_____

_____

_____

_____

MED DECISION MAKING: ☐ Physically Present ☐ Personally Repeated: assessment, diagnosis, plan of care
☐ Review of decision making confirms the resident's documentation, with the following modifications and/or summary comments:

_____

_____

_____

_____

_____

_____

_____

Complete this section only if documented below >50% of visit time involved counseling and/or coordinating care.

TIME: _____ minutes ☐ **> 50% of visit time involved counseling and/or coordination of care**

Attending physician's signature: _____

Unless they are using the counseling section for time-based coding, teaching physicians must complete two of the three check boxes and provide narrative documentation in each of the three key component subsections on this form for initial inpatient care and inpatient consultations. They are permitted to eliminate one of the subsections for patients receiving subsequent inpatient care. Following this documentation, the physicians may submit a claim for the combined E/M care that was provided and documented on the physician presence form and on the resident's medical record for the visit. Therefore, compliant coding for teaching physicians also relies on the resident's documentation, and this calls for residents to use properly designed IMR-type forms, including documentation of the NPP to warrant the level of care provided, so that a teaching physician can readily determine the level of care provided.

Physician Presence and Private Insurers

At the present time, I am unaware of any insurers establishing specific rules to govern billing for services by physicians at teaching hospitals. It would be advisable for physicians in this circumstance to obtain written confirmation of their policies from the major insurers with whom they participate. In most cases, it is reasonable to hope that they will accept documentation such as the form shown in Figure 21.1, particularly if they appreciate that it is sufficient to meet CMS compliance rules.

Billing Exception to Physician Presence Requirements in Certain Primary Care Centers

CMS provides a different set of specialized rules and conditions for teaching physicians working in a graduate medical education program that has been granted a "primary care exception."[2(pp 4-5)] According to the CMS guidelines, the types of residency programs most likely to qualify for this exception include family practice, general internal medicine, geriatric medicine, pediatrics, and obstetrics and gynecology.

When supervising residents in this situation, a teaching physician may submit claims for outpatient new patient and established patient medical services provided by the residents *without* being present or repeating the critical elements of the key components. This exception is allowed only for care involving level 1, 2, or 3 services, which would be warranted by an NPP of severity ranging from minor to moderate. CMS also requires that the physician must attest in writing that the primary care center meets all of the conditions required for payment under this exception. The upper section of the IMR-type form in Figure 21.2 provides a documentation prompt that advises physicians of this requirement. All of these required conditions are listed in the middle section of the form, with check boxes to verify that they have been met so that the teaching physician can submit claims for these E/M services without personally evaluating the patients. The last section of the form provides a graphic interface with check boxes for the physician to efficiently complete required documentation of the extent of his or her participation in the review and direction of services. The CMS criteria require that the attending physician review the care either during or immediately after the patient visit (therefore checking one of the first two boxes provided in this final section) and must confirm review of all of the listed E/M elements: medical history, physical examination, diagnoses, and tests and treatments ordered.

Figure 21.2

Sample Form for Teaching Physician to Document Under Approved Primary Care Exception This customized sample form is applicable only for the special exception for outpatient care in primary care settings.

Patient Name:	Record #_____ Date: ___/___/___

Teaching Physician in a Qualified Primary Care Center Setting: Complete ALL of the following elements of compliance

(ALL 9 of these elements must be verified as Yes to permit billing by MD without personally evaluating patients)

(Under these circumstances, claims may be submitted only for E/M care at levels 1, 2, or 3)

	Yes	No
1) Services performed in a qualified ambulatory center		
a) The patients must all consider the center their source for health care	☐	☐
b) Residents follow the same group of patients throughout their residency program	☐	☐
2) Resident has completed more than 6 months of an approved residency program	☐	☐
3) Teaching physician was supervising no more than 4 residents during time of care	☐	☐
4) Teaching physician was in close proximity to the residents	☐	☐
5) Teaching physician was immediately available	☐	☐
6) Teaching physician had no other responsibilities at the time of this service	☐	☐
7) Teaching physician assumes management responsibilities for the patients seen by the residents	☐	☐
8) Teaching physician ensures that the services furnished by the resident are appropriate	☐	☐

Resident Physician's Name_____ Resident physician's signature: _____

Physician must document extent of participation in review and direction of services furnished to patient:

As the attending physician for the indicated evaluation and management service, I attest that

☐ during the patient visit   ☐ immediately after the patient visit

I have specifically reviewed with the resident physician the following elements of medical care:

☐ medical history   ☐ physical examination

☐ diagnostic impressions   ☐ record of tests and therapies ordered

Attending Physician's Name_____ Attending physician's signature:

Billing for Physician Presence for Teaching Physicians Supervising Procedures

Although not included in the scope of this book, physicians should be aware that CMS also provides sets of specific rules for teaching physicians to report services when working with residents performing a wide range of procedures, including surgery, psychiatry, obstetrical care, pathology, radiology, and other services. The use of customized forms that incorporate the requirements for these services into documentation tools is extremely helpful in ensuring compliance for these services as well.

"INCIDENT TO" DOCUMENTATION FOR PHYSICIANS WORKING WITH NONPHYSICIAN PRACTITIONERS

The CMS *Medicare Carriers Manual* offers a separate set of regulations governing payment for services provided by clinicians who are commonly referred to as "nonphysician practitioners." This category includes NPs, PAs, clinical nurse specialists, and certified nurse midwives who are working together with physicians. This section examines how these rules affect documentation and payments for E/M services in the outpatient setting.

NPPs Documenting the NPP

It is coincidental that the common acronym applied to the term "nonphysician practitioner" is identical to the acronym used throughout the book for "nature of presenting problem." To avoid confusion, this chapter will use an italicized *NPP* as an abbreviation for nonphysician practitioner and continue to use the nonitalicized format to represent the nature of presenting problem.

Medicare payment for services provided by these *NPPs* "depends on whether the service is directly billed by the nonphysician practitioner under his or her own billing number or billed 'incident to' under the physician's billing number."[4(p 14)] The specific CMS billing criteria for payment indicate that when providing care that is not under direct physician supervision, licensed *NPPs* should submit claims using their own provider identification number. Under these conditions, they receive payment for services "to a uniform 85 percent of the physician fee schedule."[4(p 14)] However, "services provided by NPs, CNSs (clinical nurse specialists), PAs, and CNMs (certified nurse midwives) are paid at 100 percent of the physician fee schedule if they are billed by the physician as incident to services in a physician's office or clinic." Therefore, even though the nonphysician clinicians provide the medical care, when "incident to" criteria are met these services may be submitted to Medicare under the supervising physician's provider identification number, and the payments will be made at the same level as if the physician had provided the care directly.

The specific CMS criteria that must be met and documented in order to bill services "incident to" physician supervision for care provided to Medicare patients include all of the following:

1.   The *NPP* who is providing the medical services must be employed by the physician.
2.   While the E/M services are being performed, "the physician must be in the office suite. . .and be immediately available to provide assistance and direction if needed."[4(p 15)] The physician who is present at the time of the visit is not required to be the same physician who initially evaluated the patient and initiated treatment.[5]
3.   A physician must have provided direct personal care to the patient at some time prior to the "incident to" service, initiating the course of treatment that is being monitored and reassessed by the NP or PA.
4.   The physician must personally furnish additional subsequent services with sufficient frequency to indicate ongoing active management of the course of treatment.

Local Carrier Medicare Policies Regarding "Incident to" Services

These criteria listed by CMS do not include a requirement restricting the levels of care permissible to bill for "incident to" services. However, some Medicare carriers may have established an additional criterion that "incident to" care is restricted to codes 99211–99213. This type of policy might be based on an invalid assumption that level 4 and level 5 care provided to an established patient would only occur for a new medical problem, which would not be eligible for "incident to" services on the basis of CMS's third requirement. Practices should determine whether their local carrier has this type of restriction, or whether it permits "incident to" billing regardless of the level of care.

For physicians working collaboratively with *NPPs*, these criteria call for each medical practice to establish policies regarding the circumstances under which patients should be seen by a physician, by an *NPP* with the practice submitting claims under the *NPP's* own billing number, and by an *NPP* providing care "incident to" a physician service with the practice submitting claims under the billing number of a physician present in the office during the patient's visit. Evaluating these possibilities and establishing the documentation requirements for them benefits from analyzing three sets of circumstances for outpatient services that might involve an *NPP*:

1. A new patient visit (CPT 99201–99205) or consultation visit (99241–99245)
2. An established patient with an established medical problem
3. An established patient with a new medical problem

Compliant Billing and Documentation for New Patient or Consultation Visits

For new patient or consultation visits, Medicare requires the physician to be directly involved in the patient's care to submit a claim using the physician's billing number. If such patients are evaluated solely by an *NPP*, the claim must be submitted with the *NPP's* billing number because the CMS requirements preclude "incident to" billing of a service for a patient's initial visit or consultation. If an *NPP* contributes to the care provided by a physician, for example, by reviewing and documenting details of the past, family, and social history and review of systems, the *NPP* should sign this section of the record to confirm the care performed. However, under this circumstance, the *Documentation Guidelines* require that the physician also provide "a notation supplementing or confirming the information recorded by others."[6] This confirmation is provided by the physician's signature at the bottom of each page reviewed plus any supplemental documentation. If the physician then completes the remainder of the care, the service is billed under the physician's billing number.

Design for Compliance and Efficiency
Physicians and *NPPs* both benefit equally from the use of the same IMR forms for initial patient visits, such as those illustrated in Appendix D and in the CD-ROM accompanying this edition.

Compliant Billing and Documentation for an Established Patient With an Established Problem

When a patient with an established problem returns for a follow-up visit under the care of an *NPP*, it is appropriate for the *NPP* to use an established patient form (eg, the IMR established outpatient visit form shown in Appendix D). If no physician is present and immediately available in the office suite, the claim should be submitted using the *NPP's* own billing number, which CMS will pay at the level of 85% of their normal physician fee schedule. However, when all the criteria for "incident to" services have been met, the claim may be submitted using the billing number of a physician who is present and available in the office at the time of the visit, even if that physician has not previously provided care for this particular patient. Claims submitted in this fashion result in payment at 100% of the CMS physician fee schedule.

Design for Compliance and Efficiency
Adding a small "incident to" section to the established patient IMR form will assist *NPPs* in accurately documenting that their care has met all of CMS's criteria for

"incident to" billing. A graphic interface with check boxes permits rapid documentation. This template also reminds the *NPP* of the need to schedule follow-up appointments with the patient's physician at appropriate times to ensure "ongoing active management of the course of treatment." Figure 21.3 illustrates a sample template that can be added to the established patient visit forms used by *NPPs* to meet this documentation requirement.

F i g u r e 21.3

Sample Template for NP or PA Documentation of "Incident to" Services. This check-box template may be added near the end of an established patient visit IMR form, before the location of the *NPP's* signature. On an IMR form, for example, it can be inserted between the section for documenting the NPP and the section for documenting care when counseling and coordination of care dominate the time of a visit. Although this template does not document that the *NPP* is employed by the physician, it does document that all the other CMS criteria for "incident to" billing have been met.

Physician present in office during E/M visit (and immediately available):

☐ Dr. A   ☐ Dr. B   ☐ Dr. C

☐ Patient evaluated and treated for an established medical problem

☐ A physician provided direct care to initiate the current management or course of treatment of this problem

☐ A physician last provided care to this patient for this problem on ____/____/____

Compliant Billing and Documentation for Established Patient With a New Problem

During a patient's scheduled appointment with an *NPP* for care of an existing problem, the clinician might encounter a new medical problem when taking the history or performing the examination. Each practice should have a policy to address these circumstances, since, in addition to addressing the patient's established problem, it will most often be in the patient's best interest to also initiate evaluation and/or treatment for the new medical concern rather than scheduling a separate appointment for the patient to see a physician. Under this circumstance, the *NPP* has two options that will be compatible with CMS guidelines: (1) initiate the care for the new problem and submit a claim for the visit under his or her own billing number, or (2) ask the available physician to participate in the evaluation of the patient's new medical problem, then submit the claim for the visit under the physician's billing number.

As already noted, the CMS criteria preclude submission of claims as "incident to" when an *NPP* provides care for a new problem during an established patient visit. However, when the NPP identifies a new problem, it is permissible to ask the physician who is present in the office to personally evaluate the new problem and document the related medical history, examination, and/or medical decision making (only two out of the three key components must be performed and documented during an established patient visit). The physician should also document the severity of the NPP and sign the medical record. Because a physician is personally involved in the care of the patient, regardless of the fact that the *NPP* initiated care during the visit, the practice may legitimately submit a claim under the physician's identification number and receive payment for the appropriate level of care at the full CMS physician rate.

"Incident to" and Private Insurers

Private insurers do not necessarily adhere to CMS policies regarding coding and billing practices for practices that employ *NPPs*. It would be advisable for these practices to obtain written explanation of their policies in this regard from the major insurers with whom they participate.

SUMMARY

The CMS has established stringent guidelines for physicians billing for care that has been coordinated with other clinicians. Section 15016 of Part 3 of the *Medicare Carriers Manual* describes the documentation and coding criteria for teaching physicians who are providing care in coordination with resident physicians. Section 2051 includes the requirements for physicians submitting claims for care provided by *NPPs* who are providing care "incident to" a physician's care plan and presence and availability and the time of the visit.

Structured medical record forms can assist physicians and their clinician colleagues to be aware of these requirements and to document their care in a manner that ensures compliance with CMS regulations.

References

1. Johnston D. University agrees to pay in settlement on Medicare. *New York Times.* December 13, 1995:A18.

2. Health Care Financing Administration. HCFA Carrier Manual Instructions Medicare Final Rule for Teaching Physicians, June 28, 1996. Section 15016. Supervising Physicians in Teaching Settings. http://www.vcu.edu/amsweb/HS%20Comp/Regulations/teachphysicguide.pdf. Accessed April 24, 2008.

3. Centers for Medicare and Medicaid Services. *Medicare Carriers Manual*, Part 3—Claims Process, Transmittal 1780, Change Request 2290, November 22, 2002. http://www.asahq.org/Washington/Sec.15016%20Nov02Rev.pdf. Accessed April 24, 2008.

4. Medicare Payment Advisory Commission. Report to the Congress: Medicare Payment to Advanced Practice Nurses and Physician Assistants. June 2002. http://www.medpac.gov/publications/congressional_reports/jun02_NonPhysPay.pdf. Page 14. Accessed April 25, 2008.

5. Centers for Medicare and Medicaid Services. *Medicare Carriers Manual*, Part 3—Claims Process, Transmittal 1764, Change Request 2222, August 28, 2002. Page 5. http://www.cms.hhs.gov/Transmittals/Downloads/r1764b3.pdf. Accessed April 25, 2008

6. Health Care Financing Administration. *Documentation Guidelines for Evaluation and Management Services.* Chicago, IL: American Medical Association; 1997:6.

PART 5

Quality in the Evolving Health Care System

To assist with reading about Intelligent Audit forms for E/M audits in Chapter 25, readers are advised to print copies (preferably using a color printer) of these forms from part 4 of the accompanying CD-ROM.

Selected reading for an abridged overview of Practical E/M and the effective use of IMR:

Intelligent Medical Record Format Option 1: Written (Paper) and Transcription

The "format" of the medical record is the medium used to record, store, and retrieve the medical information collected during the course of a visit. The three formats in current use are written records on paper, dictated records transcribed onto paper, and electronic health records. The characteristics of each format affect how data is entered, as well as how it is stored and utilized. When implementing Practical Evaluation and Management (E/M) methodology in different medical record formats, our paramount requirement is to retain all of the compliance, efficiency, usability, and quality care benefits that this approach brings to clinicians. Attaining these goals requires us to analyze the strengths and weakness of each format, and then determine how to effectively adapt them to achieve the functionality of an intelligent medical record (IMR). This chapter analyzes the optimal means of integrating the IMR into formats that store data on paper, both written and transcribed. The next chapter addresses this issue in the format of the evolving electronic health records environment.

SEPARATING DATA ENTRY FROM DATA STORAGE AND RETRIEVAL

The features of different medical record formats can be separated into two categories: (1) data entry and (2) data storage and retrieval. *Data entry* describes how clinicians document their findings, impressions, and recommendations in the medical record. *Data storage and retrieval* describes how the record is stored and subsequently viewed. Examining the strengths and weaknesses of each of these components separately improves our ability to understand the impact that different formats exert on achieving our goals for effective medical records and quality patient care.

Until the introduction of electronic health records, physicians had only one alternative for storing and retrieving medical records. All of their documents, including the history and physical, laboratory reports, radiology reports, consultation letters, legal correspondence, and so on, resided in physical folders. Because paper was the only storage format, physicians had to accept its weaknesses as well as its strengths. They did, however, have two options for data entry: they could write their records directly onto the paper, or they could dictate them and have them transcribed onto paper for storage. Until recently very few physicians, if any, combined these two data entry options into a hybrid. Most either wrote 100% of the medical history and physical, or they dictated 100% of it.

After publication of the *Documentation Guidelines for Evaluation and Management Services* in 1995,[1] physicians began using a variety of templates, printed on paper and often completed by their patients, in an effort to fulfill the requirements for obtaining and documenting past medical history, family history, and social history (PFSH) and review of systems (ROS). Some physicians continued to dictate the remainder of their record, thereby creating a partial hybrid by adding the paper template to the transcribed dictations in their charts. In some instances, however, physicians simply dictated, "PFSH and ROS: see attached template," but they neglected to address the positive responses patients had documented on those paper forms. This created not only compliance issues, but also quality-of-care issues.

What Distinguishes the IMR Medical History Template for an Initial Visit?

While many physicians and now electronic health record designers have created a variety of templates to help physicians efficiently document selected portions of the medical history, many of these efforts have failed to ensure documentation of a *complete* PFSH and ROS and/or to achieve optimal efficiency for performing this documentation. In contrast, IMR templates are distinguished by design that ensures full compliance and maximizes physicians' efficiency for obtaining and documenting the chief complaint, PFSH, and ROS.

Efficiency is maximized by designs that permit and encourage patients to successfully complete the check-box graphic interface questionnaire quickly and accurately. Physicians can visually scan the completed forms in seconds to identify any positive responses, which they can then investigate further and record patient responses using the format (writing or dictation) that is most convenient for each of them.

The forms also meet all of the compliance requirements specified by the Current Procedural Terminology (CPT®) coding system and the *Documentation Guidelines*. The design and content intrinsically elicit sufficient information from patients to record a complete PFSH and ROS in all cases. This ensures compliant documentation of these elements for any level of E/M care, and it also provides a thorough medical background to help clinicians have a complete picture of their patients' health. The IMR forms also follow the *Documentation Guidelines* rules for distinguishing between past medical history and ROS components, which are frequently confused in self-designed templates. The IMR employs the check box interface, which ensures compliant documentation by requiring that the patient provide a "yes" or "no" answer for every inquiry, avoiding the "selection list" interface, which fails to permit patients to adequately *document* their negative responses. Finally, the narrative sections of the IMR permit physicians to describe details of patients' positive responses, and the signature lines permit physicians to confirm that they have reviewed all this data. Any medical history template that meets all of these criteria, as described in detail in Chapter 10, should certainly be considered "intelligent."

DATA STORAGE AND RETRIEVAL

The traditional data storage system utilizes a paper medical record, which is stored in folders and filed in chart racks in the medical office. The folders contain each patient's collected medical history and physical (H&P) forms, regardless of whether the data entry mode is writing or dictation, as well as all their other medical documents.

Because the written (paper) record world may be considered "low tech," it has always been credited with the theoretical advantages of being low in cost and easy to use. In today's medical environment, we have come to appreciate that these presumed advantages no longer hold true. One concern that draws the attention of most physicians is lack of accessibility to the chart, which is an inherent property of this format. Paper storage creates a significant hassle factor because physicians do not have immediate access to their records at all times.

In modern medical practice, offices are faced with the challenge of providing the physical chart to multiple locations, such as in-office laboratory, in-office testing facilities (eg, cardiac testing), in-office treatment centers (eg, physical therapy), nursing stations, and physicians' work areas. This problem is magnified when physicians have multiple offices, requiring transport or transmission of significant amounts of data between separate facilities. The physician's office staff spends significant time "pulling" charts, filing charts, and searching for charts when they are not where they belong; ie, they can be misfiled or in a location other than the file room. The charts are also not accessible to the physician after hours, unless he or she carries them from the office. Of course, when physicians take charts home, there is also the risk of loss or damage, as well as inconvenience when someone else is unable to access the record. In addition to the hassle factor for everyone in the office, the lack of timely access to patient records when they are needed has a dramatic negative impact on patient care.

The costs involved in maintaining a filing system for paper records are also significantly greater than most physicians appreciate. These include the relatively small expense of paper folders and labels and the rental cost (including taxes) for the space to store the files. There are additional costs for storing older records and for shredding outdated files. The most significant cost, however, accrues from the manpower cost of staff time performing "chart pulls and returns." The processes of retrieving and refiling records are not confined to patient visits with the physician. They also occur for ancillary testing in the office, treatment services in the office, transport to satellite offices, filing reports and correspondence, sending information to other physicians, and answering telephone inquiries from patients, physicians, and outside facilities.

To assess the cost-effectiveness of each record storage and retrieval option, it is very important for physicians to be aware of the costs they incur by using the paper storage/retrieval format. Figures 22.1 and 22.2 provide a diagnostic tool for calculating a reasonable estimate of the cost of maintaining paper records, per physician per month. Figure 22.1 is a weekly log for each member of the administrative staff to monitor the time he or she spends filing and retrieving medical records. Monitoring this effort closely for one or more weeks provides the critical data required to complete the calculations in Figure 22.2. This second chart is a shorthand calculation that can be completed by the physician, office manager, or accountant. It also includes consideration of transcription costs, which can contribute to the overall expense of the paper storage format. The final step on this worksheet provides the cost per physician per month for maintaining paper medical records.

This cost figure provides valuable insight when comparing the cost of an electronic health record to that of a physician's current chart storage system. In multiphysician practices, converting from paper storage to an electronic record system should result in less staff time attending to charts, and this may translate into lower overall staff costs in a large practice. In a small group setting (one to three physicians), on the other hand, it will generally not be possible to reduce the size of the staff because of the other services they provide. However, although actual staff costs may not be reduced, their time should be redirected to more productive tasks when the office converts to an electronic health record.

Paper Is Costly

By applying an analysis using the tools shown in Figures 22.1 and 22.2 in typical practice settings, it appears that the pure cost of maintaining paper files, without adding transcription costs, ranges (at a minimum) between $1,500 and $2,500 per month per physician (although I have heard estimates as high as $3,500 per month per physician). Transcription costs can drive these figures several times higher.

When I presented this information to a group of approximately 150 practice administrators, to be conservative, I quoted a minimum figure of $1,000 per physician per month (without transcription) to maintain (store and retrieve) medical records in the paper format. The administrators unanimously advised that this figure was far too low.

Figure 22.1

Chart Pull Data Log. Example of a data log sheet to track staff time required for "chart pulls and returns." The log must include all staff interactions with the medical record, including patient visits, phone calls, adding reports and other papers, and any other reason for chart access. This provides the time factor for the cost calculations in Figure 22.2.

CHART PULL TIME SHEET Name:_____

Date	# Clinicians Present	Time Spent	Task

TOTAL TIME SPENT: _____ hours

Estimating the Cost of Maintaining Paper-Format Medical Records

---

Step 1: Cost of chart pulls per month
  a) Time per week for all staff and all chart pulls (total from chart pull time sheets for entire staff)
            ___hrs.
  b) Multiply by 4 (to extrapolate to hrs/month)   ___hrs.
  c) Multiply by average clerical staff salary ($____ per hour) = $____
  d) Multiply by 1.25 (to account for benefits) = $____
     (may use an actual multiplier, if available)
  e) Divide by number of clinicians   (# = ___)
COST OF CHART PULLS/PHYSICIAN/MONTH: $____

Step 2: Cost of materials for new charts per month
  a) Cost of each folder $____
  b) Cost of blank labels per folder $____
  c) Cost of date and letter labels per folder $____
  d) Add a + b + c for total cost per folder $____ *(commonly $2.00 – $2.50 per chart)*
  e) Multiply "d" by number of new patients + consultations per month (# = ___) for cost/mo.
     $____
  f) Divide by number of clinicians (# = ___)
COST OF CHART MATERIALS/PHYSICIAN/MONTH: $____

Step 3: Cost of space for active and stored charts
  a) Monthly rental for file space $____
  b) Monthly cost of real estate taxes for files $____
  c) Add a + b real estate monthly cost $____
  d) Divide by number of clinicians (# = ___)
COST OF CHART SPACE/PHYSICIAN/MONTH: $____

Step 4: Cost of transcription (optional)
  a) Monthly transcription expenses (total) $____ *(or may do this for each MD)*
  b) Divide by number of clinicians (# = ___)
COST OF TRANSCRIPTION/PHYSICIAN/MONTH: $____

TOTAL COST/MD/MONTH (add totals from steps 1–4) $____

DATA ENTRY

A primary concern for physicians must be that their medical record system functions successfully at the point of care. This success is a direct consequence of the interface designs and data entry characteristics of the system used, and how well these meet the evaluation criteria of quality of care, usability, efficiency, cost-effectiveness, data integrity, and compliance.

Written (Paper) Format for Data Entry

Information entry by *writing* offers multiple advantages. It is a highly efficient format for entering information in the graphic interfaces of an IMR. The written (paper) format further enhances efficiency by allowing information gathering and medical record data entry to be performed by individuals other than the physician—specifically, the patient and other members of the medical staff. Writing also provides a concise approach to the narrative interface, which is used for documenting the history of present illness (HPI), details of positive responses to the ROS, and abnormal findings on the physical examination. Brief narrative descriptions also frequently provide supplemental information for positive responses in the PFSH and for precise descriptions of diagnoses and management options in the Medical Decision Making (MDM) section of the record. For most physicians, writing during the patient encounter does not interfere with the flow of the visit or disrupt the patient-physician relationship. Additionally, the written format is by far the most cost-effective means of entering data into the medical record.

The most obvious potential drawback to directly writing information in the medical record is legibility (or, rather, lack of legibility). As discussed in Chapter 5, the first general principle of medical record documentation presented in the *Documentation Guidelines* states, "the medical record should be complete and legible."[1] That is, if the record is not legible, it fails the standard of compliance, and it also creates challenges in providing quality patient care. It will also fail an audit based on the basic principle that "if it wasn't documented, it wasn't done," because when auditors cannot read the physician's notes, they conclude that the information was not documented (and consequently not performed). Therefore, to meet compliance requirements, physicians whose handwriting is illegible must chose from among three possible solutions:

1. Employ dictation for the narrative and MDM portions of the record.
2. Perform data entry on a keyboard.
3. Practice and achieve legible handwriting.

Critique of Data Entry Options

From the data entry perspective, there are three drawbacks to using the written (paper) format for IMR: (1) illegibility, (2) illegibility, and (3) illegibility. It is somewhat surprising that a professional with the technical skills to thread a catheter into the pulmonary artery or to remove a gallbladder through an endoscope would be unable to write legibly.

The transcription alternative is often quite costly: $2,500 per month for 30 years of practice will cost as much money as sending your 2.4 children to college and medical school, even if you consider the rising cost due to inflation.

The third option, data entry on a keyboard while seeing patients, presents numerous drawbacks. Not all physicians are proficient typists, and of those who are, very few can (or would choose to) process medical information, type 60 words per minute, and maintain eye contact with patients all at the same time.

However, bookstores have many guidebooks to help people rapidly improve their penmanship. They are inexpensive and require only a small investment of time in the evening for a week or two. It is an interesting option!

Transcription Format for Data Entry

Data entry using the transcription format has one indisputable benefit—it is always legible. As noted in the discussion of the written format, legibility is a required standard for E/M compliance. The *dictation format* is also generally physician-friendly, and it works extremely well for reporting narrative components of the medical record: the HPI, details of positive ROS responses, abnormal examination findings, and the short-response portions of the MDM.

There are, however, also significant drawbacks to implementing the transcription format for data entry, particularly when it is used conventionally to dictate 100% of the details of an encounter. The potential problems include increased cost (when compared with writing), transcription errors, and possible delay in receipt of the transcription. Transcription costs can be eliminated by switching to the use of voice recognition software; however, physicians using this technology must dictate at a conversational rate rather than the rapid-fire speech pattern they are accustomed to using with a transcriptionist, thereby decreasing documentation efficiency. Some physicians who dictate prefer to do so during the patient visit, but this may interrupt the optimal flow of care and could be distracting to the patient. Physicians who dictate between visits face a potential loss of time and the possibility of leaving out some of the information discovered during the visit.

In addition, dictation can have a negative impact on physician efficiency. First, by dictating the entire medical record, a physician loses the significant time-saving potential of having patients and staff document portions of the medical history. Further, stopping to dictate between patient visits results in some loss of time and efficiency and the possibility of leaving out some of the clinical information and/or findings discovered during the visit. This latter problem may be increased exponentially for those who dictate at the end of the day or even days later, introducing quality concerns and even potential liability issues in the event of litigation. This alternative also interferes with a physician's time at home with family.

How 30 Words per Minute Can Be Faster Than 75 Words per Minute

Besides the legibility issue, most physicians who favor dictation over writing are also convinced that it is faster than writing, pointing out that they can write only 25 to 30 words per minute, while they can intelligibly dictate 70 to 80 words per minute (reduced, as noted above, when using voice recognition software rather than a transcriptionist). While at first reading this seems to point to dictation being faster than writing, careful analysis reveals that this may not be the case. When a physician who dictates spends 3 minutes obtaining an HPI from the patient, dictating this information may require an extra 30 seconds. However, the physician who records the history by writing will usually do so synchronously with obtaining the history; it therefore requires a total of only 3 minutes to both obtain and record the HPI. It is not possible to be faster than zero additional seconds for recording a patient's medical history.

HYBRID 1: WRITING (PAPER) PLUS TRANSCRIPTION

For physicians who prefer dictation, Practical E/M recommends a hybrid approach, which integrates concise transcription for narrative sections of the medical record with writing used in the graphic sections of IMR forms. This approach maximizes efficiency, while minimizing added costs.

The hybrid requires significantly less dictation than the traditional, all-inclusive dictation. In this format, the usual paper IMR form serves as the "master" information template, and the transcription is linked directly to it. The paper form contains all of the documented graphic interface materials, and advises anyone reading the chart to refer to the transcription when the physician has dictated narrative information.

This option allows physicians to dictate all, or just part, of one or more of the narrative portions of the medical record. Since the written and dictated materials are stored together, they are linked into a single medical record document. An example of the completed physical examination template of a hybrid IMR is shown in Figure 22.3. The associated dictation for the narrative of abnormal findings is shown in Figure 22.4.

F I G U R E 22.3

Example of Physical Examination IMR Template Indicating Associated Transcription The box indicating dictation is located below the shaded examination check boxes on the right.

PHYSICAL EXAMINATION:		Ear, Nose, and Throat								
GENERAL (at least 3 measurements of vital signs) BP sitting-standing 120/80 mm Hg PULSE 72/min					HT 5 ft 10 in BP supine _/_ mm Hg RESP _/min		WT 155 lbs TEMP__ (F-C)			
				Normal/AB					Normal/AB	
	GENERAL APPEARANCE	Stature, nutrition	☒	☐	NECK	MASSES AND TRACHEA	Symmetry, color	☒	☐
COMMUNIC. & VOICE		Pitch, clarity	☒	☐		THYROID	Size, nodules	☒	☐
HEAD/	INSPECTION	Lesions, masses	☒	☐	EYES	MOTILITY AND GAZE	EOMs, nystagmus	☒	☐
FACE	PALPAT./PERCUSSION	Skeleton, sinuses	☒	☐	RESP.	RESPIRATORY EFFORT	Inspiratory-expiratory	☒	☐
	SALIVARY GLANDS	Masses, tenderness	☒	☐		AUSCULTATION	Clear	☐	☐
	FACIAL STRENGTH	Symmetry	☒	☐	CVS	HEART AUSCULTATION	RRR no GRM	☐	☐
ENT	PNEUMO-OTOSCOPY	EACs; TMs mobile	☐	☒		PERIPH VASC SYSTEM	Edema, color	☒	☐
	HEARING ASSESSMENT	Gross/weber/rinne	☒	☐	LYMPH	NECK/AXILLAE/GROIN/ETC	Adenopathy absence	☒	☐
	EXT., EAR, & NOSE	Appearance	☒	☐	NEURO/	CRANIAL NERVES	II-XII	☒	☐
	INTERNAL NOSE	Mucosa, turbs.	☐	☒	PSYCH.	ORIENTATION	Person, place, time	☐	☐
	*AFTER DECONGES.	Septum, OMCs	☐	☒		MOOD AND AFFECT	Comments	☒	☐
	LIPS, TEETH, AND GUMS	Mucosa, dentition	☒	☐		*ROMBERG		☐	☐
	ORAL CAVITY, OROPHR.	Tonsils, palate	☐	☒		*TANDEM ROMBERG		☐	☐
	HYPOPHARYNX	Pyriform sinuses	☐ NV ☐			*PAST POINTING		☐	☐
	LARYNX (MIRROR)	Structure, mobility	☐ NV ☐				☒ See attached dictation		
	NASOPHAR. (MIRROR)	Choanae	☐ NV ☐						

1. problem focused = 1-5 elements [level 1]　　2. expanded = 6-11 elements [level 2]　　3. detailed = 12 or more elements [level 3]
4. comprehensive = document every element in basic areas *and* at least 1 element in each optional area (level 4 or 5)　　*optional

NV indicates "not visable"

F I G U R E 22.4

Example of Physical Examination Transcription Associated With Template in Figure 22.3

Physical Examination (Significant Findings)

EARS: Impacted cerumen was cleaned from the left external auditory canal, revealing mild thickening of the posterior portion of the TM and mild positive pressure on pneumo-otoscopy (note: the patient was performing Valsalva maneuvers prior to the examination). The right tympanic membrane has normal appearance and mobility. Weber is midline; air conduction is greater than bone conduction bilaterally.

NOSE: Mild inferior turbinate congestion bilaterally. Following spray, there is a mild septal deviation high to the right, and there is a large middle meatal polyp visible on the left.

MOUTH: Enlarged soft palate and uvula.

LARYNX AND NASOPHARYNX: Not visible secondary to 4+ hyperactive gag reflex.

In summary, for those physicians who prefer to dictate, this hybrid maintains the IMR's advantages of (1) patients and staff entering written medical history data directly into the chart, (2) physicians rapidly documenting the normal/abnormal physical examination findings into the check-box section of their form, and (3) physicians completing check-box and selection list portions of the medical decision-making component. The physician dictates only (some or all of) the amount of information required for the narrative sections, resulting in significantly reduced dictation time and lowered transcription costs.

An additional benefit of employing a hybrid model H&P over a pure dictated H&P is that the final appearance of the completed record of a visit is a superior reference model for both physicians themselves and other reviewers, including other physicians, insurers, and/or attorneys. The different components of the H&P are more clearly identified, and it is far easier and faster for someone examining the record to identify the normal and abnormal history responses and examination findings. The advantages are particularly noteworthy in the event of an E/M compliance review, where the hybrid H&P provides the audit protection of an IMR form, including documentation of levels of risk, complexity of data, and nature of the presenting problem to report medical necessity. Appendix F presents a side-by-side comparison of the appearance of the hybrid IMR record and a conventional dictated H&P, illustrating the advantages to a viewer in understanding the content of the record and also the logic underlying the physician's diagnostic process. Although the example in this appendix is designed for electronic health record screens, the appearance is equally adaptable to hybrid paper records, as illustrated in Figures 22.3 and 22.4.

SUMMARY

This chapter provides details on using an IMR in two of the three medical record formats, writing and transcription. It also introduces two creative concepts in assessing medical record formats. First, it considers the features of data input separately from the goals for data storage and retrieval. Second, it formalizes the analysis of "hybrid" formats. Hybrid formats allow physicians to combine the best features of two or more of the three basic formats to achieve optimal compliance, efficiency, productivity (cost-effectiveness), quality of care, data integrity, and physician usability.

Reference

1.   Health Care Financing Administration. *Documentation Guidelines for Evaluation and Management Services.* Chicago, IL: American Medical Association; 1995.

Intelligent Medical Record Format Option 2: Electronic Health Records

Currently there is a powerful drive to move the future of medical records into the electronic environment. Political, economic, and quality improvement forces are all seeking the benefits that electronic health records (EHRs) promise in the areas of medical quality, patient safety, information sharing, cost-effectiveness, evidence-based medicine, and clinical decision support at the point of care.

Examining the use of the electronic format for medical records with the same criteria we applied to written and dictated medical record formats provides insight not only into the potential strengths and weaknesses of these systems, but also into the potential modifications that will allow them to incorporate the advantages of Practical Evaluation and Management (E/M) functionality and intelligent medical record (IMR) tools.

PUBLIC AND PRIVATE SECTOR DEVELOPMENTS IN ELECTRONIC HEALTH RECORDS

On April 27, 2004, President George W. Bush issued an executive order calling for widespread adoption of health information technology (HIT) over the succeeding 10 years, stressing the improvements in safety and efficiency this initiative can bring. This order also established the Office of the National Coordinator for Health Information Technology; Dr. David Brailer was appointed to that post in May 2004.

National Policy Statement on Health Information Technology

The stated goal of the President's executive order is "to provide leadership for the development and nationwide implementation of an interoperable health information technology infrastructure to improve the quality and efficiency of health care."[1]

The executive order continues with details of the responsibility of the National Coordinator for HIT, which "shall be consistent with a vision of developing a nationwide interoperable health information technology infrastructure that:

(a) Ensures that appropriate information to guide medical decisions is available at the time and place of care;

(b) Improves health care quality, reduces medical errors, and advances the delivery of appropriate, evidence-based medical care;

(c) Reduces health care costs resulting from inefficiency, medical errors, inappropriate care, and incomplete information;

(d) Promotes a more effective marketplace, greater competition, and increased choice through the wider availability of accurate information on health care costs, quality, and outcomes;

continued

(e) Improves the coordination of care and information among hospitals, laboratories, physician offices, and other ambulatory care providers through an effective infrastructure for the secure and authorized exchange of health care information; and

(f) Ensures that patients' individually identifiable health information is secure and protected."[1]

At the time the first edition of this book was written, there was a bipartisan bill pending in Congress that was aimed at providing incentives for physicians and hospitals to adopt EHRs and health information exchange. On May 12, 2005, the *New York Times* reported joint support for this proposal by Newt Gingrich and Hillary Rodham Clinton.[2] The Centers for Medicare and Medicaid Services (CMS) initiated such programs on a trial basis in 2008. There are also ongoing initiatives to establish uniform standards to promote electronic interconnectivity and interoperability, and the sharing of health information among physicians, hospitals, laboratories, pharmacies, and quality improvement organizations. These goals were the focal point of the second Executive Order on Health Information Technology, issued by President Bush on August 22, 2006.[3]

EHRs and E/M Compliance

To date, despite the fact that CMS is separately urging physicians to achieve E/M compliance and to actively pursue the implementation of EHRs, I am not aware of any organized initiative to require that EHR designs meet standards of the Current Procedural Terminology (CPT®) coding system for promoting E/M compliance.

SEPARATING DATA ENTRY FROM DATA STORAGE AND UTILIZATION

Both of the traditional medical record formats—writing and transcription—use the same data storage and utilization technology: physical charts containing information stored on paper documents. Therefore, any comparison of these two formats results in consideration of the relative advantages and disadvantages of only their data entry component. This discussion has primarily centered on the legibility benefits of transcription versus the lower costs of written records.

The introduction of the electronic record format has brought with it an absolute reversal of this focus on data entry. Regardless of whether an assessment of EHRs involves physicians, administrators, economists, politicians, or HIT specialists, the evaluations have concentrated almost exclusively on the potential advantages of *electronic data storage and utilization* when compared with paper storage. The reviews emphasize the ability of EHRs to enhance physicians' access to information and thereby increase quality of care and promote patient safety.

Curiously, these discussions have by and large excluded any assessment of the data entry characteristics intrinsic to the design of the electronic history and physical (H&P) component of EHRs, particularly from the perspective of physician usability. In reality, structuring the data entry process of EHRs seems to have been left to individual software companies and their various consultants. There has been no organized effort to scrutinize the resulting EHR designs in terms of their ability to satisfy the criteria for a functional medical record: quality of care, efficiency, compliance with E/M coding and documentation principles, data integrity, productivity, and physician usability.

Anecdotal reports and surveys indicate that as many as 50% of physicians' efforts to adopt EHRs have resulted in failure. These reports indicate that difficulties with the data entry features of EHRs are a common cause of these problems. This concern was underscored at the Second Health Information Technology Summit in 2005, when Dr. Mark McClellan, who was then the medical director of CMS, reported "Forty percent of all electronic record implementations fail."[4]

This chapter's evaluation of the EHR format looks first at the benefits electronic records provide through their data storage and utilization component. It then considers some of the difficulties encountered in the rarely evaluated data entry component. Finally, it evaluates the underlying reasons for data entry problems in existing software designs and discusses options for successfully addressing them.

EHR DATA STORAGE AND UTILIZATION

Advantages of EHR Storage and Utilization

Data utilization efficiency, in the form of accessibility to medical records at all times, is an unquestionably strong suit of the EHR. Physicians can access an individual patient record any time and from any location, as long as they have Internet access to the computer housing their EHR software. An additional benefit of electronic data storage is the ability of multiple authorized users to access the same medical record at the same time. This feature has developed growing importance as the increasing technical complexity of medical care requires multiple personnel within a medical practice to have simultaneous access to the same medical record. For example, a cardiologist can be reviewing a patient's record at the same time his or her technician is entering the results of a stress test into the same record.

Once data has been stored in an EHR, there are several projected dividends for physicians using this format. The system should allow interconnectivity and interoperability, providing for the direct upload of hospital information, laboratory reports, radiographic reports and images, and clinical decision support (information about specific diseases and treatments) into the appropriate patient record in the EHR. It should also provide clinicians with the ability to employ computerized physician order entry (CPOE), which allows prescriptions, laboratory studies, and radiology studies to be ordered electronically. Digitization of clinical data in EHRs offers the potential for a variety of data utilization benefits, including:

- Access to specific patient records on the basis of clinical criteria (eg, to identify all patients taking a specific medication).

- Rapid data collection to evaluate clinical criteria such as treatment outcomes and side effects.

- Providing deidentified data to centralized organizations that use the information for evidence-based medicine studies.

- Future potential for increased reimbursement. Currently, Medicare and private insurers are initiating "pay for performance" (labeled PQRI, the Physician Quality Reporting Initiative, by CMS) protocols theoretically intended to promote "quality care" through payment incentives based on physicians' meeting specified performance measures. These programs require patient care information from physicians to gauge their care against established guidelines; this clinical information is most easily compiled from the stored data in EHRs.

What "Performance" Is Going to Be Paid?

Current pay for performance pilot studies of quality care include (1) evaluating implementation of *preventive care measures* (eg, screening mammography, stool tests for occult blood, and colonoscopy) and (2) evaluating the use of management protocols for specific chronic illnesses that physicians have already diagnosed (eg, diabetes,

---

continued

hypertension, and congestive heart failure). The *CPT* codebook for 2008 includes approximately 190 Category II codes, described as "supplemental tracking codes that can be used for 'performance measurement.'[5 (p 439)] These codes are specifically for reporting to CMS under its PQRI program. Additional protocols, such as acute care and surgical criteria, are under active consideration by specialty societies. At this time, valid measures of physicians' medical skills and insight, such as effectiveness in making correct and timely diagnoses, do not appear to be under consideration.

Disadvantages of EHR Storage and Utilization

Cost can be a significant obstacle physicians must address when weighing possible adoption of an EHR. In our current economically constricted medical environment, it is challenging for physicians to consider any purchase that involves significant cost but generates little or no direct income benefit (although the financial incentives from "pay for performance" offer the possibility of slight future economic benefits, it currently appears that these will be more than offset by corresponding decreases in the underlying payment rates and increases in practice expense costs). There can be significant up-front and ongoing costs for these systems, which usually include hardware, software, technical support, and/or equipment insurance. For larger medical groups, as discussed in Chapter 22, a portion of this added cost might be recaptured by elimination of the expense of maintaining paper charts, and manifest as a reduced number of clerical personnel. Ultimately, the initial cost of EHR systems may be lowered by the use of Internet-based application service providers (ASPs), which provide centralized servers for the electronic record and therefore significantly reduce hardware and technical support costs for the medical practice.

Another priority concern about the data storage component of EHRs relates to maintaining the privacy of patient information. Physicians must ensure that any electronic records system meets requirements of the Health Insurance Portability and Accountability Act of 1996 (HIPAA) with respect to both data storage and transmission. Finally, there is the important consideration of what happens to the medical data entered into the system if the physician ultimately finds the system unacceptable. Physicians require a guarantee, in the event of a failed conversion to an EHR, that all entered data can be recovered in a form adaptable to their future medical record system requirements.

EHR DATA ENTRY

Standards for Data Quality

Electronic health records offer significant promise for improving the quality of health care through the potential benefits of their data storage and retrieval features. Fulfillment of this promise, however, requires quality data input to achieve these desired benefits. This necessitates that the data input design of EHRs have the capability to meet physicians' quality of care standards, as well as the ability to fulfill physicians' usability standards for *data entry* at the point of care.

As noted earlier, there has been a surprising lack of discussion and analysis of the options currently available for data entry into the H&P component of EHRs. There has also been an absence of standardization for the data elements that ought to be entered into the electronic H&P, not only for the purposes of E/M compliance but also to ensure that the data entered can be applied in a meaningful fashion to outcomes studies and evidence-based medicine. Because uniform standards have not yet been established to define what data elements are required or how they should be entered, there is a significant possibility that EHRs (as currently designed) may be subject to the common enemy of software systems, "garbage in, garbage out." This lack of standards for patients' clinical information has the potential to impair or invalidate the potential benefits of these systems.

More About "Garbage In, Garbage Out"

The benefits envisioned for studies that promote evidence-based medicine will be limited by the quality of the information used to create that evidence. No matter how ideal the software system that processes the data may be, the quality of the results will only be as good as the quality of the data entered. If the data entered into EHRs is unreliable, nonspecific, or generic, the conclusions of the studies based on this data will be unreliable, and they could lead to incorrect recommendations that would have the potential to negatively impact quality of patient care.

The questions that need to be asked about the functionality of clinical data entry and the H&P component of existing EHR systems include:

- Do the interfaces for each section of the electronic H&P permit (and preferably facilitate) the entry of precise, individualized patient information (ie, quality data)?
- Are the H&P data entry interfaces optimally efficient? Do they allow comprehensive data to be entered easily during the process of patient care?
- Do the programs facilitate E/M compliance?
- Do the programs promote optimal patient care?

The answers to these questions about the quality of data entry should correlate well with the probability of long-term success of physician adoption of these systems, as well as with the degree to which implementation of EHRs is successful in positively transforming medical practices and enhancing patient care.

Advantages of EHR Data Entry

The major benefit of the electronic H&P data entry screens of most of the currently available EHRs has been the provision of compliant graphic interfaces for the past, family, and social history (PFSH), review of systems (ROS), and physical examination sections of the medical record. These have guided physicians toward more complete medical histories and more thorough physical examinations. Additionally, in the medical decision making (MDM) section of the record, the selection lists for medications, X-rays, and laboratory tests allow integration of the medical record with computerized physician order entry software programs.

Disadvantages of EHR Data Entry

Most of the challenges associated with the electronic format relate to the data entry component of current systems. There appear to be two underlying causes for these problems: (1) requiring physicians to personally enter all clinical information into the electronic H&P (often by keyboard and mouse clicks), and (2) suboptimal design and functionality features of the electronic H&P. These issues warrant a systematic review of the H&P design and data entry characteristics of EHRs and their potential adverse effects.

Some of the obstacles, challenges, and problems related to data entry arise from EHR designs that require physicians to enter all clinical data directly into the computer. Being assigned to be the data entry specialist for electronic records creates several highly significant problems for physicians:

- Most physicians do not type well enough to enter substantial amounts of written information efficiently, as is required for quality care in the narrative sections of the medical record (describing abnormal findings in the ROS, recording a precise and descriptive history of present illness, and providing descriptive details of the abnormal findings in the physical examination).
- Most *physicians* prefer to maintain eye contact with their patients during the care process, rather than paying attention to the computer screen.
- Most *patients* prefer for their physicians to maintain eye contact with them during the care process.
- Entering *meaningful* narrative data into the computer while providing patient care is not a time-efficient or user-friendly process for most physicians.

Current EHR systems have attempted to address these issues by eliminating most or all of the keyboard entry for the physician. However, to accomplish this, many of these systems have eliminated the ability to enter free-text narrative descriptions into the record (as discussed later in this chapter). These two constraints (requiring the physician to perform the data entry and the elimination of the ability to enter free-text narrative descriptions) account for many of the adverse effects of employing the electronic format upon quality of care, efficiency, compliance, usability, and data integrity. Our goals are first to classify and explain these issues, and then to develop options that address them.

The Physician as Data Entry Operator

From their inception, the basic assumption governing data input for electronic records systems now on the market has been that the physician must be the data entry person. While this assignment may be in keeping with the tradition of physicians entering their own written data or dictating their own transcriptions, some significant and undesirable consequences have resulted from requiring physicians to use keyboard or point-and-click data entry techniques during the patient care process.

One of the most obvious consequences is a frequent "impersonalization" of the interaction with the patient at the point of care, which occurs as a result of placing a laptop computer in the space between the patient and the physician or when a physician is required to turn away from the patient to enter data by using a keyboard. The need to ensure correct markings in check boxes, correct choices from "pick lists," and/or accurate typing of free text requires significant, and sometimes nearly continuous, physician attention to the computer screen, resulting in loss of eye contact with the patient and depersonalization of the encounter. This can leave a patient with the impression that the computer screen has more of the physician's attention than the patient and his or her medical issues.

This burden on the physician to be responsible for the input of all the medical record data eliminates most of the efficiency gained in other IMR formats by using patients and staff as data entry personnel for a large part of the medical history. The five or more minutes of physician time saved per new patient visit when patients complete documentation of the PFSH and ROS on paper templates are lost because of the requirement that the physician has to ask all the questions and enter the patient's responses into the electronic screens. Although it is possible to design an electronic record that permits staff and patients to directly enter data into the software system, this option is rarely a feature of current systems. Further, implementation of this solution would necessitate adding more hardware (and cost) to the system. It would also potentially require greater patient education and assistance.

There are two possible mechanisms offered for physicians to enter medical information into most current EHR systems: (1) typing on the keyboard and (2) point-and-click entry using the mouse. Because it is not practical for most physicians to type a detailed narrative while actively taking care of patients, most EHRs substitute one of two variations of a *graphic* interface to compile those sections of the medical record deemed suitable for narrative description:

■ Point and click from "pick lists" of pre-entered words and phrases. Systems will apply this option to the HPI, abnormal PFSH and ROS responses, the physical examination, and clinical impressions and recommendations.

■ Recalling a preformed generic macro that has a general description related to the patient's chief complaint. The physician fills in a few variable sections of this macro through either pick lists or limited keyboard entry. This approach is most often applied to the HPI and/or the physical examination.

Defining a Distinction Between "Templates" and "Macros"

Electronic record vendors and physicians often use the terms *template* and *macro* interchangeably, regardless of the format of a physician's medical record. For clarity, Practical E/M and Practical EHR "reserve the term 'templates' for structured graphic interface designs"[6(p 212)] that have the distinguishing feature that they "contain structure but not substance."[6(p 193)] In other words, templates do not provide actual documentation until there is active entry of information, such as by checking a box or picking an element on a selection list. The IMR forms and screens are built on structured templates.

In contrast, the term *macro* is reserved for graphic or narrative interface designs that contain not only structure but also substance, in the form of preloaded clinical information. When entered into a patient's H&P, they provide automatic clinical information, which may appear in the form of prechecked boxes on a graphic form or a precreated narrative text containing nonspecific generic medical history or examination information. Macros are inherently noncompliant, because preloaded information substitutes automation for documentation. As summarized in *Practical EHR*,

Although this preloaded information may invite the physician to perform a small amount of modification, eg, typing a few additional words or filling in several blanks from a drop down "pick list," the software automatically pre-enters the majority of information. This functionality eliminates the requirement for physicians to obtain and/or document original information related to the present visit. It documents the software's ability to print the same information in case after case rather than documenting the patient's actual status at the time of the visit. All such preloaded information fails to meet compliance requirements for performing and documenting the patient's status on the date of the visit. It also permits and promotes "problem-focused" care, while using previously recorded information to justify submitting claims for "detailed" or "comprehensive" care, even when these higher levels of care may not have been performed and/or may not be medically necessary.[6(p 59)]

CONSEQUENCES OF LOSS OF NARRATIVE ENTRY OPTION: QUALITY OF CARE AND USABILITY

From the perspective of Practical E/M methodology, the most significant negative effect of the limitations on physician data entry options is the loss of the ability to enter original narrative or free-text entries into the medical record. As a result, physicians using EHR systems programmed with one of these two alternative options do not have the ability to efficiently or effectively enter the individualized, patient-specific history and examination details that are essential components of quality care. The EHRs that use one of these "limited-vocabulary" approaches record less accurate and less precise information than formats employing a narrative interface. In most cases, the process of trying to enter *meaningful* descriptive data by using these limited-vocabulary formats is also significantly slower and more cumbersome than entering a straightforward free-text description into a written or dictated medical record. Most importantly, it is simply not possible for either generic macros or "pick lists" of sequential words and phrases to duplicate the multilayered, in-depth descriptions included in the narrative sections of a written, dictated, or typed IMR. The portions of the medical record that are most significantly affected by the loss of narrative detail include the HPI, explanations of positive responses to the PFSH and ROS, descriptions of abnormal physical examination findings, and individualized details of clinical impressions and therapeutic options.

How to Evaluate Electronic H&P Data Input Functionality

It is possible for physicians to pre-evaluate the effect of generic macros and pick lists on their efficiency of data entry and on the quality of the information they are able to enter into their medical records. I strongly recommend that any physician considering an EHR system install a demonstration version of the software and use the following two-part trial run before making a commitment to a system. This will provide insight into the data entry characteristics of the system being tested and provide the opportunity to analyze the impact of this format on usability, efficiency, entry of meaningful data, and providing quality patient care.

Preliminary Setup

1. First load the EHR demonstration program software into the type of computer hardware (desktop, laptop, or tablet PC) you will use when seeing patients.
2. Next, collect four or five real patient records of single encounters that represent patients with significant medical problems (I suggest you select charts representing the number of patients you would normally see in about 1 hour).

   Alternatively, you may use the imaginary summaries shown in Appendix A. However, if you choose to use these sample charts to simulate a realistic data entry experience, please add a complete PFSH and ROS with some positive responses, including your descriptions of the details of the abnormalities.

Trial Run 1

1. Pretend these charts are your actual patients providing you with their medical information.
2. Enter all the information from these charts, word-for-word, as you would while having a dialogue with the patient.
3. Analyze the time, effort, and ability to enter detailed in-depth narrative information using the data entry options of the demo EHR system to reach a conclusion about the user-friendliness and efficiency of the system for your individual practice style and requirements.

Trial Run 2

1. Make a second copy of your selected charts.
2. Ask an honest observer (eg, your spouse, a relative, a trusted friend, or a member of your medical staff) to play "pretend patient," using the charts as a script.
3. Interview your "patient" while entering the information in real time into the EHR. Continue to enter through a pretend examination and MDM while explaining findings and recommendations to the patient.
4. Have your honest observer evaluate his or her impressions, feelings, and reactions to the addition of active computer data entry during his or her visit.

As noted earlier, the loss of a free-text narrative interface can result in a significant negative impact on quality of care, which is our prime criterion for measuring the value of medical records. Pick lists require the physician to select from a limited collection of short phrases and combine them in an attempt to describe a complex situation. Because the short phrases must be general enough to fit multiple patients, they lack the subtleties and nuances that distinguish one patient's medical history, physical examination, and decision making from another's. They are also inadequate to distinguish a patient's first visit from his or her second visit, the second visit from the third visit, and so on. It may be slightly less obvious, but prewritten *narrative* macros have essentially the same consequence. The description has to be so generic that, even with the limited modifications these allow, the medical record of one patient with chronic sinusitis will read almost identically to that of every other patient with chronic sinusitis. These options compel physicians to categorize medical conditions in a general fashion, omitting the often subtle differences that distinguish individual patients because of the difficulty they create for recording such patient-specific and visit-specific information.

Medical History Impact

Loss of the narrative entry capability has its most obvious impact on the HPI, where the evolution of symptoms and responses varies in almost every case. A valid HPI also requires a "chronological description"[5(p3)] of the course of each patient's illness. It is not possible to pre-program a chronological description, which differs for every patient and every visit. The impact on the PFSH and ROS sections of the history may be even more profound. While EHRs offer a variety of well-designed *graphic* interface templates for documenting "yes" and "no" responses for the PFSH and ROS, there is generally little or no provision for documenting the *details* of the positive responses. However, accurately documenting the details of these additional patient problems is mandatory for compliance and can directly affect the completeness of patient care and determination of the level of E/M care (ie, E/M code level) warranted by the nature of the patient's problem(s) (NPP). Therefore, the inability of physicians to address and document these details, due to the absence of a narrative interface, has a negative impact on quality of care, compliance, and productivity.

Physical Examination Impact

The loss of the narrative interface for the physical examination section presents problems similar to those observed for the HPI. The limited vocabulary provided by pick lists or preloaded generic macros does not adequately enable the physician to document complete, detailed, and precise descriptions of abnormal examination findings. The resulting text tends to homogenize the descriptions, so that the abnormalities sound similar or identical for every patient. For example, every inflamed eardrum tends to be described in exactly the same words as every other inflamed eardrum, making it seem as though they all look alike. This impairs physicians' ability to accurately monitor the course of disease processes.

MDM Impact

The use of pick lists for recording medical impressions and treatment recommendations also eliminates the patient-specific descriptions that help physicians document the particular characteristics of each patient's medical situation. In reality, every patient with congestive heart failure is not identical to every other patient with that diagnosis, and the clinical impressions and management options vary on the basis of these differences. The narrative interface permits inclusion of descriptive terms that describe the physician's impressions of severity of a problem (eg, "mild," "moderate," "severe," or "life-threatening") and its likelihood of being a correct diagnosis (eg, "possible," "probable," "unlikely," or "rule-out"). Individualized descriptions also enhance the quality of care by enabling physicians to customize each patient's treatment to his or her specialized needs. Such free text descriptions also provide a written record of the physician's thought process concerning possible alternative diagnoses, the reasons for selecting a particular treatment regimen, and a blueprint for potential future management options. These are insights that would likely not otherwise be apparent several months later or on review by another clinician.

Benefits of Narrative Description for Impressions and Treatment Options

For example, the physician evaluating a patient with chest pain whose EHR replaces the narrative interface of the Impressions/Differential Diagnosis section with an *International Classification of Diseases, Ninth Revision* (ICD-9-CM) diagnosis code pick list might select ICD-9 code 786.50 (symptoms involving respiratory system and other chest symptoms; chest pain; chest pain, unspecified) from the system's pick list. However, the physician loses the option of entering a short narrative description to clarify his or her thought process; eg, "mild localized chest pain, doubt myocardial infarction, probable reflux esophagitis or possible costochondritis." Even though the EHR's format allows the other possible diagnoses to be listed, pick-list entry is unable to record the physician's subjective concerns or value-weighted considerations of the different probabilities. Further, if the ICD-9 codes selected are automatically being transmitted to a practice management system for use as billing codes, claims submission guidelines prohibit the entry of these important rule-out diagnoses. All of these limitations again result in the records of all patients with similar diagnoses reading essentially the same, and the MDM loses much of its ability to assist the physician as a blueprint for future care.

Impact on Developing the Differential Diagnosis

There is another, previously unaddressed problem that occurs as a direct consequence of using macros and pick lists to compile the HPI. To use these options quickly and efficiently, physicians need to make a mental diagnosis before obtaining the history, often based solely on the patient's chief complaint. They need to make this diagnosis prematurely, to select the "correct" pick list or "correct" macro that provides the "standard" history to "fit" their tentative diagnosis. In other words, *the tentative diagnosis generates the history*, which has been preprogrammed with a set of predetermined generic descriptions.

This approach turns the methodology of the medical history upside-down. It eliminates the benefits of using free-text narrative, which Practical E/M recommends for HPI. The narrative interface allows each patient's medical record to "tell a story," reflecting the medical diagnostic process of developing a differential diagnosis from the dynamic medical history. The key to the narrative documentation approach is that it provides a true reflection of the process whereby *the history guides the diagnostic process*.

Problems With Using a Tentative Diagnosis to Standardize the Medical History

The EHR data entry systems that begin the medical history with a preprinted macro or pick list restrict the incentive and ability to ask the individualized "magic questions,"

continued

whose answers point to the correct diagnosis, because the format makes it cumbersome or impossible to record such questions and the patient's answers to them. This restriction particularly impacts the physician's flexibility in dealing with more unusual and challenging cases, which call for creativity and customized approaches.

Using a chief complaint to select a diagnosis-specific medical history macro or pick list can result in reduced flexibility in obtaining the history, and therefore in diminished diagnostic insight. These limitations can lead to an increased reliance on routine laboratory and radiographic testing. This approach may therefore result in increased testing costs. It can also make it more difficult to recognize when test results do not fit the patient's history (an occurrence that should normally trigger repeat testing or reconsideration of the patient's overall medical picture). Finally, this scenario can leave the physician and patient at a loss when test results are normal; without the foundation of an individualized history, the medical record may lack the basis to help the physician explain the patient's symptoms or determine subsequent care.

EHR DATA INPUT AND E/M COMPLIANCE ISSUES

Although many EHRs have attempted to integrate E/M coding calculations, these efforts generally utilize the conventional approach of measuring the amount of documentation as the sole criterion for determining the level of E/M codes, without regard for the NPP as an assessment of illness severity and medical necessity.

Some coding engines ask physicians to enter their estimate of the level of history, physical examination, and MDM and then calculate an E/M code based solely on these three key components. This option leads to the same high level of unreliability for coding and documentation that is commonly encountered in audits of physicians' charts using similar estimates with their current paper records.

Other EHRs automatically total the boxes checked in the graphic interface areas of the three key components, using these totals to calculate an E/M code. However, these automated systems have several critical drawbacks. First, they lack the ability to measure whether a checked "abnormal" PFSH, ROS, or physical examination element has been sufficiently explained (in narrative terms) to satisfy the rules of the *Documentation Guidelines for Evaluation and Management Services.*[7] Merely checking a symptom as "yes" or an examination element as "abnormal" (or an exam element related to the HPI as "normal") is insufficient to fulfill the documentation requirements. A second challenge can arise for determining the number of HPI elements documented, if these are not entered as separately identified questions, and particularly for inability to register whether the documentation has included the required "*chronological description* of the development of the patient's present illness."[5(p 3)] There are several additional concerns related to the MDM component. The software usually has no ability to assess whether a listed diagnosis is under active consideration for the current visit (this should "count" toward supporting the level of care) or if it is simply listed as background information (which should not "count"). Further, current systems almost uniformly lack the ability for physicians to document a number of the MDM elements that are necessary for determining E/M codes, including amount of data ordered, complexity of data reviewed, risk of the presenting problem(s), risk of diagnostic testing, and risk of treatment options.

Critically, most EHRs have not integrated the essential Practical E/M concept that the NPP determines medical necessity and the level of care (ie, E/M code) warranted and appropriate for the patient's medical problems. This level of NPP should guide the amount of care and documentation that must be performed or exceeded for coding compliance. In fact, most EHRs do not even provide physicians with the opportunity to consider or document the NPP.

It is important for EHR systems to upgrade their software so that physicians can enter all of the missing elements of E/M documentation, including the NPP. Then their functionality should be modified to facilitate compliant code selection and documentation based on the CPT descriptions of the levels of care warranted by severity of the NPP.

Auditors have pointed out several other significant E/M compliance concerns that need to be addressed in EHR systems:

- If the electronic H&P does not enable physicians to enter narrative explanations of positive responses for PFSH and ROS, then the mere documentation of positive responses will not satisfy the requirements of the *Documentation Guidelines.*

- Those EHR systems that *automatically* default the entire graphic interface sections of the record to "negative" or "normal" responses (a functionality that is commonly described as "documentation by exception") present a significant compliance issue. Since these records do not require the physician to enter information individually for each question or each examination element, there is no validation that each item of care was actually performed. In other words, such systems do not document which components of care were actually performed; they only document that the system does automatic entry. Auditors readily discover this problem when every chart from a given physician documents *identical* comprehensive care for every patient and for every visit, even those visits where the NPP warrants only problem-focused or expanded problem-focused care. The significance of this automatic documentation problem is highlighted by the fact that such records almost always present all negative responses for every aspect of care other than those related to the patient's chief complaint. To an experienced auditor, this finding makes all the charts from that physician suspect for compliance problems and potentially for false claims.

- Similarly, the use of pick lists or prewritten macros in lieu of sections that would otherwise call for narrative data entry often generates nearly identical documentation among the records of all the physicians' patients. This can occur for multiple visits with the same patient, as well as for visits of different patients who have similar diagnoses. What an auditor sees is documentation of a computer's ability to print out the same report over and over again, rather than documentation of the actual delivery of medical care the physician provided during each patient visit. There is no way to determine to what extent the care was actually performed, or how much of the documentation is merely a function of the preprogrammed architecture of the software. Further, automated data entry fails to support whether the care was medically necessary.

- Some electronic H&P designs employ a feature that automatically inserts an exact, word-for-word copy of the complete PFSH and ROS from the patient's initial visit into these sections of each of the patient's subsequent visit (this functionality is commonly described as "copy forward"). However, this duplicate information does not represent the patient's current medical history information, only a duplication of the patient's status from a prior visit. While the *Documentation Guidelines* allows the physician to inquire about (and document) *changes* in health since the previous visit, it does not permit credit for these portions of the medical history without obtaining either an update or a complete *new* review. This automated insertion of previous and outdated information not only creates an E/M compliance problem, it also raises significant quality of care concerns and potential medical liability issues. If the physician simply accepts the old PFSH and ROS data without questioning the patient about changes in general health, there is the possibility of overlooking critical health issues that could adversely affect patient care. For example, automatically bringing forward a copy of a three-month-old ROS, which states that a patient does not have chest pain, provides no information that the patient has not experienced chest pain during the intervening three months since that previous visit.

A Representative Audit

Several years ago, a Medicare carrier requested that I review the E/M documentation of a physician who the carrier's medical director believed was committing fraud. The carrier provided printed charts for multiple visits for each of 10 patients. For each patient, the record of each visit read word-for-word exactly the same, except for variations in their vital signs. Further, the records for patients with similar illnesses were also almost word-for-word identical.

From an auditor's perspective, these medical records provided zero documentation of the care provided. They demonstrated only that a computer has the capability to print the same macro an infinite number of times, without significant variation. I therefore concurred with the medical director that the documentation present in the medical records did not support the E/M codes submitted. The Medicare carrier pursued a fraud complaint against this physician (I was not advised of the outcome or the magnitude of the penalty).

APPEARANCE OF THE COMPLETED H&P

Although most current EHRs use some combination of graphic and narrative interface components, most reformulate the appearance of all this information into the pure narrative text form of conventional dictated medical records that physicians stored in traditional paper records. However, as noted in Chapter 22, this model creates significant challenges in identifying details of patient encounters for physicians themselves as well as for outside reviewers. Compliance audits of such records detect significant insufficiencies due to multiple missing E/M components and failures to meet documentation requirements. Often the missing features result in a document that indicates only problem-focused care.

The appearance of IMR screens and forms provides a superior model for both physicians reviewing their own records and outside reviewers. They are far easier to read and to identify normal and abnormal responses and examination findings. Further, they provide significant audit protection in the event of a compliance review. Appendix F provides a side-by-side comparison of the appearance of each section of an IMR-style presentation with the matching sections of a conventional dictated record, demonstrating the IMR's advantages for ease efficiency of review, searchability, and compliance.

ELECTRONIC H&P DATA ENTRY AND LOSS OF EFFICIENCY

In most EHR systems, the electronic format's requirement for physician data entry eliminates the dramatic efficiency achieved when patients and staff directly enter data into the PFSH and ROS portions of the record. When compared with systems that permit patient data entry, the loss of this option adds an additional 5 or more minutes of the physician's time to each new patient visit. Additionally, attempting to enter enriched narrative descriptions into a pick list or a prescripted generic macro is cumbersome and less efficient than narrative writing or dictation, and often it cannot be successfully accomplished during patient care (or at all).

At HIT conferences, individual physicians, physician organizations, and EHR industry representatives all report evidence that physicians implementing EHRs in their practices initially find that it takes significantly longer to provide and document patient care than it did using their old paper or dictation formats. However, within 6 to 12 months, those physicians who continue using their EHRs are often working as quickly as they did under their old system (writing or transcription for data entry). Interestingly, there are no reports of what transpires to bring about this return to "normal" efficiency. This topic is of critical importance. It warrants thorough investigation so that physicians, administrators, and software developers can understand the barriers to EHR implementation that are inherent to currently available systems, and so that they can develop effective solutions that do not compromise the quality of documentation in medical records. These parties also need to be certain that the increase in speed after 6 to 12 months truly represents an increase in efficiency rather than a decrease in the level of care provided and/or integrity of the documentation.

Theory of Why Data Input Efficiency "Recovers"

Reports show that 6 to 12 months after introducing electronic records, physicians either return to their normal speed of working with patients, or they may abandon their attempt to convert to the EHR. We need to understand (1) how and why this efficiency transformation may or may not occur, and (2) whether this insight can help ensure that more medical practices are able to make a smooth and effective transition to the electronic format without experiencing a decrease in efficiency and productivity.

My personal observations of physicians working with these systems, and logical analysis of their use, have both led me to conclude that a significant factor in the return to a normal timeframe for seeing patients is a choice by the physicians to cease trying to input customized, patient-specific narrative information. They are only able to increase their speed of data entry by entering the similar generic information designed into the software on every similar patient, to "get the work done." Speed may also increase if the physician uses defaults to enter negative responses for all PFSH and ROS questions and normal responses for all physical exam elements. For most of the EHR systems currently available, those physicians who relinquish narrative data entry concepts increase their speed, but do so at the expense of quality information input. Those clinicians who decide not to relinquish narrative data entry either continue spending more time on each visit or they reject the EHR system. In summary, systems with these current H&P design features require physicians to adapt to the functionality of their software; the functionality of the software lacks the flexibility to adapt to the physician's optimal workflow and the medical diagnostic process.

This hypothesis is based on my observations of the use of these systems in three contexts: (1) the sample texts I have seen that were created using these types of data entry designs, (2) demonstrations by physicians using these systems to enter HPI and other abnormal medical information, and (3) my own impressions, based on my work with demonstration versions of these systems, that the only *efficient* data entry they allow is for limited general descriptions. However, speed is not efficiency, which requires that there not be any loss of compliance, quality of documentation, or quality of care.

ADDRESSING EHR DATA ENTRY CHALLENGES

One of the primary sources of problems interfering with quality data entry using currently available EHR systems is the elimination of narrative interfaces, which, if available, would enable physicians to enter free text into the medical record. The basis for the absence of narrative entry capability is likely the fundamental premise that physicians should personally perform all data entry directly into the computer, combined with the realistic assessment that narrative entry by keyboard is impractical for most physicians.

Applying the principles of Practical E/M to an assessment of electronic H&P design and utilization leads to the conclusion that improving data entry functionality and compliance can be achieved by introducing modifications that permit narrative data entry, allow data entry by physician extenders, and improve E/M documentation and coding capabilities.

The following section provides a review of several options that some companies have begun to offer to introduce more flexible data entry capabilities into their software. Implementing hybrid formats allows software systems to combine elements of writing, dictation, typing, and point-and-click mouse entry to create multiple data entry options that utilize the strengths of one format to solve the problems created by the weaknesses of another format. One of our goals, as we analyze the potential of incorporating hybrid formats into electronic H&P designs, is to retain the significant advantages offered by the data storage and utilization component of electronic records. At the same time, another goal is that these systems should also accommodate the positive data entry features of written and dictation formats, especially the efficient use of the narrative interface in appropriate areas, to successfully address the problems associated with the data entry component of many EHRs. Providing multiple data entry options for the electronic H&P should make physician adoption of EHRs more appealing and less complicated, by allowing physicians to select an EHR system offering the design features and functionality that are best suited to their own practices.

HYBRID SYSTEMS

In the discussion of written and dictated formats in Chapter 22, we introduced the concept of hybrid medical records, which harness the strengths of one format to overcome potential weaknesses in another, according to each physician's particular needs. Hybrids also increase the flexibility and usability of a system by allowing individual physicians to choose the features of each format that best fit their personal preferences for each portion of the H&P, while continuing to meet the compliance requirements of the CPT coding system.

In hybrid 1 (writing plus transcription), discussed in Chapter 22, the dictation format introduced a valuable alternative to writing for data entry in medical records that use paper for storage and utilization. For physicians whose handwriting is illegible, the benefit of dictation (ie, legibility) for entering the narrative sections of the paper medical record outweighs the negative aspect of its additional cost. For physicians who write legibly, the cost-effectiveness and potential time saving of writing their narratives usually far outweigh any benefit from dictation.

A primary strength and promise of the electronic record format lies in the data storage and utilization component. The data entry component presents multiple potential obstacles, not only to physician usability but also to entering the meaningful data required to fulfill this promise. The application of the hybrid concept to electronic records allows physicians to benefit from the electronic format for data storage, while blending one or more different formats to overcome the weaknesses of direct data entry by the physician into the computer. Three EHR hybrid options offer reasonable possibilities for improving the data entry functionality of EHRs.

Hybrid 2: Scanning (Virtual Storage and Utilization) for Paper Records and Data

Scanning physician paper records for electronic storage dramatically remedies two important weaknesses of the traditional paper storage system that uses writing and/or dictation as the data entry format. As discussed in Chapter 22, the negative features of paper records (including IMRs on paper, with or without transcription) are related to the cost of data storage and retrieval and particularly to the limitations of accessibility to the records.

Hybrid 2 maintains the effective data entry functionality of written and dictated medical records. However, all the documents that would normally be stored in a paper chart are instead scanned electronically and stored in a computerized filing software program, which provides an electronic environment for data storage and retrieval. This system stores not only the written or transcribed medical record forms, but also the images of laboratory reports, X-ray reports, and correspondence. The paper forms are scanned, and electronic information can be downloaded, into a server that files the images into a "folder" for each patient.

These electronic folders with their stored documents are accessible to the physicians and other authorized persons at any time, and from any location, through password-protected computer access. By replacing storage in a physical paper chart with virtual storage, hybrid 2 solves the medical record access problem.

The data storage and retrieval costs of systems based on hybrid 2 can be evaluated by using worksheets similar to those shown in Figures 22.1 and 22.2. Some staff time is still involved for scanning documents into the system, but this is greatly reduced from the time required to file and retrieve traditional paper record charts. The remaining costs that must be included in the calculations are the costs of the scanning system itself. These include either the purchase and maintenance costs for an in-office hardware and software scanning system, or monthly access charges for an Internet-based virtual storage system.

Analysis of Hybrid 2

Hybrid 2 is a paper medical record stored in an electronic environment. When compared with a paper chart system, it is usually more cost-effective. Most important, it resolves the access problems related to the data storage and utilization component of written records, while maintaining the effectiveness of the written (and dictated) data entry component. For example, a physician who is pleased with a paper-based IMR system can readily replace the paper storage system with virtual storage without compromising *quality of care* or *compliance*. Office *productivity* will increase because of reduced costs of information storage and utilization. *Efficiency* and *physician usability* will also increase because of the immediate availability of patient records at all times and in all locations.

The weakness of hybrid 2 is that it lacks the functionality of a true EHR. Data is not entered digitally into the storage environment. Therefore, this system lacks the essential capabilities of a true electronic record, including searchability of data, interconnectivity and interoperability with other electronic systems, clinical decision support capabilities, and automated reporting of performance measures.

Hybrid 3: EHR Plus Dictation for Data Entry

In the last three to four years, a significant number of EHR systems have incorporated a hybrid option that is a first step toward addressing the data entry problems caused by the lack of a narrative interface. This solution offers physicians the option of dictating the narrative sections of the medical record, which previously had required typing or suboptimal documentation through use of pick lists or prewritten generic macros. The dictation can be entered digitally into the appropriate section of the EHR by a transcriptionist or through an integrated speech recognition software program. Hybrid 3 is an electronic record with an enhancement that introduces a dictation option to address the "loss of effective narrative interface" problem common to many EHR systems.

Analysis of Hybrid 3

The strength of hybrid 3 is that it provides physicians with an optional method of entering free-text narrative information into the EHR system, while maintaining all the benefits of electronic data storage and utilization. Although the physician remains the sole data entry operator (DEO), he or she can enter detailed free-text narrative without using the keyboard. For physicians who are comfortable with dictation, this hybrid restores the efficiency, quality of care, and usability benefits provided by a narrative interface. Another major benefit of including the narrative interface is restoration of the analytical methodology whereby obtaining the medical history guides the development of the differential diagnosis, which is then confirmed by the physical examination and/or testing. The return to this approach also discourages reliance on blanket testing to determine a diagnosis. In addition, allowing free-text input addresses E/M compliance concerns related to the HPI, positive responses in the PFSH and ROS, the physical examination, and the impressions and management option elements of MDM.

There remain weaknesses of hybrid 3 that warrant further consideration and improvement. The most easily remedied is that some systems fail to provide a narrative option in all the sections of the H&P where it is required. Others that include the narrative option have failed to eliminate the problematic pick lists and pre-entered macros, leaving physicians with the ability to choose an intrinsically noncompliant documentation option.

When assessing the option of speech recognition software, recent systems have achieved excellent accuracy with only a small amount of "training" for the software; however, they require physicians to speak at conversational speed rather than the high-speed dictation they commonly use with transcriptionists. If, however, the system uses human transcriptionists, there will be an associated increase in cost.

There are also several electronic H&P data entry issues that are still not optimally addressed by hybrid 3. This approach still lacks the option of allowing (or encouraging) patients and medical staff to enter data directly into the program. Also, it fails to address E/M compliance concerns related to inability to document some elements of the MDM (ie, complexity of data and the three elements of risk) and failure to consider the NPP. Finally, it fails to address the needs of physicians who prefer writing to dictation.

Perhaps the most important innovation of this hybrid is that it recognizes the benefit of introducing a nonelectronic format option for data entry into an EHR system, while still employing the electronic format for data storage and utilization. It also recognizes that someone other than the physician, ie, a professional DEO (the transcriptionist), can input the data in the electronic environment. This opens the door to the next option of incorporating the strengths of writing as well as dictation into the data entry component of EHRs.

Hybrid 4: EHR With Full Data Entry Flexibility

Hybrid 4 recognizes the advantages and benefits of offering multiple format options to physicians for the data entry component of the electronic H&P. It maintains all the functionality of electronic storage and utilization while providing full flexibility for physicians to choose among all three data entry formats (writing, dictation, and direct computer entry) for each section of the medical record. Realizing that the EHR is likely to be accepted in the future as the standard format for the storage and utilization of medical records, the goals of this hybrid system are as follows:

1. Allow physicians to customize their EHR by selecting from among all the format options for data entry.
2. Include both graphic and narrative interface options in all appropriate sections of the electronic H&P.
3. Allow options for data entry by nonphysician personnel (ie, staff and patients).
4. Fulfill E/M compliance requirements for medical records.
5. Allow for integration of new data entry options in the future.

Systems that use the Practical E/M methodology and IMR templates with paper storage fulfill all of these goals, but they lack the benefits of an electronic data storage and utilization component. Hybrid 4 is an EHR that retains all the benefits of electronic data storage and utilization, while also designing the electronic H&P with full IMR features and functionality and permitting physicians to enter data by writing, dictation, and/or direct keyboard input.

The key factor that imparts hybrid 4 with this flexibility is eliminating the EHR requirement that the physician personally type or point and click with the mouse to enter all clinical information into the computer system. The primary benefits of EHRs derive from what we can accomplish with quality medical data once it has been entered into the system. How this information is entered and the identity of the individual performing the data entry are of secondary significance; eliminating this clerical task frees the physician to devote increased time and attention to patient care. It is the quality and usefulness of the medical data entered that is of paramount importance. Our goal should be "quality in, quality out."

Indirect Data Entry Options

In this approach, just as for hybrid 3, one dictation option is for the physician to use an audio recorder (or dictate into the computer's microphone) as a "data transfer medium," with secure Internet upload to convey medical information to a professional transcriptionist.

Hybrid 4 extends this potential by allowing the physician to use legible writing as another optional data entry modality. One means of accomplishing this goal is for the physician to write on a paper IMR template and scan it for Internet upload as another "data transfer medium" to convey medical information to a DEO, who actually enters the documentation into the software instead of the physician.

Figure 23.1 compares the effectiveness of the physician and the professional DEO in entering data into the digital data entry medium of electronic records. As noted in this chart, the cost of time for a professional DEO is significantly lower than the cost of time for a physician, who is also far less skilled at entering data into computer systems than the DEO.

F I G U R E 23.1

Effectiveness of Professional DEO Compared With Physician for Data Entry Into Computer

	Physician as DEO	**Professional DEO**
Ability to enter data rapidly	Poor	Excellent
Accuracy in entering data	Poor	Excellent
Effective use of physician time and productivity	Low	High
Impact on efficiency of care	Negative	None
Impact on patient-physician relationship	Negative	None
Cost of the entry professional	Very high	Low

Direct Data Entry Options

Voice recognition software allows transcription of physicians' dictation directly into the electronic H&P, as described for hybrid 3. There remains a question whether the software's transcription should be reviewed for accuracy, although ideally the system should retain the original voice file for verification if needed.

A relatively new hardware and software device now allows a creative option for entry of written material directly into the electronic H&P. The digital pen and paper system uses a pen with a digital camera and memory chip linked to software that prints forms matched to the screens of an electronic H&P superimposed on unique microdots that identify the patient, the date, and the type of form. This system allows patients to complete their IMR medical history forms with the digital pen and have their responses immediately uploaded into the H&P, so that their information is available when the physician enters the room. Physicians who prefer to write the narrative portions of the H&P can use the digital pen for entering both check-box components and narrative components of the record, thereby duplicating their accustomed workflow with patients. Although the digital pen is highly accurate for transcribing check boxes in the graphic portions of the record, its accuracy for legible handwriting is currently less than 90%. This suggests the advisability of using a proofreader to make final corrections as needed, which is a relatively low-cost addition. In addition, because of its digital paper component, the digital pen also retains an image of the actual written document in the EHR software, again providing a mode of verifying accuracy of the transcription.

Another option that has recently become available programs EHR software into tablet PC hardware with handwriting recognition. Practical E/M methodology recommends that the screens on the tablet PC should have an appearance similar to that of the physician's IMR templates. The physician holds the tablet PC and writes data directly onto the screen, exactly as he or she would work while holding a clipboard with paper, and may dictate during or after the encounter as well. Ironically, this option for data entry brings us full circle, back to the electronic equivalent of an IMR on paper. Both the physician and staff can enter both graphic and narrative data directly into the electronic H&P. Practices might also allow patients to use tablet PCs to complete the PFSH and ROS graphic interface sections of the initial visit forms in the office; however, this adds a significant hardware cost, and many patients are still not comfortable with computer entry. There are several significant concerns with the current functionality of the tablet PC approach. It can be cumbersome for writing narrative information that is more than one line in length, it has the usual challenges with physician illegibility, it interrupts physicians' work with patients when it makes a transcription error that must be corrected, and it does not retain an image of what the physician wrote (therefore eliminating the option of using a proofreader to confirm the conversion of handwriting to digital text). Physicians considering this option should perform thorough testing to see how well it fits with their optimal workflow.

Overview of Hybrid 4

Integrating hybrid 4 plus IMR screens into electronic H&P design and functionality combines the powerful storage and retrieval capabilities of electronic records with the usability, efficiency, compliance, and data integrity features of Practical E/M, while offering physicians a full range of data entry modalities. The outcome is a highly flexible system with the ability to match physicians' optimal workflow, reinforce the diagnostic process, and meet each physician's accustomed medical record documentation preferences.

Several refinements are also needed. Screens and any paper forms used by staff or patients must be perfectly matched. This includes incorporating the ability to document the NPP and all components of MDM into the electronic H&P screens. For compliance and quality documentation purposes, documentation by exception, copy forward functionality pick lists, and preset generic macros must be eliminated as narrative alternatives, for all the reasons previously cited.

Possible Compliant Roles for Pick Lists and/or Macros

Although unacceptable as a substitute for free-text narrative documentation of multiple components of the H&P, the use of pick lists or preformulated macros is appropriate and can improve efficiency in several portions of the electronic H&P:

■ Ordering medications

■ Ordering laboratory tests

In addition, after the E/M encounter is completed, selection lists of CPT and ICD-9 codes can be an option for billing codes if the physician is performing charge entry functions on the software.

As noted, there are relative advantages and drawbacks to each of the new data entry tools available in hybrid 4, and these must be carefully evaluated by each practice. For example, although there is a cost associated with the options that employ a DEO for data entry or a proofreader to assist with digital pen entry, this expense is much lower than the expense of three other alternatives: (1) the cost and inefficiency of maintaining a paper record storage and utilization system; (2) the cost of full dictation of all records; and (3) the cost of physician time and loss of quality of care if the physician serves as the DEO for keyboard entry of all data directly into the software system.

For most physicians, some or all of these data entry tools of hybrid 4 can be readily adapted to their practice, and they offer superior usability, performance, and data integrity to designs that offer only keyboard or mouse-click entry.

Function of Hybrid 4 at the Point of Care

The following outline demonstrates how such a flexible system should function, step by step, for a new patient visit, with all the data entry options indicated as bullet points. An asterisk (*) indicates tasks performed by the physician. For physician tasks involving narrative data input, the dictation options include dictation for entry by a transcriptionist or voice recognition software. The writing options include writing on paper for indirect entry by a DEO, digital pen, or tablet PC.

1. The patient completes the PFSH and ROS portions of an IMR.
   ■ The patient can write on a paper form in the office prior to seeing the doctor (with or without a digital pen or using a tablet PC).
   ■ The office can send a paper form to the patient before the visit, by mail, fax, or e-mail.
   ■ The patient can complete the form directly from home before the visit on the physician's secure Web site.

2. The nurse (or medical technician) reviews the PFSH and ROS with the patient and documents any further details. The nurse may also enter preliminary HPI information into the record. (Note: Physicians who do not work with extenders will perform these tasks themselves.)
   ■ The extender can *write* the information.
   ■ The extender can *dictate* the information.

- The extender can *enter the information directly* into a computer by typing on the keyboard.

3. *The physician enters the examination room, reviews and completes the PFSH and ROS, and then elicits further details of the HPI, including the chronological course of the illness and ensuring that at least four elements of the HPI have been documented.

   - The physician can *write* this narrative information.

   - The physician can *dictate* the information during or immediately after the visit. (Note: If dictated, the physician also checks the appropriate boxes on paper or EHR screen for "see attached dictation.")

   - The physician can *enter the information directly* into a computer by typing on the keyboard.

4. *The physician follows Practical E/M methodology to (1) form a preliminary impression based on the patient's medical history, (2) identify the NPP, and (3) select the appropriate level of care and E/M code appropriate for the NPP. (Note: NPP is not documented at this point.)

5. *The physician performs and documents the physical examination, following IMR documentation prompts, to ensure E/M documentation compliance.

   - The physician documents the *normal* and *abnormal* examination findings on the check-box template by writing.

   - The physician may have the option to document *normal* and *abnormal* examination findings by mouse-click entry directly onto the computer screen. (Note: If using direct computer entry, the system should not allow all fields to be populated as "normal" with a single mouse click, because this would not adequately satisfy E/M compliance guidelines.)

   - The physician can document any *abnormal* examination findings and/or pertinent normal examination findings by *writing*, by *dictating*, or by *entering the information directly into the computer* by typing on the keyboard.

6. *The physician documents MDM, following IMR documentation prompts (of CPT guidelines) to ensure E/M documentation compliance.

   - For the first MDM subsection, the physician documents any *data reviewed*. The physician can document the data and results by *writing*, by *dictating*, by *entering directly into the computer* by typing on the keyboard, or by *copying and pasting* laboratory reports stored in the EHR.

   - For the second MDM subsection, the physician documents the diagnoses, management options, and data ordered, including any qualifying comments, following documentation prompts to ensure care at the level warranted by the NPP. The physician can document these elements by *writing*, by *dictating*, or by *entering directly into the computer* by typing on the keyboard. For data ordered, the physician may also use a drop-down pick-list menu of diagnostic procedures or modifiable pre-entered macros for specific conditions.

   - For the third MDM subsection, the physician documents the complexity of data reviewed and/or data ordered. The physician documents this element by checking boxes for the correct degree of complexity on a selection list located on the paper chart or delete on the computer screen.

   - For the fourth MDM subsection, the physician documents the risk levels for the presenting problems, diagnostic tests ordered, and treatment options recommended following documentation prompts (and Table of Risk) to ensure care at the level warranted by the NPP. The physician documents this element by checking boxes for the correct level of risk for each of the three categories on a selection list located on the paper chart or on the computer screen.

7. *The physician documents the final NPP.
    - The physician documents this factor by checking a box for the correct level of severity on a selection list located on the paper chart or on the computer screen.

8. *The physician completes CPT and ICD-9 coding information, either on a paper "superbill" or as direct entry into the computer.

9. When using indirect entry options, the staff provides the dictation and paper forms to a DEO. This may involve the use of in-house personnel or personnel provided through an Internet ASP company, in which case the dictation and written records are sent via a secure Internet connection.

10. The DEO enters all graphic interface documentation from the scanned documents and all dictated and written narrative data into the appropriate free-text portions of the EHR.
    - All scanned images and audio files are permanently stored as part of the electronic record for compliance purposes.

11. When the patient visit is a consultation, the EHR software transfers appropriate MDM and narrative portions of the H&P to a consultation letter template to create a customized original consultation letter from the same data input.

This hybrid integration of the data entry options of writing, dictation, and/or keyboard with the data storage functionality of an EHR provides the accessibility, searchability, interconnectivity, and interoperability benefits of EHRs with the E/M compliance, efficiency, productivity, quality care, usability, and data integrity benefits of Practical E/M methodology.

SUMMARY

It is critically important to analyze the impact of the electronic format on the functionality of each of the two components of medical records: data storage/utilization and data entry. The value of EHRs must be evaluated by using the same criteria that are applied to other medical record systems: quality of care, usability, efficiency, productivity (cost), data integrity, and compliance.

The data storage and utilization features of EHRs are recognizably superior to those of paper charts. As technology advances, these features will be required for physicians to participate in health system integration through electronic interconnectivity, with its promise of improved quality, patient safety, and cost savings. However, many currently available EHR designs present challenges to optimal H&P design and data entry functionality. These issues include the requirement for physicians to enter all data directly into the software system by keyboard or mouse clicks, absence of the ability to enter free-text narrative descriptions, and incomplete E/M compliance features. These barriers impose unacceptable restrictions on the quality of clinical data physicians can record in their electronic H&P, and therefore on the quality of patient care as well.

Recognizing the multiple benefits the EHR format can bring to our health care system, the goal of this chapter's analysis is to demonstrate our need to bring the same innovation, enthusiasm, and commitment to EHR data entry design that developers are already bringing to the data storage and utilization features. This will enable physicians to have optimal H&P designs and to choose among multiple options for data entry, including hybrid formats, to customize a system that meets their personal and professional requirements and allows them to incorporate electronic records into their practices.

References

1. Executive Order: Incentives for the Use of Health Information Technology and Establishing the Position of the National Health Information Technology Coordinator. April 27, 2004. http://www.whitehouse.gov/news/releases/2004/04/20040427-4.html. Accessed July 7, 2005.

2. Hernandez R. Gingrich and Clinton finally agree to work together on a health plan. *New York Times.* May 12, 2005:B9.

3. Executive Order: Promoting Quality and Efficient Health Care in Federal Government Administered or Sponsored Health Care Programs. August 22, 2006. http://www.whitehouse.gov/news/releases/2006/08/20060822-2.html. Accessed May 16, 2008.

4. McClellan M. CMS Quality, Efficiency and Value-Based Purchasing Policies: The Role of Health Information Technology. Presented at the Second Health Information Technology Summit; Washington, DC; September 9, 2005.

5. American Medical Association. *Current Procedural Terminology CPT® 2008.* Chicago, IL: American Medical Association; 2007.

6. Levinson SR. *Practical EHR: Electronic Record Solutions for Compliance and Quality Care.* Chicago, IL: American Medical Association; 2008.

7. Health Care Financing Administration. *Documentation Guidelines for Evaluation and Management Services.* Chicago, IL: American Medical Association; 1997.

Proposal for Designing
Educational External E/M Audits

Chapters 24 and 25 discuss two similar but separate categories of audits of physicians' evaluation and management (E/M) coding and documentation. External audits, which are addressed in this chapter, are audits of medical practices and teaching hospitals that are conducted by outside agencies, such as Medicare, the government's Department of Health and Human Services, and private insurers. We will encourage a restructured approach for these audits, which parallels the positive goals established for physicians using Practical E/M principles. Internal E/M audits, discussed in the following chapter, are formal reviews a medical practice conducts of its own medical records, sometimes as a component of a formal practice compliance program.

External E/M audits date from the inception of Medicare's 1992 program for teaching E/M documentation and coding principles to physicians. An objective review of the ways in which external E/M audits have been used since the introduction of the *Documentation Guidelines for Evaluation and Management Services*,[1] combined with an analysis of the effects of those audits on how physicians code, document, and practice medicine, provides significant insight into their impact on health care. Using this historical perspective as a focal point provides insight into the goals that external E/M audits should ideally seek to accomplish, and how they should be restructured to achieve those goals.

Internal and External Audits

E/M audits of physicians' medical records are most commonly performed by outside, or *external*, agencies, particularly Medicare and private insurers. The concept of *internal* audits for physician offices was introduced with the Department of Health and Human Services recommendations for practice compliance programs, which followed settlements under the Physicians at Teaching Hospitals (PATH) audits in the mid- to late 1990s. These programs most commonly exist in larger groups and academic centers, which train their own compliance staff to conduct these reviews and/or employ outside consultants.

CONVENTIONAL E/M AUDITS: MEASURING CODING BY DOCUMENTATION

After the introduction of the E/M coding system in 1992, Medicare followed its extensive physician-training protocol with a program of dual-purpose "friendly" audits. These were intended first to measure physicians' ability to document and code correctly, and second to provide feedback and assist physicians in improving their documenting and coding. The results of these friendly audits revealed that physicians were not successfully adapting to the new coding system. This conclusion provided an impetus for further modification of the system through the addition of quantitative measures, which were introduced in 1995 in the first edition of the *Documentation Guidelines.*

A lot can be learned from the design of these early audits. The positive lesson is that the intent of the original program was to be *educational.* This foreshadows a central theme of this chapter, which is that a primary function of audits should be to better educate physicians on the subject of documentation and coding, and to provide them with tools that promote compliant E/M practices. On the other hand, the structure of those audits has resulted in auditors and insurers focusing on a comparison of coding to documentation, in most cases without consideration of the role of severity of patient illness (the nature of presenting problem [NPP]). This has led to our current external audit system, which concentrates on financial penalties for physicians rather than on education, and which has caused a significant negative impact on the quality of medical care.

Shifting the Focus Back to Patient Care

Conventional audits concentrate almost exclusively on documentation of the three key components, and on the relationship between the amount of documentation and the E/M code the physician chose to submit. Practical E/M audits shift the focus back to the patient. The auditor starts his or her report of the review of a patient record with consideration of the NPP, and then evaluates the appropriateness of the level of care submitted (ie, the E/M code) for this severity of the patient's illness. Only then does the auditor turn his or her attention to the three key components, for the purpose of ensuring not only that an appropriate level of care was selected, but that the documentation indicates that it was also provided.

As with today's conventional E/M audits, the Medicare trial audits first considered the E/M code submitted and then compared this with the code calculated by analyzing the extent of documentation in the medical record for the three key components of E/M coding (ie, history, examination, and medical decision making [MDM]). This initial calculation was carried out without any consideration of the level of care warranted by the severity, risk, and prognosis (without treatment) of the patient's illnesses (ie, the NPP). The code calculated on the basis of the three key components was used as the reference standard against which the physician's submitted E/M code was measured. On this basis, the auditor determined whether the care was "overcoded" (ie, the submitted code was higher than the reference standard of the documentation-derived code), "undercoded" (ie, the submitted code was lower than the reference standard of the documentation-derived code), or coded correctly.

The audits that conclude there was either overcoding or undercoding do not do any further evaluation. Only in cases where the submitted E/M code matches the documentation-derived code does the auditor consider the NPP and evaluate whether the level of care indicated by the code was also "medically necessary." In this instance, if the auditor determines that, according to Current Procedural Terminology (CPT®) coding system guidelines, the submitted code is higher than warranted by the severity of the patient's illness, the chart would still be designated as "overcoded," even though the documentation of the three key components is sufficient to support the level of care submitted for billing purposes.

Medicare auditors use this same methodology for E/M audits today. The only variation observed is that many non-Medicare auditors rarely, if ever, consider the NPP under any circumstance.

Critique of Conventional Audits

The problem with current conventional audits is that they have been used for the sole purpose of economic retribution, rather than for promoting enhanced medical care and providing physicians with educational guidance to improve their medical record documentation. These audits have consistently demonstrated that most physicians do not have effective tools to facilitate sufficient documentation to support the submission of higher-level E/M codes, but they have failed to result in an effort to provide physicians with appropriate tools to rectify this state of affairs.

Medicare and private insurance companies have focused solely on detecting over-coding, and then asking physicians to refund payments in cases when they detect it. The economic consequences, particularly when Medicare extrapolates the results of a small audit over a large number of visits (discussed in detail later in the chapter) or considers added penalties for "fraud," have been so economically devastating that most physicians have been frightened into simply submitting low-level codes, even for patients with complex problems for whom they provide higher levels of care.

In practice, this "defensive undercoding" often leads to a downward spiral of negative consequences for physicians, patients, and quality of care. The low reimbursements resulting from undercoding create a powerful economic incentive for physicians to provide brief visits, which are only sufficient for problem-focused care. However, problem-focused care is often lower than the level of care and documentation warranted by the severity of the patient's illness, both medically and as defined by the CPT coding guidelines.

The conventional audit typically addresses the purely economic question, "Are we paying for more care than was delivered?" Practical E/M analyzes the same circumstance by asking, "How can we guide the physician to deliver (and document) the level of care that the physician determined (as indicated by the E/M code submitted) was appropriate for the patient's illness?"

RESTRUCTURING EXTERNAL AUDITS TO PROVIDE EDUCATION AND TOOLS

Clearly, the conventional approach to E/M audits has not been successful in helping physicians learn a methodology that would enable them to achieve coding and documentation compliance. When we can agree that teaching physicians an effective method for achieving compliance while facilitating care is a worthwhile goal for external E/M audits, it becomes possible to restructure both the perception and the presentation of external E/M audits. Their primary focus should change from one of performing punitive financial reviews to one that emphasizes educational analysis. In addition, these audits should offer explanations and support that provide physicians with both the knowledge and the tools they need to incorporate an effective E/M documentation and coding approach into their medical practices. This will encourage physicians to identify levels of care appropriate for the severity of patient illness (ie, the NPP), and it will reinforce this effort by ensuring that physicians can submit codes (and receive reimbursement) appropriate for providing those levels of care.

Step 1 of a Practical E/M Audit

A conceptual reorganization of external E/M audits begins with moving the NPP into a primary focus of every E/M review. This immediately shifts the first concern of the audit away from measuring the code submitted against the level of documentation. Instead, the initial focus of the audit is assessing the code submitted in terms of the severity of the patient's illness on the day of the visit. If the physician has not documented the severity of the NPP, the auditor should first evaluate the MDM portion of the medical record, reviewing the documentation of diagnoses, data, and management options (plus any notation of the risks and/or the NPP). From this review, the auditor develops an assessment of the severity of the patient's NPP, and the level of E/M care this severity warrants. The auditor bases this judgment on the CPT codebook's E/M coding guidelines and the clinical examples in Appendix C of the codebook. Comparing these appropriate levels of care with the E/M code the physician submitted, the auditor makes a reasonable determination, which will be recorded in the audit report, of whether:

- the level of care (ie, E/M code) submitted *does not exceed* the level of care warranted by the NPP, per CPT coding guidelines, or
- the level of care (ie, E/M code) submitted *exceeds* the level of care warranted by the NPP, per CPT coding guidelines.

In cases in which the level of care submitted is within CPT coding system guidelines for the NPP, no further explanation is required. However, if the submitted code is found to exceed that suggested by the CPT coding guidelines, the next step for the auditor to take should be educational. Under this circumstance, the auditor's report to the physician should include:

- the CPT coding system's definitions for the different types (ie, severity) of NPP,
- the auditor's assessment, based on the documentation in the medical record, of the patient's type of NPP on the date of service,
- several clinical examples from the CPT codebook[2] in which NPPs are of comparable severity to that of the patient visit under review, and an indication of the appropriate level of care according to the CPT codebook, and
- the maximum level of care deemed appropriate for the selected type of NPP, according to CPT coding descriptors for the type of service performed.

This information could be presented effectively by providing a documentation tool for the physician's future guidance, such as the one shown in Figure 24.1.

Step 2 of a Practical E/M Audit

The second step for this type of external audit is the comparison of the E/M code submitted with the level of care documented in the medical record. (In cases where step 1 concludes that the code submitted *exceeds* CPT coding system indicators for the NPP, step 2 would compare the E/M code deemed appropriate for the NPP with the level of care documented in the medical record.) The auditor's task in this step is to compare the code submitted with the level of care documented, with three important additional considerations.

FIGURE 24.1

NPP and Appropriate Levels of Care for an Outpatient Initial Visit* The CPT code level associated with each type of NPP is derived from the CPT coding system descriptors of the different levels of care for the type of service submitted. The proposed definitions for 'low to moderate' and 'moderate to high' were introduced in Chapter 5.

Type of NPP	CPT Coding System Definition
Minor (level 1)	Problem runs definite and prescribed course, is transient in nature, and is not likely to permanently alter health status; OR has a good prognosis with management and compliance.
Low (level 2)	Problem where the risk of morbidity without treatment is low; there is little to no risk of mortality without treatment; full recovery without functional impairment is expected.
Low to moderate (level 2)	A problem where the risk of morbidity without treatment is low to moderate; there is low to moderate risk of mortality without treatment; full recovery without functional impairment is expected in most cases, with low probability of prolonged functional impairment.
Moderate (level 3)	Problem where the risk of morbidity without treatment is moderate; there is moderate risk of mortality without treatment; uncertain prognosis OR increased probability of prolonged functional impairment.
Moderate to high (levels 4, 5)	Problem where the risk of morbidity without treatment is moderate to high; there is moderate risk of mortality without treatment; uncertain prognosis or increased probability of prolonged functional impairment.
High (levels 4, 5)	Problem where the risk of morbidity without treatment is high to extreme; there is moderate to high risk of mortality without treatment OR high probability of severe prolonged functional impairment.

* The lowest level of NPP, "minimal," does not apply to the initial visit type of service. Also, as reviewed in Chapter 5, the CPT codebook frequently uses the undefined levels of "low to moderate" and "moderate to high," which are associated with various E/M code levels for different types of service.

Source: American Medical Association. *Current Procedural Terminology CPT® 2008*. Chicago, Ill: American Medical Association; 2007.

The first consideration is that the audit itself must be compliant. The auditor's review must follow only the CPT coding system guidelines and the *Documentation Guidelines*. The use of alternative audit tools currently employed by a number of Medicare carriers and private insurers must be prohibited.

The second consideration is a shift of the auditor's perspective. Since step 1 of the audit ensured that the level of care indicated by the submitted (or corrected) E/M code did not exceed the extent of care warranted by the NPP, the auditor's analysis of the extent of care documented should be different from that conveyed in a conventional audit report. If the auditor finds insufficient documentation to support the E/M code, rather than concluding that the physician "overcoded," he or she should report that the care warranted for the code (according to CPT coding system guidelines) either "was not provided or was insufficiently documented." This change in point of view is more than semantics; it represents a significant change in the conceptual approach to E/M audits. This revised perspective will also change the emphasis of the audit report from punitive to constructive, guiding physicians on the extent of care that CPT coding system guidelines and the *Documentation Guidelines* state they must provide and document to support the E/M code they submitted.

Should There Be Financial Consequences for "Underdocumentation" and Improper Code Selection?

To promote care that is appropriate, high quality, and cost-effective, external audits should shift their primary focus away from imposing financial penalties to educating physicians about the relationships between severity of patient illness, code selection, and extent of care provided and documented. However, the question remains about how Medicare or a private insurer should respond, either when a physician's documentation is insufficient to support the code submitted or when the code submitted by the physician exceeds the level of care warranted by the NPP.

The question of what type of response is most appropriate in these circumstances is clearly a policy decision that must be made by Medicare and each private insurer on a case-by-case basis. In keeping with the educational perspective we are advocating, and our orientation toward correcting future problems rather than imposing financial penalties for past errors, we would suggest that the first response to a failed E/M external audit should be to give the physician an opportunity to correct the problem, while temporarily deferring financial consequences pending the results of future reviews. Physicians should be provided with constructive information to help them gain the insight and tools that will permit them to document and code appropriately in the future. This approach could include the possibility that pending financial penalties resulting from the current audit would be reduced if subsequent reviews demonstrate compliant coding and documentation.

The third consideration addresses the audit report itself, recommending that its focus be educational. This can be achieved by showing the physician a table that reports details of the amount of history, examination, and MDM required for the E/M code submitted by the CPT coding system and the *Documentation Guidelines*. These standards are then compared with the extent of care the physician documented in the medical record. Figure 24.2 illustrates a prototype of a report fulfilling these requirements.

In this figure, the left-hand column lists each of the elements of the three key components. The middle column lists the level of care for each element that must be documented to fulfill the CPT coding system and the *Documentation Guidelines* requirements for the E/M code submitted. The right-hand column then reports the auditor's evaluation of the amount of documentation actually present for each E/M element in the medical record, and it uses symbols to indicate whether the documentation for each element meets the CPT coding system requirements.

An additional educational tool for step 2 would be for the auditor to provide physicians with copies of documentation prompts that would help them to ensure appropriate levels of care in future cases. For example, if the physician's documented physical examination did not support the level of E/M care submitted, as in Figure 24.2, then the auditor could add a Practical E/M documentation prompt for the appropriate specialty and type of service, such as the one shown in Figure 24.3. This prompt is appropriate for an initial outpatient visit for all single-organ-system examinations other than ophthalmology and psychiatry (which modify the description for a "detailed" examination).

FIGURE 24.2

Illustration of Analysis of Chart Documentation of Care Provided

---

Physician: **David Doctor**

Patient: **Jay J. Jones** ID No. **123456**

Date of Service: **1/5/2005**   Date of Audit: **3/30/2005**

Type of Service Submitted: **Initial office visit**   Type of Service Audited: **Agree**

Note: this type of service requires documentation for all three key components to meet or exceed the level of care required for the submitted E/M code.

E/M Code Submitted: **99204**   E/M Code Documented: **99203**

Key Component and Elements	Required for E/M Code Submitted	Care Documented in Medical Record
1. Extent of medical history (a) HPI is a true history (b) No. of elements of present illness (c) No. of elements of PFSH (d) Number of systems of ROS	Comprehensive (a) includes chronological description (b) 4 or more (c) 3 (d) 10 or more	Detailed* (a) includes chronological description† (b) 4† (c) 3† (d) 6*
2. Physical examination (a) 1997 guidelines, cardiology (b) 1995 guidelines	Comprehensive (a) All required elements and 1 element in each nonshaded section (b) Comprehensive examination	Detailed* (a) 15 elements* Missing required elements (b) Detailed exam*
3. Medical decision making (2 of 3) (a) Data ■ Amount of data reviewed ■ Amount of data ordered ■ Complexity of data (b) No. of diagnoses or Rx options ■ Number of diagnoses ■ Number of treatment options (c) Risks ■ Risk of presenting problem(s) ■ Risk of diagnostic procedures ■ Risk of management options	Moderate (a) Moderate (b) Multiple (3) (c) Moderate	Low* (a) None* ■ None* ■ None* ■ None* (b) Limited* ■ Minimal (1)* ■ Limited (2)* (c) Estimate = moderate† ■ Not documented ■ Not documented ■ Not documented

* Documented E/M care is less than required for submitted E/M code.

† Documented E/M care meets or exceeds the extent of care required for submitted E/M code.

Sample Physical Examination Documentation Prompt for Initial Outpatient Visit, Cardiology Exam

1. Problem focused = 1-5 elements (level 1) 2. Expanded = 6-11 elements (level 2)   3. Detailed = 12 or more elements [in 2 or more systems] (level 3)
4. Comprehensive = document every element in basic areas AND at least 1 element in each optional area (level 4 or 5)   ***Optional**

Currently, physicians most often do not even receive a formal analysis report following an E/M audit, just the results showing how many charts failed audit. Thus, conventional audits often conceal, rather than reveal, the guidelines by which they evaluate medical documentation. This leaves physicians in greater confusion, which motivates them to undercode, creating a financial incentive for them to reduce the levels of care they have time to provide.

In contrast, the goal of the protocol advocated in this section is to provide physicians with insight and tools that will enable them to bring their care, documentation, and coding into alignment with the severity of patient illness and into compliance with CPT coding system guidelines. This approach is designed to benefit patient care and align incentives among patients, physicians, Medicare, and private insurers. It also promotes a dialogue between auditors and physicians to improve compliance and ensure appropriate reimbursement.

Implementing the "Practical E/M" Audit Approach

The goal of these audits is to help physicians achieve compliant E/M care that is appropriate for the severity of patient illness, building on compliance to promote quality medical care. Achieving acceptance for this approach will require support from Medicare as one component of a program for training physicians in E/M compliance. Following this, physicians can hope that insurers will also accept the merit of a long-term approach to the cost-effectiveness of quality care.

AUDITORS' CHALLENGES

While it is beyond the scope of this chapter to review all the details of medical record audits, it is valuable to consider several of the challenges that confront conscientious auditors when they are reviewing medical records. This section therefore brings together a number of issues addressed previously from the physicians' perspective and considers them from the auditors' point of view. It is also valuable for physicians to appreciate the types of documentation (or lack of documentation) that create these challenges, because these situations can lead to misunderstandings and disputes in the event of an audit. It is clearly far more enjoyable to avoid such disputes than to have to contend with them.

Medical History Section: Graphic Interface for Initial Patient Visits

As noted in Chapter 1, the graphic interface that allows patients to document their own past, family, and social history (PFSH) and review of systems (ROS) must be appropriately designed to both maximize its benefits and avoid several potential pitfalls during an E/M audit. First, the graphic interface must require the patient to personally document a response to every medical question asked. Otherwise, it is not possible to ascertain whether the patient considered the inquiry or understood it. Therefore, a selection list option, which provides a long list of illnesses or symptoms and instructs a patient to circle only those with a positive response, provides inadequate documentation. Using a selection list makes it impossible to document that the patient understood or even considered those items on the list that remain uncircled. In the extreme case, when the patient circles no responses, it is not possible to know whether the patient even read the material. From an auditor's perspective, strict interpretation of the *Documentation Guidelines* permits credit only for the circled elements, as those are the only elements that have actually been *documented*. In brief, the absence of documentation is not the equivalent of documentation of a negative response. The report of an auditor encountering this situation should suggest that the physician change his or her record to a form that requires "yes" and "no" responses to each inquiry.

The next challenge in the medical history section of the records is encountered when there is no documentation that the physician actually reviewed the graphic templates completed by a patient. This may occur either because this section of the record lacks a physician verification signature (as required by the *Documentation Guidelines*), and/or it fails to acknowledge and supplement the patient's positive responses. For example, if the patient checks "yes" to an inquiry about chest pain, headache, shortness of breath, or other symptoms, the physician must investigate and document the relevance of this information. If the auditor finds no such documentation, the auditor's report should not provide credit for this section, since the physician has not demonstrated that he or she reviewed this material.

The Educational Audit Report for Lack of Documentation of Review of the PFSH and ROS

If the auditor encounters this situation, the auditor's report should cite the review requirements of the *Documentation Guidelines*. It is an educational option for the auditing organization to decide whether, in this circumstance, they also wish to point out the risk of legal dangers if the patient should suffer a significant medical consequence from a reported symptom and the physician is unable to show that the documented complaint was appropriately investigated.

Medical History Section: PFSH and ROS for Established Patient Visits

Some medical practices have either transcription or electronic systems with functionality that automatically inserts an exact copy of the complete PFSH and ROS from the patient's initial visit into these sections of the medical record at each of the patient's subsequent follow-up visits. What the auditor sees is an identical, word-for-word copy of this information in the patient's medical record for every visit. The auditor must identify this as a noncompliant documentation practice. The PFSH and ROS from an initial visit two years ago (or two weeks ago) may not be the same as the status of the patient's PFSH and ROS on the date of the visit being reviewed. For example, the patient may have been diagnosed with diabetes or lung cancer in the time that has elapsed since the date of the initial visit with this physician. When physicians rely on systems that automatically populate this important section of the medical history with a duplicate of outdated information, they usually fail to inquire about changes in the patient's health status. Not only is this practice noncompliant for documentation purposes, most important, it conceals this medically vital patient information from the physician.

The *Documentation Guidelines* permits physicians to fulfill documentation requirements for this part of the medical history by inquiring about (and documenting) any changes in PFSH and ROS since the previous visit.[1] If a physician does not perform and document this update, then an auditor must conclude that there is no

PFSH or ROS for the current visit, and that any information provided is simply a copy of outdated information. This results in a problem-focused history, according to the CPT coding system guidelines.[2]

The Educational Audit Report for Lack of Documentation of Update of the PFSH And ROS

If the auditor encounters this situation, the auditor's report should point out that an automated duplicate of the PFSH and ROS information from a prior visit, without documentation of the patient's current status, does not fulfill the requirements of the CPT coding system guidelines and the *Documentation Guidelines*.

It is an educational option for the auditing organization to decide whether, under these circumstances, they also wish to point out the risk to the physician of legal consequences if the patient should suffer a severe consequence because the physician acted (or failed to act) without knowledge of recent changes in the patient's health.

Physical Examination Section: Graphic Interface

Auditors may face a challenge with graphic interface templates for the physical examination portion of the medical record that is similar to difficulties they can encounter with templates for the PFSH and ROS. If the physician checks off a box indicating that part of the examination is "abnormal," but he or she does not provide a narrative description of the abnormality, then for purposes of compliance with the *Documentation Guidelines*, the documentation is not adequate to confirm that this part of the examination has been performed.[1] Similarly, a notation of "normal" without additional detail will fail an audit for the portion of the examination related to symptomatic organ systems.[1] According to the requirements of the *Documentation Guidelines*, the auditor should not allow credit for these portions of the examination under either of these circumstances.

The Educational Audit Report for Inadequate Documentation of Physical Exam Elements

If this section's documentation is inadequate, the auditor's report should advise the physician that the *Documentation Guidelines* require that "specific abnormal and relevant negative findings of the examination of the affected or symptomatic body area(s) or organ system(s) should be documented. A notation of 'abnormal' without elaboration is insufficient."[1]

NPP Section

An auditor's greatest challenge in assessing the NPP is that conventional medical records provide no documentation of the physician's evaluation of this integral element of E/M coding. Without specific documentation by the physician, judgment of the severity of patient illness, and its risks of morbidity, mortality, and loss of bodily function, are left entirely to the auditor's interpretation. We recommend that if the auditor feels that the severity of a patient's NPP may not be sufficient to warrant the level of E/M care submitted by the physician, he or she should request assistance from a qualified physician to make this determination. Most important, in these cases the auditor's report should emphasize to physicians the importance of documenting the severity of the NPP in their medical records.

The NPP Message for Physicians

The auditors' perspective on the challenge of interpreting the NPP should emphasize to physicians the importance of documenting their impressions of the NPP for every patient encounter. The physician is the most knowledgeable individual to judge the type of NPP that is both appropriate and reasonable for the severity of the patient's illnesses on the day of the visit, and an auditor should accept this assessment when it is documented and compatible with the overall information in the medical record.

MDM Section

The greatest challenge of the MDM section for auditors is identical to the auditor's difficulty with the NPP. Most conventional medical records lack specific documentation of the three elements of risk and/or the level of complexity of data ordered and reviewed. This leaves subjective judgments of the risks of patient illnesses, diagnostic procedures, and treatments entirely to the auditor's interpretation. Once again, even with availability of the Table of Risk from the *Documentation Guidelines*,[1] an auditor may or may not have sufficient expertise to make this determination on the basis of the remaining documentation in the medical record. If the risk of a patient's illness(es), diagnostic procedures, and management options are not clear from the medical record, the auditor should seek assistance from a qualified physician in reviewing the record.

There are two additional MDM auditing issues of which physicians should be aware. First, most physicians do not separate treatment options from "data ordered" in their documentation. This may mislead the physician into believing he or she has considered more treatments than are actually documented. This is probably a residual consequence of the "SOAP notes" approach (*s*ubjective, *o*bjective, *a*ssessment, and *p*lans) to medical records, where the "plan" section includes both diagnostic tests and treatments. For example, if a physician lists under "impression" the single diagnosis of "chronic sinusitis" and then lists under "plan" "(1) amoxicillin, (2) computed tomographic scan," this does not count as two management options. In reality, it represents only one treatment and one diagnostic procedure (or data), because the scan is a diagnostic test, not a management option. This issue can result in a dramatically unexpected audit result for the physician; specifically, this example would lead to a straightforward level of MDM at best (unless at least a limited amount of data was also reviewed), resulting in a maximum E/M code of level 2 (ie, 99202). For this reason, as noted in Chapter 16, we advise physicians that their medical record documentation should separate the conventional "plans" section into its two appropriate E/M categories: treatment options and data ordered.[2]

The Educational Audit Report for Documentation Issues in the MDM Section

If the MDM section lacks documentation of the three components of risk, the complexity of data reviewed, and/or separation of the treatment options from data ordered, the auditor's report should include suggestions that the physician incorporate these features into subsequent medical record documentation.

ELECTRONIC HEALTH RECORD CHALLENGES

The final challenge auditors may encounter concerns the review of electronic records that compile medical histories, physical examinations, and sometimes even treatment options by copy forward functionality, using preformatted macros, and/or pick lists. When every record reads almost exactly the same as every other record, with the exception of one or two modified elements that relate solely to a problem-focused appraisal of a patient's presenting problem, the auditor's interpretation must be that the physician has provided only problem-focused care. This care has simply been plugged into a standard record that documents only the ability of the computer to automatically print the same information repeatedly, rather than accurately documenting the care that was actually performed. This is often described as "cloned" documentation. In this circumstance, credit for care can be given only for those elements that are individualized to that particular visit. The auditor should also advise the physician that such standardized repetitive elements do not fulfill the requirement of documenting the care that was actually provided.

An Auditor's Perspective on Repetitive or "Cloned" Documentation

When reviewing a series of charts where the documentation has been compiled by pick lists or prewritten macros, I have quickly become frustrated by the fact that I am looking only at the computer's ability to repeatedly print the same information, regardless of whether the care was actually provided. It feels like playing a game of cards when 50 of the cards in the deck are all the jack of clubs. There is a limited amount of information there, but not enough to really play cards. Providing information that appears identical in every case is the equivalent of providing no meaningful information (ie, the auditor's interpretation of "garbage in, garbage out").

Therefore, the accurate audit of such records can give credit only for the uniquely documented information, not for the automatic information. In summary, *automation is not documentation.*[3] In addition, the greatest concern with the use of automation is for the quality of care. When most of the elements of each record are identical, then most of the individual features of a patient's health and of his or her illness are lost. There is little basis for providing ongoing quality care.

Potential solutions for existing electronic health records with preloaded graphic templates, preentered generic macros, or "automatic" pick lists might include:

- requiring the physician to build the history and physical examination one check box at a time rather than providing a default template, or

- providing an additional check box for the physician to attest that each of the elements checked by default was actually performed, with the additional mandatory requirement for original narrative documentation of details for both pertinent positive and pertinent negative history elements and for pertinent positive and negative physical examination findings. Finally, the software also has to allow the physician to remove checks from boxes for those elements of care that were not performed.

Although these options would add some documentation time, they would also result in more individualized histories and physical examinations, which would demonstrate compliant care, documentation, and coding.

MAINTAINING AUDIT INTEGRITY

Physicians, Medicare, and private insurers must all be able to trust that the outcomes of E/M audits are accurate, consistent, and reliable. There are several approaches to ensuring the integrity of external (or internal) E/M audits, by applying checks and balances within the audit system itself. First, on occasion, an auditor should re-review the same chart two months after the first audit, and then compare the results for *intra-auditor consistency*. Second, there should be test cases where multiple auditors review the same chart and the audits are compared for *inter-auditor consistency*. Finally, auditors must be required to make formal written audit reports available to physicians, showing the results of each audit and providing the rationale for the findings. These reports not only provide educational feedback to clinicians, but they also allow review of the audit process and assurance that the auditors are following the principles described in the CPT codebook and in the *Documentation Guidelines*. It is advisable that these types of checks and balances be included in any auditor training protocol, such as will be proposed in Chapter 27.

Auditors Need to Use Compliant Tools as Well

The Centers for Medicare and Medicaid Services (CMS) has created a major problem for E/M compliance by permitting the use of noncompliant audit tools by many individual Medicare carriers. The most common of these tools fails to consider medical necessity and distorts the MDM component of E/M documentation by giving excessive credit for "new problems" (eg, a newly sprained ankle is credited as "multiple diagnoses," which is illogical and inappropriate) and inadequate credit for established problems regardless of their severity.

Some medical groups have taken advantage of this noncompliant tool, finding a variation of "new" problems for every visit; when combined with a prescription medication, this interpretation leads this noncompliant tool to assign moderate- or high-complexity MDM for every visit. With some aggressive documentation of history and examination, these groups will submit level 4 or level 5 codes for every visit, without considering medical necessity. The use of these noncompliant and unsanctioned audit tools has compromised the integrity and credibility of the Medicare carriers. The situation calls for CMS to require E/M compliance from all of its carriers.

Auditors as well as physicians require compliant tools. Everyone should have access to the same tools and be trained in the same coding and documentation methodology. For auditors, software tools should facilitate accurate application of the E/M guidelines in the CPT codebook and *Documentation Guidelines*, perform accurate coding calculations, and generate automated customized reports to send constructive information to physicians. Requiring that such tools be mandatory for the audit process promotes inter-auditor and intra-auditor consistency and provides a credible and reliable system for physicians.

Automated Downcoding of E/M Services

Appendix C of this book extends the content of this chapter by identifying a number of noncompliant *automated* E/M downcoding practices used by some commercial insurers in lieu of formal E/M audits. It discusses options that medical practices can use to respond to such practices, and it also presents strategies for responding to requests for medical record documentation as part of a formal external audit.

SUMMARY

Medicare and private insurers have used conventional E/M audits, almost exclusively, as an economic weapon rather than as an educational tool. That approach has not succeeded in improving E/M care or documentation. It has only achieved economic intimidation and provided a strong incentive for physicians to submit lower-level E/M codes, so that Medicare and private insurers can lower payments for each E/M visit. Because the payments for these low-level codes are inadequate for the time required to provide patients more comprehensive care, the consequence is that this economic disincentive discourages physicians from providing higher levels of E/M care for patients who have moderately severe and severe illnesses. This leads to increased reliance on sophisticated testing, and it sometimes results in more visits than would otherwise be required to solve the patient's problems. Thus, paradoxically, the outcome of this economically motivated effort to decrease E/M expenditures is an actual increase in overall medical costs, combined with a negative impact on quality of care.

These results of conventional external audits indicate the need for a different approach to E/M auditing, which should be focused on educating clinicians and providing them with tools that they can use to ensure compliant care and documentation. This approach should also prove beneficial for Medicare and private insurers, because when clinicians provide the appropriate level of E/M care, patients benefit from the most cost-effective diagnostic methodology. However, the health care system also needs CMS to set an example of compliance by requiring its carriers to use only compliant audit tools and to ensure that its auditors are appropriately trained.

References

1.   Health Care Financing Administration. *Documentation Guidelines for Evaluation and Management Services.* Chicago, IL: American Medical Association; 1997.

2.   American Medical Association. *Current Procedural Terminology CPT® 2008.* Chicago, IL: American Medical Association; 2007.

3.   Levinson S. *Practical EHR: Electronic Record Solutions for Compliance and Quality Care.* Chicago, IL: American Medical Association; 2008:99.

Internal E/M Audits for Practice Benefits

Audits of evaluation and management (E/M) records can (and should) be constructive! The preceding chapter showed how the introduction of Practical E/M principles can transform *external* audits from being an instrument for destructive imposition of economic penalties into a constructive educational tool to boost physician compliance. *Internal* Practical E/M audits offer even more significant benefits to practices reviewing their own medical records. In addition to providing constructive feedback to physicians by identifying potential issues with compliance, quality, and productivity, they can act as a catalyst to help physicians work together with their coding staff to identify medical record problems and to introduce solutions to remedy them.

Many larger practices employ professional coders, who fill multiple essential roles related to the following:

■ Proper coding for accurate claims submission

■ Review of Medicare and insurer explanation of benefits (EOB) reports, including analysis of payments and denials, filing of appeals, and interpretation and explanation for physicians about payer policies on payments

■ Documentation and coding reviews for accuracy and compliance

■ Involvement in a practice's formal compliance program

Although most small medical practices do not currently employ a professional coder, perform internal audits of their E/M documentation and coding, or have a formal compliance program, they can achieve significant benefit from introducing Practical E/M audits, performed either by a physician who understands E/M compliance or by an outside coding consultant. For large and small practices alike, the benefits of implementing internal Practical E/M audits include the following:

■ Audit reports generate positive and constructive feedback to physicians, not only encouraging compliance but also promoting quality, efficiency, and productivity.

■ Proper documentation of these audits demonstrates many of the elements of a formal office coding compliance program.

■ Establishment of a compliant internal audit program gives the practice the insight needed to identify and address inappropriate or automated E/M downcoding by private insurers.

■ Experience with internal audits provides the expertise to evaluate and respond to noncompliant external audits by Medicare carriers or private insurers.

THE PHILOSOPHY OF PRACTICAL E/M AUDITS

The actual review of E/M records in a Practical E/M audit begins in a very similar fashion to conventional audits. The coders *who* perform the audits need no major new skills in chart review, and *what* steps they take in evaluating medical record documentation and coding are essentially unchanged from the protocols they are currently accustomed to using. However, there are significant changes in the *why*, the *how*, and even the *when* of performing this type of audit.

The *Why* of Performing Practical E/M Audits

Conventional internal E/M audits generally have the intent of identifying documentation and coding errors and then providing physicians with a list of rules to follow while performing and documenting patient care. However, this approach has been unsuccessful in providing physicians with a usable and reliable means of achieving compliant E/M records. Physicians do not want to memorize long lists of coding rules or be required to interrupt patient care and communication to look them up. Personal survey of more than a thousand professional coders reveals that few ever encounter even a single physician who is able to consistently achieve compliance for aligning the three critical E/M measures of documentation, code selection, and medical necessity while using conventional medical record forms.

The goals of Practical E/M audits go significantly beyond identifying documentation and coding problems. They are designed to lay the groundwork for resolving physicians' E/M problems. The reviewer delves more deeply into the documentation features that are creating these problems. This insight allows physicians to understand and appreciate the advantages of adopting IMR designs that inherently overcome these fundamental E/M challenges while at the same time matching physicians' optimal patient care workflow rather than interfering with it.

The *How* of Performing Practical E/M Audits

Overview of Conventional E/M Audit Tools
Achieving compliant E/M documentation and coding requires compliant E/M auditing. Practical E/M rejects commonly encountered audit tools that substitute noncompliant assumptions and calculation shortcuts for accurate auditing. Many of the conventional tools also focus on "counting" quantitative aspects of documentation, while overlooking the qualitative and substantive aspects of medical records that should be incorporated into constructive audits.

Areas of Compliance Concern With Conventional Audit Tools

Some of the areas of compliance concern encountered with conventional paper E/M audit tools include the following:

1) Medical history component

   a) History of present illness (HPI) – Inability to consider whether documentation presents a true medical history, including a chronological description of the development of the patient's illness, rather than just an "extended" chief complaint

2) Physical examination

   a) Inability to assess whether organ systems that are documented as being *abnormal* also include documented descriptions of the "specific abnormal findings"[2(p 11)]

   b) Inability to assess whether affected or symptomatic organ systems that are documented as being *normal* also include documented descriptions of the "relevant negative findings"[2(p 11)]

---

continued

3) Medical decision making

    a) Number of diagnoses and/or management options – the most commonly employed shortcut tool confuses whether a problem is "new" or "established" with the "number" of diagnoses; it also fails to attribute any credit to the number of management options

    b) Amount and/or complexity of data – some audit tools fail to weigh complexity of data; most audit tools fail to report absence of documentation of this factor in the medical record

    c) Levels of risk of complications, morbidity, and/or mortality in three categories related to presenting problem(s), diagnostic procedures, and management options; most audit tools fail to report absence of documentation of this factor in the medical record

4) Nature of the presenting problem(s) (NPP)

    a) Most commonly used audit tools fail to consider the role of medical necessity in determining appropriate levels of care

    b) Most audit tools also fail to report absence of documentation of this factor in the medical record

Conventional audit tools also generally require multiple steps of coding calculations. In addition to being time consuming and requiring uncreative busy work for experienced coders, this audit approach commonly leads to a singular focus on comparisons of medical record documentation to code selection, excluding considerations of medical necessity, usability of medical records, care and documentation efficiency, and quality of care. Although current software audit systems eliminate the unpleasant manual code calculations, they generally continue to be encumbered by most of the compliance issues accompanying conventional paper audit forms, particularly inclusion of noncompliant measures for medical decision making (MDM) and lack of consideration of medical necessity.

Overview of Practical E/M Audit Tools

In contrast, the Practical E/M audit approach emulates intelligent medical record (IMR) forms for physicians by providing intelligent audit (IA) forms. These help coders address all of these conventional audit problems by incorporating the actual documentation and coding guidelines presented in the Current Procedural Terminology (CPT®) codebook and the *Documentation Guidelines for Evaluation and Management Services*[2] into effective audit tools, thereby ensuring accurate and consistent audits. By replacing the complex multilayered calculations required during conventional E/M audits with easily performed comparisons of levels of care entered onto color-coded audit templates, IA forms also:

- Eliminate calculation drudgery
- Increase audit efficiency
- Help coders focus on the more important creative work of identifying physicians' documentation patterns, the sources of compliance errors, and the development of educational reports that pave the way for effective physician solutions

(Section 4 of the accompanying CD-ROM provides printable color copies of these forms for outpatient services and inpatient care.)

The *When* of Performing Practical E/M Audits

There is an optimal timing schedule for medical practices introducing this type of audit. Because the purpose is educational, and the goal is correcting and eliminating E/M challenges, the initial Practical E/M audit should be considered a "current status" audit. This should be scheduled in the context of identifying current documentation and coding problems as a precursor to introducing medical record strategies and forms that will eliminate those problems. As discussed below, part of this overall review will include assessments of (1) the financial risks involved in the event an external audit of current medical record practices and (2) the potential increased productivity rewards projected to result from introducing compliant protocols and medical record forms.

How Many Charts Should Be Audited?

There are a number of good reasons to review no more than a small number of representative charts from each physician. First, my personal impression, based on experience auditing large numbers of E/M charts and confirmed by other expert coders, is that a review of five or six charts (half of which should be new patient or consultation visits and the other half established patient visits) is sufficient for a qualified coder to identify consistent documentation and coding patterns with a high degree of certainty. Of course, additional charts can be reviewed if patterns do not emerge, or if a physician feels that further reviews would be beneficial; however, neither of these issues has arisen in my experience. In addition, by avoiding a large sample size, the results of the audit cannot be considered "statistically significant." As a result, there are no valid financial implications that would require significant repayments if the sample audit reveals some degree of overcoding or underdocumentation.

Assuming that the current status audit leads to effective reviews and a mandate to implement IMR-type medical record forms for the practice, experience shows that it is wise for coders to monitor the charts created during the early stages of the implementation. Even though the overall instruction to physicians is that it is mandatory to complete every section of IMR forms, experience shows that any protocol that changes current documentation habits (eg, documenting levels of risk and the NPP) commonly needs to be reinforced one or more times before physicians assimilate these habits into their normal patient care workflow. This initial monitoring would be followed approximately six to eight weeks later by a "postimplementation" audit. Once again reviewing five or six medical records per physician, the coders can confirm accurate matching of code selection to severity of patients' NPP, presence of sufficient levels of care and documentation to support the codes selected, and documentation of all components of the E/M record to ensure audit protection. The conclusion of this review should confirm both the audit protection features and productivity benefits of the new program when compared with the findings of the preliminary "current status" audit.

PROTOCOL FOR PERFORMING INTERNAL PRACTICAL E/M AUDITS

While the steps involved in the Practical E/M medical record audit are conceptually similar to those of traditional audits, it is valuable to point out some of the nuances and potential "gray areas" of these reviews before looking at the innovative aspects of Practical E/M reports. Please print copies of the IA forms from Part 4 of the accompanying CD-ROM to illustrate the following steps.

Step 1: Confirming the Correct Type of Service

The preliminary step of an internal audit is confirming that the physician has identified the correct type of service. To accomplish this, the auditor needs to confirm that the selected type of visit matches the requirements in the CPT codebook for that service. It is particularly important to be certain that all documentation requirements are met for consultation services, including the request for consultation and provision of an appropriate written report to the referring physician. (This information is reviewed in more detail in Chapter 9.) Once the correct type of service is identified, the reviewer can select an IA form designed for that specific type of service, fill in the demographic information on the cover sheet, and proceed to review the documentation in the medical record.

Step 2: Auditing the Level of History Documented

The auditor next reviews the medical history portion of the medical record and records the findings by circling the appropriate number of elements for past, family, and social history (PFSH), review of systems (ROS), and HPI (including confirmation of an appropriate chronological description of the course of the illness) in the top section of page 1 of the four-page IA form. The form guides auditors to identify the lowest level of the three elements circled and assigns this as the level of history documented by circling the corresponding level in the final column. The auditor may transfer this result to page 4 at this time or later in the audit.

Step 3: Auditing the Level of Physical Examination Documented

The middle and bottom sections of page 1 provide templates for circling the level of physical examination documented, as interpreted by both the 1997 and 1995 *Documentation Guidelines*. The appropriate guidance is present for interpreting the level of documentation both ways, as well as check boxes to denote when a physician does not adequately document abnormal and/or pertinent normal findings.

Auditors are reminded that for a "detailed" examination," the 1995 *Documentation Guidelines* require the physician to record an "extended" examination, not only of the affected body area or organ system, but also of the "other symptomatic or related organ system(s)."[3(p 9)]

A Common Problem for Exam Documentation Based on the 1995 *Documentation Guidelines*

It is noteworthy that most coders report that they encounter very few medical records where physicians relying on the 1995 *Documentation Guidelines* actually document a "detailed" physical examination. While physicians may document an "extended" examination of the organ system related to the chief complaint, their documentation of the other symptomatic or related organ systems is almost always "limited," which supports only an "expanded problem focused" examination.

After documenting the results determined by both sets of guidelines, the auditor will transfer the *higher* of these two levels to the corresponding section of page 4.

Step 4: Auditing the Level of MDM

Page 2 of the IA form provides a template for circling the levels of the multiple elements and subcomponents of MDM. As pointed out previously, it is unusual for physicians using conventional medical record forms to document a significant number of these subcomponents, leaving this assessment to the judgment of a reviewer.

Since Practical E/M emphasizes the importance of physicians documenting *all* the subcomponents of E/M care, the IA forms provide for placement of an asterisk to denote those subcomponents that have not been documented.

The IA form instructs the reviewer how to identify the correct level of MDM directly from the multiple subcomponents documented. This value is circled in the column on the right and transferred to page 4.

Step 5: Auditing the Level of the NPP

The template on page 3 permits the reviewer to circle the level of the NPP based on the CPT definitions (with the addition of Practical E/M's added definitions for "low to moderate" and "moderate to high"). Coders are also encouraged to refer to the clinical examples provided in the CPT codebook's Appendix C to identify the types of medical problems appropriately matched to these various levels of severity of illness. It is also extremely unusual for physicians using conventional medical record forms to document the NPP, again leaving this assessment to the judgment of a reviewer. The IA forms provide for placement of an asterisk to denote whenever a medical record is lacking this documentation. After completing this determination, the reviewer transfers it to the appropriate section of page 4.

When the medical record lacks documentation of the NPP, it becomes necessary for the auditor to use his or her judgment to make this determination. A reasonable assessment can usually be inferred from the diagnoses documented, diagnostic tests ordered, and management options recommended, as well as the overall sense of the severity of illness conveyed in the medical history. The auditor may also seek physician assistance if there is a significant question about the appropriate level of severity for the NPP.

Since it can often be challenging for a reviewer to determine a reasonable level of NPP just from the documented history and physical (H&P), it is far preferable for the experienced physician who is caring for the patient to make this determination at the point of care. For example, a diagnosis of "headache" could indicate levels of severity that range from the common mild tension headache (low NPP) to the possibility of an intracranial aneurysm (very high NPP). From a compliance standpoint, the physician and the auditor will both be happier when the physician documents a realistic assessment of the NPP at the time of the visit. It helps the physician establish the appropriate level of care for the patient, and it conveys this information to an auditor for a fair and reasonable review of the appropriateness of the care provided. (This documentation also becomes particularly valuable in the event of an external audit.) When an internal audit identifies a physician who fails to provide this documentation, the auditor should always urge that physician to add this information to his or her medical records to prevent problems in the event of an external audit.

Step 6: Deriving Two Levels of Care, Determined by the Key Components and by the NPP

The final page of the IA form brings together the audit results of the three key components and the NPP from the first three pages. It provides instructions that incorporate the CPT rules, based on the type of service, for considering two of three or three of three of the key components to interpret the level of care documented on the basis of the key components. The form provides a separate determination for the level of care warranted by the NPP.

The terminology of Practical E/M's overall assessment of the audit differs from the descriptions used in conventional audits, which basically compare only the code submitted and the level of care supported by the medical record documentation, only occasionally considering the NPP under limited circumstances. A Practical E/M summary compares all three factors (E/M code selected, level of care documented in the medical record, and level of care warranted by the NPP) in the following sequence:

- First, the E/M code submitted is compared with the level of care warranted by the NPP. Ideally, these two levels should match in every case. If the code selected is higher than warranted by the NPP, it is identified as "overcoding." If the code selected is lower than warranted by the NPP, it is identified as "undercoding."

- Next, as in a conventional audit, the E/M code submitted is compared with the level of care documented by the three key components. If the documentation fails to be sufficient to support the submitted code, it is identified as "underdocumentation for the E/M code submitted."

- Finally, and most important, the E/M code warranted by the NPP is compared with the level of care documented by the three key components. If the documentation is insufficient to support the warranted level of care, it is identified as "underdocumentation for the level of care warranted by the NPP."

THE AUDITOR'S ROLE IN ASSESSING LEVELS OF CARE AND THE NPP FOR PHYSICIANS USING IMR FORMS

When performing immediate postimplementation audits and ongoing E/M compliance audits for practices that have implemented a Practical E/M program, coders and reviewers will pay particular attention to the physicians' selection of appropriate levels of the NPP. This is because correct use of the IMR forms should ensure that the provision and documentation of care for the three key components is consistently sufficient to fulfill the requirements of the levels of care (ie, the E/M code) selected.

A physician using an IMR should have documented his or her impression of the NPP for the visit on the final page of the form. If this has not been documented (or if the physician is using a different type of form that lacks this capability), one of the auditor's primary responsibilities is to inform the physician of the need to make this determination and to complete this section of the chart.

Alternatively, when the physician has documented the NPP, the auditor should consider whether the selected severity seems "reasonable" for the documented impressions, management recommendations, and the patient's medical history. This review may include reference to the CPT coding system guidelines and clinical examples. One of the benefits of internal audits is that the auditor can discuss any concerns with the physician who provided the care to be sure that there is ultimately an agreement on the appropriate level of severity of NPP.

For convenient reference, Table 25.1 shows a summary "auditing prompt," correlating NPP levels of severity with levels of care. The table is derived from the E/M coding descriptors in the CPT codebook for the outpatient services that auditors evaluate most frequently. Auditors can create similar tables for other types of service, such as hospital inpatient care, by following CPT coding guidelines and E/M descriptors.[1]

TABLE 25.1

Auditing Prompt Correlating Level of Care With NPP* for Outpatient Office Visits

Initial Visit		Established Patient Visit		Outpatient Consultation	
E/M Code	Type of NPP	E/M Code	Type of NPP	E/M Code	Type of NPP
99201	Self limited or minor	99211	Minimal	99241	Self limited or minor
99202	Low to moderate severity	99212	Self limited or minor	99242	Low severity
99203	Moderate severity	99213	Low to moderate severity	99243	Moderate severity
99204	Moderate to high severity	99214	Moderate to high severity	99244	Moderate to high severity
99205	Moderate to high severity	99215	Moderate to high severity	99245	Moderate to high severity

* The type of NPP must equal or exceed the severity level shown to support the indicated E/M code. Ideally (for internal audits) the type of NPP should be equal to the severity level shown for the selected level of care.

Source: *CPT 2008.*[1]

For example, an NPP of "low to moderate" calls for level 3 care for an established patient visit (CPT code 99213) but for level 2 care for a new patient visit (CPT code 99202) or consultation (CPT code 99242). This association enables the auditor to apply CPT coding guidelines to compare the level of care (E/M code) selected by the physician with the type (or severity) of NPP he or she has documented in the medical record. When the selected code is either higher or lower than the level of care indicated by the NPP, the auditor will note this discrepancy in the audit report as either overcoding or undercoding. Ideally, the auditor should discover and confirm that the physician is consistently following the documentation prompts for the NPP that guide him or her to select the level of care warranted by the NPP, which benefits both the physician's quality of care and productivity.

Addressing Cases Where the Level of Care Selected Differs From the Level of Care Warranted by the NPP

In cases where the audit findings do not confirm alignment of selected E/M code with the documented level of the NPP, the auditor should be equally concerned regardless of whether the submitted code is higher or lower than the level of care warranted by the NPP:

■ If the selected code level is higher than warranted by the patient's NPP, it indicates that there is insufficient medical necessity to support submitting that level of care. In this "overcoding" situation, the auditor should suggest lowering the submitted E/M code, but this would be solely on the basis of medical necessity rather than on the extent of documentation of key components.

■ If the selected code level is lower than warranted by the patient's NPP, it indicates that the physician has chosen to provide insufficient complexity of care. The resultant undercoding has the potential to affect both quality of care and physician productivity. Under this circumstance, the auditor should constructively suggest that the physician can submit a higher level of care (ie, E/M code) when faced with similar cases in the future. (Note: If the key component documentation in the chart also supports a higher-level E/M code than the one submitted, then the auditor can recommend increasing the code to the proper level for the reviewed case as well.)

Clinical Impact of Selecting Levels of Care Lower Than Warranted by the NPP (Undercoding)

Conventional E/M audits, whether internal or external, do not commonly evaluate situations in which the E/M code selected is *lower* than the level of care that is indicated by the NPP. This is because these audits are oriented to satisfying the rules of a "coding game," and they direct little or no attention to the quality and appropriateness of care. The consequence of this oversight is easily illustrated by examining a clinical example from Appendix C in the CPT codebook. The first sample patient visit listed for E/M code 99205 states, "initial office visit for a patient with disseminated lupus erythematosus with kidney disease, edema, purpura, and scarring lesions on the extremities plus cardiac symptoms."[1]

For the purposes of this example, let's assume that the physician submitted E/M code 99203 and accurately documented care appropriate for this code (ie, a detailed history, detailed physical examination, and MDM of low complexity). An auditor applying a conventional E/M audit approach to this medical record will first calculate the documentation-derived E/M code, which will be 99203. Next, the auditor will compare this to the submitted code of 99203 and conclude that the coding "passed audit." In the event that the auditor considers the NPP, he or she should conclude in this case that the NPP is high and therefore that there is sufficient medical necessity to support the submitted 99203 level of care. This medical record therefore passes a conventional E/M audit.

On the contrary, this example should not pass audit. From the Practical E/M audit's perspective of quality of care and optimal productivity, our concerns with this example should be obvious. This patient has a high NPP, with high morbidity and a life-threatening illness. Clearly, as confirmed in Appendix C of the CPT codebook, this patient warrants the level of care compatible with E/M code 99205 (ie, comprehensive history, comprehensive examination, and complex MDM). From a liability perspective, the 99203 care in the example reports that the physician has provided a level of care lower than the standard set by the three specialty societies that approved this clinical example.

In this example, either the physician has performed an extent of care that was lower than indicated by the NPP, or the physician actually provided an appropriate level of care, but failed to perform adequate documentation and coding of that care. The medical record has "passed" the conventional audit. However, the conventional audit approach has failed the patient and the physician, because it provides no measure of the appropriateness of the level of care the physician selected, thereby permitting "undercoding." The Practical E/M internal audit protocol specifically addresses this problem and corrects it.

Table 25.2 illustrates the section of a sample internal E/M audit that compares the submitted E/M codes against the appropriate level of E/M code indicated by the NPP. The auditor can employ color-coding or symbols to demonstrate whether the submitted E/M code is:

- higher than warranted by the NPP,
- lower than warranted by the NPP, or
- appropriate for the level of care warranted by the NPP.

T A B L E   25.2

Illustration of Audit of Submitted E/M Codes Based on NPP

Demographics*	E/M Code Based on NPP	E/M Code Submitted
Record 1	99203	99203
Record 2	99202	99203[†]
Record 3	99204	99203[‡]

* Indicates multiple information sections, which may include audit date, physician name, patient name, patient account number, date of visit, and so on.

[†] Submitted E/M code is higher than warranted by NPP.

[‡] Submitted E/M code is lower than warranted by NPP.

Comparing Consideration of the NPP for Internal versus External Audits

Internal audits can be more particular in matching the selected E/M code to the NPP than the protocol recommended for external audits in the previous chapter. External audits can reasonably evaluate only one aspect of appropriateness of the NPP: whether the submitted code is, or is not, *higher* than the level of care warranted by the NPP. This is done to evaluate for possible *overcoding*.

When a medical practice is evaluating its own medical records, however, it is equally important for the reviewer to pay close attention to whether the submitted code might be *lower* than the level of care warranted by the NPP. This approach enables the practice to identify not only *overcoding*, but also possible *undercoding*. The goal for internal audits is that the E/M code selected should be precisely in agreement with CPT coding system guidelines, avoiding both overcoding and undercoding. Guaranteeing precise agreement with the CPT coding system guidelines for the NPP ensures both appropriate levels of care and appropriate levels of reimbursement.

Does the physician need to be certain of the patient's diagnosis to select an appropriate NPP? In many cases, it will not be possible for the physician to be absolutely certain of the diagnosis until the patient returns with laboratory test results, radiology reports, or consultation letters. However, neither this information nor a final diagnosis is required for the physician to determine the NPP. Appendix C in the CPT codebook clearly demonstrates that when the NPP leads the physician to realistically believe that a severe illness is the potential cause of a patient's problems, and he or she proceeds with an evaluation of this possibility, then it is reasonable to document that the NPP is high.

In the headache example provided earlier in this chapter, if the physician documents a significant possibility of the patient having an intracranial aneurysm, and confirms the seriousness of this possibility by obtaining an urgent or emergent neurology consultation, then it is reasonable for him or her to indicate that the severity of the NPP is high.

COMPILING EDUCATIONAL INTERNAL AUDIT REPORTS

The results of individual chart audits are compiled into Practical E/M audit reports, which are designed to be educational and constructive. These can include the collected IA reports for each chart reviewed, a graphic table that compiles the results of the individual reports, and a narrative summary of the findings. For current status audits of physicians who are using conventional records, these reports should clearly report E/M compliance issues, identify the underlying factors causing the problems, and presumably lay the foundation for adoption of an approach and tools that will resolve the problems while optimizing quality and efficiency. When used for postimplementation audits of practices using IMR forms, the reports should confirm compliant documentation and coding, spotlight any questions about identification of appropriate levels of the NPP, and form the core of an office compliance program.

An optimal summary report begins by identifying the levels of care (ie, E/M code) submitted, documented, and warranted by the NPP for each medical record audited. This fundamental information can be supplemented by including findings related to two prevalent medical record problems that frequently contribute to noncompliant documentation:

- Performance of a *comprehensive* medical history. This fundamental tenet of Practical E/M documentation is needed to ensure that the physician has obtained sufficient information about a patient's health to make an accurate assessment of the NPP.

- Documentation of *all* the elements of E/M coding. To ensure compliant documentation and audit protection, physicians must *document* those elements that are commonly left out of conventional medical records: (1) complexity of data to be reviewed; (2) the risks associated with the patient's presenting problem(s), the diagnostic procedures ordered, and the management options recommended; and (3) the NPP.

Reporting the Levels of Care Submitted, Documented, and Warranted by the NPP

As already emphasized, in compliant medical records the E/M code selected should match the level of care medically indicated by the NPP, and the documentation of the three key components should demonstrate that the level of care provided meets or exceeds the CPT descriptors for this level of care.

The audit results shown on page 4 of individual reviews can be transferred to the portion of a graphic table that compares the E/M code submitted, the level of care documented by the three key components, and the level of care warranted by the NPP.

Table 25.3 builds on the audit form shown in Table 25.2, adding the column that reports the E/M code determined by the physician's documentation. It illustrates the section of a graphic internal audit report that compares (1) the extent of E/M care appropriate for the NPP at the time of the visit (based on CPT coding guidelines) with (2) the E/M code submitted and (3) the E/M code calculated from the documented extent of care. The Table can employ color-coding or symbols to demonstrate whether:

- There is, or is not, sufficient documentation of the three key components to support the E/M code submitted
- There is, or is not, sufficient documentation of the three key components to support the E/M code warranted by the NPP

Table 25.3

Sample of Audit Comparing Code Submitted, Code Calculated From Documentation, and Level of Care Appropriate for NPP

Demographics*	E/M Based on NPP	E/M Submitted	E/M Based on Documented Care
Record 1	99203	99203	99204
Record 2	99202	99203[†]	99203
Record 3	99204	99203[‡]	99202[§]
Record 4	99204	99203[‡]	99203[‖]

*Indicates multiple sections, which may include audit date, physician name, patient name, patient account number, date of visit, and so on.

[†]Submitted E/M code is higher than warranted by NPP.

[‡]Submitted E/M code is lower than warranted by NPP.

[§]Documented care is lower than submitted E/M code and lower than warranted by NPP.

[‖]Documented care is lower than warranted by NPP.

The auditor's accompanying written report should summarize the number of records where the E/M code submitted was higher than warranted by the NPP, lower than warranted by the NPP, and appropriate for the NPP. It should also summarize results of the comparison of the level of care performed, based on the documentation of the three key components, with the E/M code submitted and the E/M code appropriate for the NPP. This should show the total number of audited records where:

■   The documented level of care supports the selected E/M code

■   The documented level of care is insufficient to support the selected E/M code.

There is, of course, no category of "excess documentation" of the three key components. Physicians may provide a higher level of care than called for by the NPP based on their personal judgment of the level of care that they feel is medically indicated for each patient at each visit. Sometimes, for example, it requires a more extensive physician examination to medically confirm that the patient does not have a more serious illness.

Above and Beyond

In my own medical practice, I followed the philosophy that every new patient should have at least a comprehensive medical history and a detailed specialty-specific head and neck examination. Although this amount of documented care clearly exceeded the minimum requirement for a patient with a low NPP (eg, a patient presenting with a straightforward viral upper respiratory infection), this was the level of care I personally wanted to provide for my patients—to make sure that they had nothing more than that simple viral upper respiratory infection.

In many cases, the result of providing this level of care was the discovery of additional medical issues, either related or unrelated to the patient's presenting complaint. Such findings enhanced quality of care, improved patient relations, increased my personal satisfaction as a physician, and often led to higher levels of care and increased productivity because of the increased number and/or severity of medical problems.

The comparison of these three levels of care is the centerpiece of Practical E/M audit reports. It emphasizes that the level of care warranted by the NPP is the medical standard for judging the appropriateness of both the E/M code submitted and the level of care provided (and documented). The focus of this internal audit approach is not only on meeting the compliance requirements of the CPT coding system guidelines, but also on the appropriateness of the extent of care the physician provides. It therefore becomes a tool that helps physicians achieve their goals for providing quality care, while also helping them obtain the correct level of reimbursement for these services.

Reporting the Quality of Medical History Documented

Internal audits can help physicians to achieve their patient care, productivity, and compliance goals by evaluating whether sufficient medical history was obtained (and documented) to enable the physician to adequately assess the present illness and the patient's overall health picture. Physicians cannot formulate a reliable differential diagnosis or reasonably judge the severity of a medical problem (ie, NPP) either by investigating only a few characteristics of the chief complaint without obtaining a true medical history or by eliciting a history of the course of the patient's illness but including details about only one or two elements of the HPI. They also cannot consider related medical problems or the context of a patient's overall health without obtaining sufficient information about a patient's PFSH and ROS.

This portion of a Practical E/M internal audit report analyzes and reports the chronological description and number of elements of the HPI (1 to 8), the number of elements of the PFSH (1 to 3), and the number of organ systems reviewed and documented as part of the ROS (1 to 14). While performing each audit, the coder notes the amount of documentation for each of these three subcomponents of medical history on page 1 of the IA form. As the medical record is being evaluated, these findings can be transferred to a table such as the one shown in Table 25.4, reporting how many elements were documented for each of the three factors.

Table 25.4 illustrates the section of a sample audit report that shows the extent of HPI, PFSH, and ROS documented in the medical record of a patient seen for an initial outpatient visit or consultation. The auditor can utilize color coding or symbols to demonstrate when the extent of documentation reveals that the physician documented less than required for a comprehensive history; ie, less than an extended history of the present illness, less than a complete PFSH, and less than a complete ROS.

TABLE 25.4

Sample Audit of Amount of Medical History

Demographics*	E/M Code Submitted	No. of Elements of HPI	No. of Elements of PFSH	No. of Elements of ROS
Record 1	99203	4	2[†]	7[†]
Record 2	99203	2[†]	1[†]	2[†]
Record 3	99203	6	3	12

* Indicates multiple sections, which may include audit date, physician name, patient name, patient account number, date of visit, and so on.

[†] Documentation is less than "extended" for the HPI, or less than "complete" for the PFSH and ROS, based on the guidelines published in the *Documentation Guidelines*.[2]

In an accompanying written report, the reviewer will include a summary of the number of records reviewed that included a comprehensive medical history and the number that did not. The auditor should also have the freedom to expand on the quantitative analysis shown in Table 25.4. In particular, if the physician's notes fail to address the patient's positive responses to the questions listed in the PFSH and ROS, the report should point out the problems this lack of documentation can create in the areas of:

- Compliance; eg, "an external audit would probably not give credit for sections of the PFSH and/or ROS that lack documentation that the patient's responses were reviewed and included in the care process."
- Productivity; eg, "an external audit reaching this conclusion could result in downcoding and negative financial consequences for the practice."
- Quality of patient care; eg, "the patient's documented concerns could indicate additional medical conditions, care of which would benefit overall health."
- Possible professional liability issues; eg, "a documented patient concern that was not addressed could progress to a serious or life-threatening condition."

Reporting Documentation of Commonly Overlooked Subcomponents

As discussed in detail in Chapter 16, the CPT coding set defines multiple subcomponents of MDM, and the vast majority of physicians fail to document four of these in their medical records:

- Complexity of data to be reviewed
- Risk of significant complications, morbidity, and/or mortality associated with the patient's presenting problem(s)
- Risk of significant complications, morbidity, and/or mortality associated with the diagnostic procedures ordered
- Risk of significant complications, morbidity, and/or mortality associated with the possible management options

Similarly, unless they are using IMR forms, physicians do not document the NPP, which confirms the level of medical necessity for the care provided, as part of their H&P. However, by documenting all of these commonly missing elements, physicians can ensure that they are the individuals making these subjective assessments about severity and complexity, not an outside reviewer whose judgment of these critical factors may not be accurate or reliable.

While performing each individual audit, coders note on page 2 of the IA form (with use of an asterisk) any of these MDM elements that have not been documented. On page 3, they report whether the NPP has been documented. As each medical record is being evaluated, these findings can be transferred to a table such as the one shown in Table 25.5, recording a "yes" or "no" to indicate whether the record contains documentation of each of these three factors.

T a b l e 25.5

Sample Audit of Documentation of Specific Elements of MDM and NPP This table reports whether each record contains documentation of the complexity of data, the three levels of risk defined in the CPT codebook, and the NPP.

Demographics*	Documentation of Complexity of Data	Documentation of 3 Levels of Risk	Documentation of NPP
Record 1	No	Yes (1/3 documented)	No
Record 2	No	No	No
Record 3	No	No	No

* Note: "Demographics" may include multiple sections, which may consist of audit date, physician name, patient name, patient account number, date of visit, etc.

In the accompanying written report, the reviewer will include a summary of the number of records reviewed that included documentation of these components of E/M documentation and those that did not.

EDUCATIONAL MATERIALS FOR PHYSICIANS

The graphic reports illustrated in Tables 25.2 to 25.5 form the centerpiece of a quality-of-care–focused internal E/M audit. The information in these four tables can also be combined into a single integrated spreadsheet analysis form; an example of the appearance of this all-in-one table is presented in Table 25.6.

Table 25.6

Sample of an Integrated Spreadsheet This table includes, in addition to the code submitted, the information from Table 25.2 (level of care appropriate for the NPP), Table 25.3 (level of care based on documentation of the three key components), Table 25.4 (the level of medical history documented), and Table 25.5 (the presence or absence of commonly overlooked subcomponents). Shading and symbols shown can be translated to color-coding for ease of review. For space considerations, this table should be created in a "landscape" orientation.

Demographics*	1: E/M Code		2: E/M	3: Sufficiency of Hx			4: MDM Elements and NPP			Comments
	Submitted	By 3 Key Components	By NPP	HPI	PFSH	ROS	Data Complexity	3 Levels of Risk	NPP	
Record 1	99203	99204	99203	4	3	12	No	Yes (1)	No	
Record 2	99203†	99203	99202	2	1	2	No	No	No	
Record 3	99203‡	99202§	99204	6	2	1	No	No	No	
Record 4	99203‡	99203‖	99204	1	2	7	No	No	No	

* Indicates multiple sections, which may consist of audit date, physician name, patient name, patient account number, date of visit, and so on.

Code submitted:

† Submitted E/M code is higher than warranted by NPP.

‡ Submitted E/M code is lower than warranted by NPP.

Code determined by three key components:

§ Documented care is lower than submitted E/M code and lower than warranted by NPP.

‖ Documented care is lower than warranted by NPP.

Sufficiency of medical history (Hx):

　Lists the number of elements documented for HPI, PFSH, and ROS

　Shaded boxes indicate documentation of less than an "extended" HPI, complete PFSH, and/or complete ROS

Documentation of MDM Elements and NPP:

　Indicates whether each component was documented

　Shaded boxes indicate components that were not documented

Whether presented individually or in an integrated sheet, the information in these tables can be accompanied by an additional narrative summary to inform physicians of the overall findings of the audit, emphasizing the relationships between severity of illness, NPP, code selection, medical care performed, and documentation.

Narrative Summary Report

The final document is a narrative report interpreting the results shown in the graphic table(s). The auditor should have this explanation programmed as a word processor macro, and then fill in the details of the audit results shown in the tables. The report should first explain the CPT coding principles of selecting the appropriate E/M code based on care warranted by the patient's NPP, filling in the findings related to Table 25.2. This is followed by a summary of the findings comparing the level of care provided with the levels submitted and medically indicated, as shown in Table 25.3. The report then summarizes the findings in Table 25.4 and 25.5 regarding the amount of medical history documented and presence or absence of documentation of the elements of MDM and NPP. If the auditor uses a combined graphic format shown in Table 25.6, the appropriate sections of the single table can be referenced in the narrative.

Optional Additional Reports

The coder performing an internal audit also has an *option*, if even greater depth seems appropriate, of creating a detailed analysis of the documentation in each medical record reviewed. This "Summary Report," which is illustrated in Figure 25.1, shows in greater detail the audit findings revealed in the IA forms.

F I G U R E 25.1

Illustration of Analysis of Chart Documentation of Care Provided This Summary Report is based on an audit in which the code submitted was level 4 and the auditor determined that the code indicated by the NPP was also level 4, but the level of care documented met requirements only for level 3. In this example, the code submitted and the code warranted by the NPP are the same, but this will not always be the case.

Summary Report

Physician: **David Doctor**

Patient: **Jay J. Jones** ID No. **123456**

Date of Service: **1/5/2005**   Date of Audit: **3/30/2005**

Type of Service Submitted: **Initial office visit**   Type of Service Audited: **Agree**

Note: this type of service requires documentation for all three key components to meet or exceed the level of complexity for E/M code.

E/M Code Documented: **99203**   E/M Code Submitted: **99204**   E/M Code by NPP: **99204**

Key Component and Subcomponents	Care Documented	Required for Code Submitted	Required for Code Indicated by the NPP
1. Extent of medical history (a) No. of elements of present illness (b) No. of elements of PFSH (c) Number of systems of ROS	**Detailed*** (a) 4† (b) 3† (c) 6*	**Comprehensive** (a) 4 or more (b) 3 (c) 10 or more	**Comprehensive** (a) 4 or more (b) 3 (c) 10 or more
2. Physical examination (a) 1997 guidelines, cardiology (b) 1995 guidelines, cardiology	**Detailed*** (a) 15 elements* (b) Detailed examination*	**Comprehensive** (a) All required elements, 1 element in each non-shaded section (b) Comprehensive examination	**Comprehensive** (a) All required elements, 1 in each of non-shaded sections (b) Comprehensive examination

continued

F I G U R E 25.1 (cont'd)

Illustration of Analysis of Chart Documentation of Care Provided This Summary Report is based on an audit in which the code submitted was level 4 and the auditor determined that the code indicated by the NPP was also level 4, but the level of care documented met requirements only for level 3. In this example, the code submitted and the code warranted by the NPP are the same, but this will not always be the case.

Summary Report

Physician: **David Doctor**

Patient: **Jay J. Jones** ID No. **123456**

Date of Service: **1/5/2005**   Date of Audit: **3/30/2005**

Type of Service Submitted: **Initial office visit**   Type of Service Audited: **Agree**

Note: this type of service requires documentation for all three key components to meet or exceed the level of complexity for E/M code.

E/M Code Documented: **99203**   E/M Code Submitted: **99204**   E/M Code by NPP: **99204**

Key Component and Subcomponents	Care Documented	Required for Code Submitted	Required for Code Indicated by the NPP
3. Medical decision making (2 of 3)	**Low***	**Moderate**	**Moderate**
(a) Data	(a) None*	(a) Moderate	(a) Moderate
■ Amount of data reviewed	■ None*		
■ Amount of data ordered	■ None*		
■ Complexity of data	■ None*		
(b) No. of diagnoses or Rx options	(b) Limited*	(b) Multiple (3)	(b) Multiple (3)
■ Number of diagnoses	■ Minimal (1)*		
■ Number of treatment options	■ Limited (2)*		
(c) Risks	(c) Estimate = moderate	(c) Moderate	(c) Moderate
■ Risk of presenting problem(s)	■ Not documented		
■ Risk of diagnostic procedures	■ Not documented		
■ Risk of management options	■ Not documented		

* Documented E/M care is less than warranted by NPP.

† Documented E/M care meets or exceeds care warranted by NPP.

This Summary Report for each record reviewed begins with an assessment of the type of service documented and an indication of whether this agrees with the E/M code submitted. It next indicates whether the type of service requires sufficient documentation for all three of the key components to meet or exceed the requirements for the submitted code and indicated code, or whether two of three components are sufficient (eg, established outpatient visit). The focus of the table is to convey a section-by-section analysis of each medical visit, indicating the amounts of care documented for each subsection of the three key components and comparing these with the levels called for by the E/M code submitted and by the NPP.

Each Summary Report can also be accompanied by its own brief explanatory narrative. This can also be a preloaded report in the auditor's word processor, which can then be customized to reflect the individual findings of each chart audited. It would include written explanations of the reasons shown in the Summary Table that any documentation failed to meet the requirements of the *Documentation Guidelines*. The goal of the written report is to help the physicians appreciate the standards for providing and documenting care so they can apply these principles to future patient care.

Sample Narrative Report to Accompany Chart Shown in Figure 25.1

Most of this text can be standardized as a preloaded word processor report. The individual information that is added in relation to each audit report is shown in *italics*:

The E/M code submitted (*99204*) is appropriate for the NPP, which was determined to be "*moderate to high*." However, the documented level of care *does not* support this code, achieving *only level 3* care.

1. The medical history *does not* meet the CPT coding system requirement of being "*comprehensive*," due to documenting *fewer than 10* organ systems in the review of systems.

2. The physical examination *does not* meet the CPT coding system requirement of being "*comprehensive*," due to documentation of less care than required by either the 1995 or 1997 *Documentation Guidelines*.

3. Finally, the MDM *does not* meet the CPT coding system requirement of being "*moderate complexity*," because *only one* of the three elements of the MDM shows moderate complexity, and CPT coding system guidelines require at least two of the three elements to meet this level. Because there is *no* data reviewed or ordered, the number of documented diagnoses or treatment options should have been *three or more*. Otherwise, the submitted E/M code would need to be lowered. In addition, *none* of the three elements of risk has been documented in the medical record. At least one of these elements should be documented to confirm your medical impressions at the time of the visit.

The auditor's instructional commentary is, of course, customized to the findings of each audit. For example, consider how this report might be written for a chart whose only documentation in the ROS subsection of medical history reads "review of systems, noncontributory." While the physician may incorrectly believe that this brief statement provides sufficient documentation that he or she performed a comprehensive ROS, the auditor must interpret this as zero documentation of an ROS, and this would be indicated in the Summary Table. In the narrative section of the report, the auditor's responsibility is to inform the physician why his or her documentation does not fulfill the requirements of the *Documentation Guidelines*. The auditor may include a specific reference from the *Documentation Guidelines* that describes the requirements for this portion of the medical record. For example, the report might state the following[2]:

> Regarding the review of systems (ROS), the AMA publication *Documentation Guidelines for Evaluation and Management Services* indicates that "A ROS is an inventory of body systems obtained through a series of questions seeking to identify signs and/or symptoms which the patient may be experiencing or has experienced . . . a complete ROS inquires about the system(s) directly related to the problem(s) identified in the HPI (History of Present Illness) plus all additional body systems."
>
> The specific guideline for documentation required for a physician to report a complete ROS states, "At least ten organ systems must be reviewed. Those systems with positive or pertinent negative responses must be individually documented. For the remaining systems, a notation indicating 'all other systems are negative' is permissible. In the absence of such a notation, at least ten systems must be individually documented."
>
> Most auditors recommend that physicians document the responses to the questions asked for all of the 10 or more systems required, rather than using the default of 'all other systems negative.' This approach not only ensures E/M compliance but also provides precise medical information to support the patient's future care.

In summary, internal audit reports should be oriented to providing information to physicians about both accurate coding and documentation and the level of care that is appropriate for the patient's illness(es). The first part of these audits addresses selection of a level of care (E/M code) appropriate for the severity of the patient's illness. It also stresses the importance of the physician obtaining (and documenting) a complete medical history to be able to judge the patient's entire clinical picture and its severity.

The second part of these reports follows the more conventional audit practice of comparing the submitted code to the level of care documented in the medical record. The added feature in this section is that the auditor considers not only the E/M code submitted, but also the appropriate level of care identified by the NPP. The goal of this part of the audit is to educate the physician that his or her care, and the documentation of that care, should equal or exceed the level of care indicated by the patient's NPP.

INTERNAL AUDITS AND FEEDBACK TO PHYSICIANS

Medical practices that have a compliance program also have an assigned compliance physician (or a physician committee), who works with the auditor to confirm audit findings and to assist with any educational reviews provided to his or her fellow physicians. One of the compliance team's responsibilities is to discuss any discrepancies in selection of levels of care (ie, E/M codes) with a physician whose charts have been reviewed. This includes code selection that is either higher or lower than the level of care indicated by the NPP. We also recommend that these medical practices conduct compliance workshops on this topic several times per year. These meetings should include clinicians, nurses, medical assistants, auditors, and administrators. The compliance team can present selected (de-identified) charts as the basis for an open "coding forum," as discussed in Chapter 14. The forum presents a patient's illness and medical assessment as the basis for discussing the selection of an appropriate E/M code, as warranted by the NPP. The goal of such forums is to make sure that everyone is "on the same page" in understanding the relationship between illness severity, the NPP, and code selection. The staff should strive to achieve consistent agreement on these relationships as they apply to medical problems that are commonly seen in the practice's specialty. Discussion of more unusual cases in these forums should also help to improve consistency and ensure reasonable agreement among clinicians in the practice. Physicians and staff should appreciate that the effort invested in these workshops is repaid in office productivity and audit protection.

Some of the additional features of medical records that the auditor and compliance physician are responsible to review include:

- documentation of consultation requests and consultation letters,
- appropriate physician signatures confirming review of graphic templates in the medical history section,
- documented details about positive patient responses on the graphic templates in the medical history section,
- documented details about abnormal and pertinent normal physical examination findings, and
- documented clinical impressions and therapeutic recommendations that are clear and understandable (a "blueprint for care"), because this information is a strong indicator of quality, efficiency, and cost-effectiveness in ongoing patient care.

Concerns in any of these areas should be discussed with individual clinicians. General comments on these topics should also be discussed at the scheduled compliance workshops.

INTERNAL AUDITS AND THE OFFICE COMPLIANCE PROGRAM

For academic or private practices interested in creating a compliance program, the E/M internal audit protocol provides a cornerstone for a functional system that benefits physicians and patients while satisfying compliance requirements. The practice benefits from internal reviews and discussions concerning proper code selection and appropriate supportive documentation by achieving enhanced quality of care, efficiency, and productivity. By creating a formal system that includes both audit reports and records of formal discussions of E/M compliance, the practice also establishes a protocol that fulfills most of the seven elements of a compliance program, as cited by the Department of Health and Human Services:

- Established compliance policies and procedures
- Qualified and empowered compliance officer
- Effective education and training
- Effective monitoring and auditing
- Corrective action plans
- Disciplinary enforcement
- Effective communication

A medical practice implementing a compliance program is required to create a written compliance protocol that outlines its policies and procedures, including programs for corrective action and discipline in the event of noncompliance. The E/M audit reports and meetings described in this chapter fulfill the requirements for monitoring and auditing, education and training, and effective communication. A complementary program is required for review of non-E/M procedures, but these audits are usually less challenging than E/M reviews.

THE OFFICE COMPLIANCE PROGRAM AS A BASIS FOR MONITORING MEDICARE AND PRIVATE INSURERS

Once an office has established an internal audit protocol, the billing staff should report any instances of automated E/M downcoding by private insurers directly to the physicians and auditors involved in the program. The office should perform its own formal E/M audit of the medical record in question. When this confirms the physician's appropriate code selection and documentation, the practice should file a formal appeal with the insurer. If the insurer asks for a copy of the medical record to perform a formal review, the practice should provide a copy of the medical record in question after the insurer agrees (preferably in writing) to provide the name and credentials of the reviewer. The insurer should further agree to provide, for each chart reviewed, a detailed written audit report that includes clear explanations of how the reviewer has applied the CPT coding system's coding and documentation rules. If the insurer's audit disagrees with the practice's own internal assessment, this formal report will make it possible for the practice to demonstrate the flaws in the insurer's analysis and pursue appropriate appeals.

Overview of Dealing With Insurer Audits

Once the physician is performing compliant coding and documentation, it is essential to ensure that other parties are also "playing by the rules." In the past (and continuing today), when physicians were not certain of being compliant, the private insurers would "audit" their charts and provide summary results, without providing information about the credentials of the auditor, the tools the auditor used, detailed findings of the audit, or the reliability of the audit.

Physicians should not willingly accept these practices. Physicians using Practical E/M methodology can be confident in both the appropriateness of their E/M code selection and the compliance of their medical record documentation. They are therefore in a secure position to challenge the findings of the insurer's auditor. This must be done to ensure that all parties, not just the physicians, are held responsible for adhering to the CPT coding system guidelines of E/M coding and the *Documentation Guidelines*.

This program of physicians auditing insurer downcoding reverses the usual scenario of the insurer auditing the physician. The medical practice can now effectively identify circumstances where private insurers may be engaged in noncompliant downcoding practices. As an added benefit, the practice's records of these audits of insurer coding errors can form a substantial database for the office compliance program, thereby serving two purposes at once:

- ensuring payment of E/M services at proper levels, without downcoding, in compliance with CPT coding principles; and
- fulfilling the requirements of the office compliance program.

SUMMARY

A medical practice's own internal E/M audit program should focus on quality of care and physicians' compliance education, while also addressing office efficiency and productivity. It should be based on the CPT coding system methodology of correctly identifying, and then providing and documenting, the appropriate level of care indicated by the severity of the NPP.

Effective audit reports should provide both analysis and guidance for physicians, including (1) avoiding E/M code selection that either exceeds or is lower than the level of care warranted by the NPP, (2) emphasizing the role of a comprehensive medical history in evaluating the significance of each patient's illness, and (3) analyzing the amount of medical care documented in the medical record. The information in these audit reports first indicates whether the submitted code is higher, lower, or appropriate for the level of care warranted by the NPP. It then indicates whether the medical history is comprehensive, to facilitate a reasonable assessment of the patient's NPP. Next, it assesses proper documentation of commonly excluded MDM elements and the NPP. Finally, it indicates whether the documentation is sufficient or insufficient to support the E/M code submitted and the level of care appropriate for the NPP.

Medical practices can implement their own internal E/M audits to further compliance, quality care, and productivity. These audits form the basis of a formal coding compliance program, and they also allow physicians to appeal noncompliant insurer downcoding and to critique external audits for potential noncompliance.

References

1.   American Medical Association. *Current Procedural Terminology CPT® 2008*. Chicago, Ill: American Medical Association; 2007.

2.   Health Care Financing Administration. *Documentation Guidelines for Evaluation and Management Services*. Chicago, IL: American Medical Association; 1997.

3.   Health Care Financing Administration. *Documentation Guidelines for Evaluation and Management Services*. Chicago, IL: American Medical Association; 1995.

Proper Use of Modifiers
With E/M Services

Correctly submitting claims and receiving proper reimbursement for evaluation and management (E/M) services that are performed on the same day as a procedure, or for E/M services that are performed during the global period of an unrelated procedure, requires physicians to understand the compliant use of modifiers. This necessitates consideration of the concepts of the Current Procedural Terminology (CPT®) coding system that govern relationships among different services and the codes representing them. The Introduction section of the CPT codebook presents an overview of how modifiers are used, and Appendix A of the codebook provides a comprehensive list of all the modifiers and the circumstances under which they should be used.[1]

Many of the procedure services listed in the CPT codebook include the provision of some related E/M care. Physicians are advised not to submit E/M codes for the E/M care that is included in the procedure code. For example, on the day that a gastroenterologist performs a scheduled colonoscopy, the physician should not submit a claim for the E/M services related to the procedure (ie, history, examination, and medical decision making that relate to the medical problem associated with the procedure). Furthermore, claims adjustment software systems employed by Medicare and private insurers are programmed to deny payment automatically when an E/M service is submitted during the global period of a procedure, as described later in this chapter.

There are some qualifying circumstances, however, when the physician performs E/M services that go beyond the extent of E/M care that is considered to be a component of the procedure. Under these circumstances, the CPT coding system indicates that the physician should submit a claim for these more extensive E/M services. To ensure appropriate reimbursement under these circumstances, the physician must indicate the nature of the qualifying circumstance by attaching an appropriate modifier to the E/M code. In our example, on the day of the colonoscopy, if the gastroenterologist also provided the patient with E/M care that was "significant and separately identifiable" for his unrelated gastroesophageal reflux disease, then "this circumstance may be reported by adding modifier 25 to the appropriate level of E/M service."[1]

This chapter is intended to help physicians identify and understand the circumstances that warrant the use of modifiers with E/M codes for the purpose of requesting reimbursement, and to distinguish these from the circumstances that do not warrant the use of modifiers.

Guidelines in the CPT coding system, and in the Resource-Based Relative Value Scale[2] (RBRVS), employed by the Centers for Medicare and Medicaid Services (CMS), indicate when E/M services are considered to be a component of another medical procedure or service. They also instruct physicians how to use modifiers when performing E/M services that are "separate and identifiable"[1] from the E/M care that would otherwise reasonably be included in another procedure. This chapter examines compliant usage of the three modifiers (24, 25, and 57) designated to address proper coding of E/M services performed in relation to other services. It also briefly discusses three other modifiers (21, 55, and 56) that are used to explain qualifying features of E/M codes, unrelated to other services.

Theoretically, CPT codes function as messengers, carrying information that accurately conveys the services performed, and their associated relative value units (RVUs),[2] to Medicare, Medicaid, and commercial insurance companies. In turn, physicians expect these payers to process the submitted codes and modifiers in *compliance* with the guidelines of the CPT coding system and RBRVS, and to provide appropriate reimbursement. This chapter also addresses the reality that, at present, Medicare, Medicaid, and commercial insurers do not consistently meet this expectation. While it is beyond the scope of this book to present a detailed discussion of all the insurer coding and reimbursement principles that conflict with the CPT coding system and RBRVS guidelines, it is critical to acknowledge that this issue exists, and that insurers do engage in practices that contradict what physicians have been taught about compliant coding practices by coding consultants. Once this dilemma is "on the table" for scrutiny, physicians will at least be able to examine some of their options (eg, appeals, scheduling modifications, or choosing not to participate) for responding to payer noncompliance and payers' financial disincentives to providing efficient, cost-effective, high-quality care for our patients.

E/M CARE PERFORMED DURING A PROCEDURE'S GLOBAL PERIOD

The CPT codebook provides both general and specific guidelines concerning the relationships between procedures and E/M services, indicating when it is (and when it is not) appropriate to submit codes for both services when they are performed on the same date. Several fundamental principles from the CPT codebook[1] and RBRVS[2] provide a good foundation for understanding compliant coding relationships concerning E/M services:

1. Every medical service performed should be compensated once, but only once.
   - For example, the physician should not submit a code for E/M services if another service (such as a procedure with a global period, as described below) also includes the value of that same E/M service.
2. Each CPT procedure code that has an indicated "global period" includes an assigned value (in the RBRVS) for related E/M care.[1,2] However, this value does not include E/M services that are "separate and identifiable" from the care related to the procedure.[1]
   - Physicians indicate these "separate and identifiable" E/M services by appending an appropriate modifier when they submit the E/M code for reimbursement.
3. Procedure codes that do not have an indicated "global period" (labeled in RBRVS as "XXX codes"[2]) do not include intrinsic value E/M care.
   - Therefore, physicians can submit codes for both the XXX procedure and the E/M service performed on the same date without the use of a modifier.
   - Medicare, Medicaid, and commercial insurers should recognize that these services are not related and are not components of each other, and they should provide reimbursement at appropriate levels without use of a modifier.

4. Unless otherwise specified in the description of a specific E/M code, procedures are not included in (or components of) E/M services.

    ■ That is, the CPT codebook states that "any specifically identifiable procedure (ie, identified with a specific CPT code) performed on or subsequent to the date of initial or subsequent E/M services should be reported separately. The actual performance and/or interpretation of diagnostic tests/studies for which specific CPT codes are available may be reported separately, in addition to the appropriate E/M code."[1]

    ■ An example of an "otherwise specified" exception, where a specific E/M service does include a certain procedure in its definition, occurs when an ophthalmologist performs a screening vision test (CPT code 99173). The description of the single-organ-system eye examination in the 1997 edition of the *Documentation Guidelines for Evaluation and Management Services* includes "test visual acuity."[3] Therefore, this specific E/M service does include the vision test procedure in its definition. As a result, if an ophthalmologist were to submit an E/M code plus code 99173 on the same date of service, he or she would effectively be submitting two codes for this same service of testing vision, and this would violate the first principle of compliant coding relationships. (This CPT guideline also provides that nonophthalmologists who perform a screening vision test should submit, and be reimbursed for, the 99173 code as well as the E/M service.)

    ■ Another type of exception arises for *specific guidelines* that apply to particular types of E/M service and override the general guidelines. The notable example of this circumstance is for critical care E/M services (CPT codes 99289–99296). The description in the CPT codebook for critical care specifies, by CPT code, multiple specific procedures that are included in the provision of critical care.

E/M CODES AND THE "SURGICAL PACKAGE"

The surgical package definition in the Surgery Guidelines section of the CPT codebook categorizes those specific services that are "always included in addition to the operation per se."[1] In addition to local anesthesia, topical anesthesia, immediate postoperative care, and recovery care, the list includes two categories of E/M services[1]:

■ subsequent to the decision for surgery, one related E/M encounter on the date immediately prior to or on the date of the procedure (including performing a history and physical), and

■ typical postoperative follow-up care.

Importantly, within the first category, the CPT guidelines distinguish E/M care performed *after* the physician has reached a decision to perform surgery from E/M care that leads to the decision to perform surgery. This latter situation is addressed by the correct use of modifiers 25 and 57, as described later in this chapter. Within the second category, CPT guidelines specify that this "typical" postoperative care "includes only that care which is usually a part of the surgical service. Complications, exacerbations, recurrence, or the presence of other diseases or injuries requiring additional services should be separately reported."[1] Modifier 24 is used to report these circumstances.

Considering the CPT codebook's definition of the E/M care that is included in the surgical package, we must also conclude that when a patient warrants E/M services that (1) result in the decision for surgery, (2) exceed the *problem-related* services included in the surgical package, or (3) exceed *typical* postoperative care, then the physician should indicate the amount of *additional* care by also submitting an E/M code with an appropriate modifier. The modifier indicates that this is a special circumstance, warranting E/M care greater than that which is normally expected as a part of the surgical package.

The CPT guidelines provide additional detail for coding of E/M services performed in association with diagnostic procedures, such as endoscopy, arthroscopy, and injection procedures for radiography. Follow-up care for this type of procedure is defined in the CPT codebook as including "only that care related to recovery from the diagnostic procedure itself. Care of the condition for which the diagnostic procedure was performed or of other concomitant conditions is not included and may be listed separately."[1] This is another circumstance where the CPT coding system guidelines recommend submitting the E/M service with an appropriate modifier (specifically, modifier 25).

Conspicuously absent from this otherwise comprehensive description of the surgical package is a quantitative definition of the *duration* of the postoperative period. We can look for assistance with this important billing-related information from the Medicare RBRVS, as discussed in the next section.

E/M CODES AND PROCEDURES WITH DIFFERENT GLOBAL PERIODS

The RBRVS, which was introduced in 1992 by the Health Care Financing Administration (now CMS), provides quantitative relative values for the various services with assigned CPT codes. The RBRVS definition of a "global surgical package" parallels the surgical package definition in the CPT codebook, with the inclusion of both preoperative E/M care within the 24-hour period before the procedure and postoperative E/M visits.

The RBRVS defines major surgeries as those procedures for which the duration of the global package is 90 days.[2] Minor surgeries are those procedures with a designated global postoperative period of either zero or 10 days.[2] As noted earlier, the CPT codebook provides that E/M care includes performance of a "history and physical"; this would be appropriate for a major surgery or significant procedure performed in the hospital or outpatient surgical center, which both require a written history and physical (H&P).

The RBRVS clarifies the global period concept for endoscopies and other minor surgical procedures by including the statement that "no payment will be made for a visit on the same day a minor surgical or endoscopic procedure is performed unless a separate, identifiable service is also provided."[2] The modifier descriptions in Appendix A of the CPT codebook define the concept of "separate, identifiable service," which is explained further in the "Using Modifiers With E/M Codes" section later in this chapter. In addition, RBRVS provides the following example for clarification[2]:

> Payment for a visit would be allowed in addition to payment for suturing a scalp wound if, in addition, a full neurological exam is made for a patient with head trauma. If the physician only identified the need for sutures and confirmed allergy and immunization status, billing for a visit would not be appropriate.

The Amount of Care Needed to Qualify as "Separate and Identifiable"

This deference to an example to illustrate "separate and identifiable service," rather than an actual definition, always reminds me of Supreme Court Justice Potter Stewart's often-quoted analysis of pornography: "I shall not today attempt further to define the kinds of material I understand to be embraced within that shorthand description

continued

('pornography'); and perhaps I could never succeed in intelligibly doing so. *But I know it when I see it.*[italics added for emphasis]"[4]

In teaching physicians about using modifiers, I frequently refer to this particular example from RBRVS, because it provides a reasonable image of when it is appropriate, or not appropriate, to use a modifier for E/M care performed with a minor or endoscopic procedure. Because of the method by which RVUs are determined, it is also *reasonable* to interpret that the amount of E/M care that is included in a minor or endoscopic office procedure is equal to the amount of E/M care that a physician would usually provide in this circumstance. This would include inquiring about the status of the medical problem being investigated with the procedure (ie, a brief HPI), a review of background medical health information to find out whether the patient has any pertinent changes that could affect the procedure (an update of the past medical history and review of systems), and a limited examination of the part of the body related to the procedure.

Physicians should consider that this amount of problem-focused E/M care is a component of such procedures, and they should not submit separate E/M codes for providing this level of care. This also tells us that it is appropriate to submit an E/M code (with an appropriate modifier), in addition to the procedure code, in medically indicated circumstances where the E/M care the physician performed is more extensive and addresses issues beyond those related to the procedure itself.

E/M CODES AND PROCEDURES WITH NO GLOBAL PERIODS

Some procedures do not have a "global surgical package" included in their value under the RBRVS system. These are commonly diagnostic tests, such as urinalysis, electrocardiogram, radiology studies, and vision screening tests. For such procedures that do not have an associated global package, RBRVS lists one of several alphabetical indicators in place of a number of global days.[2] These procedures thus do not include provision of any E/M care. Therefore, physicians should submit E/M codes for E/M services they provide in association with these procedures, and the codes should be submitted without the use of a modifier. The procedures in this category most commonly use one of the following alphabetical indicators:

■ An MMM alphabetical indicator applies to services related to uncomplicated maternity cases. These procedures do not fall under the general surgical package definition because the CPT coding system applies a custom definition to encompass maternity care.

■ The XXX alphabetical indicator applies specifically to procedure codes in which the "global concept does not apply."[2] The XXX label applies to all radiology services (CPT codes 70000–79999), all laboratory services (CPT codes 80000–89999), and a significant number of diagnostic "medicine" services (CPT codes 90000–99999).[2]

USING MODIFIERS WITH E/M CODES

The CPT codebook advises that modifiers provide a shorthand explanation of circumstances affecting a service, without changing its definition or its code. Without modifiers, it would be necessary to greatly increase the number of CPT codes to provide explanations for all the modifications that may affect each service.[1]

Modifiers Indicating a Change in the E/M Service Itself

There are three modifiers that primarily affect E/M codes submitted independently, without an associated procedure:

1. Modifier 21 may be used for a prolonged E/M service. Specifically, this modifier is appropriate only when the total amount of time exceeds the "typical time" indicated by the CPT descriptors for the highest-level E/M service within a given category.[1]

2. Modifier 55 is applied to E/M services in the postoperative period to indicate that the physician providing the postoperative management is not associated with the physician who performed the surgical procedure. (For proper claims payment, the physician who performs the surgical procedure must also append modifier 54 to the procedure code to indicate that another physician is providing the preoperative and/or postoperative care.)

3. Modifier 56 is applied to E/M services in the preoperative period to indicate that the physician providing the preoperative management is not associated with the physician who will perform the surgical procedure. (For proper claims payment, the physician who performs the surgical procedure must also append modifier 54 to the procedure code to indicate that another physician is providing the preoperative and/or postoperative care.)

Choosing Between Modifier 21 and the Prolonged Service Add-on Codes (99354–99357)

The CPT guidelines also provide for the use of add-on codes 99354 to 99357 to report time spent during prolonged services. These E/M codes are to be used only when there is at least 30 minutes of prolonged service. Therefore, use of modifier 21 is appropriate when the prolonged service exceeds the time for the highest level of E/M service in the appropriate category by up to 30 minutes.

Modifiers Indicating E/M Service Outside a Procedure's Global Package

The three E/M code modifiers that demand significant attention are 24, 25, and 57. Each of these modifiers is used to submit a claim for an E/M service that qualifies as an exception under the rules of the CPT coding system's "surgical package." If the E/M care were submitted without the modifier, payment would be denied because the service is by definition included as part of the surgical package. However, a physician may submit a claim, with the appropriate modifier attached, when he (or she) provides E/M services that are more extensive than those included in the surgical package.

Modifier 24: Unrelated evaluation and management service by the same physician during a postoperative period
As noted earlier in this chapter, the CPT codebook directs us that the "surgical package" does not include E/M care during the global period for complications, exacerbations, recurrences, or unrelated diseases or injuries requiring additional services.[1] Because this E/M care is *not* a component of the procedure, it is appropriate to report it (and to receive reimbursement for it). The physicians indicate these special circumstances on their insurance claims by adding modifier 24 to the appropriate E/M code.

As a practical matter, most care that warrants the use of modifier 24 will be associated with a diagnosis code that is unrelated to the diagnosis used for the original procedure. Submitting this unrelated diagnosis code provides support and justification for the use of the 24 modifier in these cases.

Modifier 25: Significant, separately identifiable evaluation and management service by the same physician on the same day of the procedure or other service

On a day when a physician performs a procedure that has an assigned global period (0, 10, or 90 days), E/M services related to the procedure are included in the surgical package. However, the CPT codebook also describes that it is appropriate to report E/M care, with an attached 25 modifier, on the same day a procedure or other service is performed if "the patient's condition required a significant, separately identifiable E/M service above and beyond the other service provided or beyond the usual pre-operative and postoperative care associated with the procedure that was performed."[1] Submitting an E/M code with a 25 modifier is also appropriate if the E/M care resulted in the decision to perform a minor or diagnostic procedure, because CPT coding guidelines specify that the surgical package includes (only) E/M care that is performed "subsequent to the decision for surgery."[1]

The CPT guidelines also advise that this "significant, separately identifiable" E/M service may be provided for the same condition, and be submitted with the same diagnosis code, as the procedure service.[1]

Problems When Submitting the Same Diagnosis Code for E/M Care and for the Procedure

As a practical matter, although CPT coding guidelines permit the physician to use the same diagnosis code for both the procedure and the E/M care submitted with modifier 25, doing so frequently results in difficulty obtaining proper payment from the insurer. The probable reason for this is that when both services have the same diagnosis code, the insurer's software is unable to appreciate that the E/M services were in fact "significant, separate, and identifiable" from the procedure itself. The result is frequently denial or delay of claims processing, necessitating appeals for payment and causing significant administrative burden for the physician's staff.

On the other hand, when the physician is able to submit the two services with unrelated diagnosis codes, this obstacle disappears. Theoretically, with different diagnosis codes for the procedure and the E/M service, plus use of the 25 modifier, there should be no difficulty with authorization for payment.

There should be no problems receiving payment for E/M services from Medicare carriers when using the same diagnosis code for both E/M care and diagnostic or minor procedures performed during initial outpatient visits or consultations. This is because Medicare carriers apply the CPT coding system principle that the E/M care included in the surgical package is only "subsequent to the decision for surgery,"[1] which does not include care leading up to that decision. It is obvious that this principle applies during initial visits and consultations. Unfortunately, this reasoning is not obvious for an outpatient established visit, where the decision to perform a procedure may or may not have been made on the same day as the procedure was performed. Without providing a copy of the medical record, there is no way to indicate that the decision to perform the procedure was made as a result of the follow-up E/M visit.

It is important to distinguish that modifier 25 is applied to E/M services performed with minor, endoscopic, or diagnostic procedures. It is not the appropriate modifier for separate and identifiable E/M care on the day of a major surgical procedure (ie, a procedure defined by RBRVS as having a 90-day global period). Modifier 57 is used to address this situation.

Modifier 57: Decision for Surgery

The CPT codebook specifies only that this modifier is used with an E/M service that results in the initial decision to perform surgery. The RBRVS provides clarification that specifically differentiates correct use of this modifier from that of modifier 25 by stating, "use of modifier 57 is limited to operations with 90-day global periods."[2]

This modifier is therefore used only when an E/M service occurs within 24 hours of an operation, a time frame that would normally include the E/M care as part of the surgical package. However, when the E/M service is the basis for making the decision to perform surgery, it introduces a special circumstance that warrants reporting the E/M care in addition to the procedure (and having that care reimbursed).

An example would be evaluating a patient emergently for acute onset of abdominal pain. When the visit results in a recommendation for immediate emergency appendectomy, the physician should submit the CPT code for the appendectomy and also the appropriate E/M code with modifier 57.

NONCOMPLIANT INSURER PRACTICES

Of course, coding and compliance do not exist in a vacuum. They are components of our current billing and reimbursement system, and this system can and does lead to problems, based on individual insurer payment policies and software systems.

Without these modifier guidelines, Medicare carriers and commercial insurers would necessarily have to program their claims processing software to provide reimbursement either for every code submitted or for only one code (the most intensive) for each visit. Faced with this choice, insurers have set their software to pay for only one service per visit. However, if they are programmed with compliant reimbursement practices, they should recognize that E/M services submitted with appropriate modifiers should be paid.

Unfortunately, numerous insurers have programmed their software to ignore some modifiers, including modifiers 24, 25, and 57. Others have elected to recognize the modifiers but also programmed exceptions that deny payment despite the modifier when the E/M service is submitted in conjunction with certain specified procedure codes. When insurer software fails to recognize modifiers and pay for these E/M services, the end result is significant obstacles to efficient care for physicians and patients. To be paid for their services, physicians who want to provide additional, unrelated E/M care in the global period of a procedure would be forced to schedule a separate visit for the patient after the global period has concluded.

The proper payment of E/M codes submitted with modifiers eliminates this problem. It allows physicians to provide more efficient medical care and patient convenience. On the other hand, noncompliant treatment of E/M codes that are properly submitted with modifiers reduces insurer credibility and creates significant perverse incentives that interfere with the delivery of high-quality, efficient, cost-effective health care.

Medicare and E/M Modifiers

Through their national policy, Medicare has generally been compliant with the CPT coding system modifier guidelines. With regard to E/M services provided on the same day as a procedure, Medicare carriers consistently provide reimbursement when the E/M codes are appropriately submitted with modifier 24, 25, or 57. However, Medicare has implemented a number of national "payment rules and policies" that contradict some of the principles of the CPT coding system.

The first of these contradictory policies concerns reimbursement for complications that occur during the global period of an operation. The CPT coding system guidelines specify that complications are not components of the "surgical package," and therefore any E/M services provided for significant surgical complications should be submitted with modifier 24. However, in direct contradiction to this guideline, Medicare policy declares that when there are complications secondary to a surgical procedure, for all medical or surgical care that does not require a return trip to the operating room, "Medicare will include these services in the approved amount for the global surgery with no separate payment made."[2]

This policy that conflicts with the CPT codebook's surgical package definition[1] exposes a significant disconnect in the health care system. Since the RVUs for each surgical procedure are calculated under CPT coding system guidelines, the value of a given surgical code does not include any consideration of care for complications. Medicare then provides reimbursement for that code based on these RVUs but makes a "policy decision" that they will not provide additional payment for the care of complications. Under the RBRVS system, *this Medicare nonpayment policy requires the physician to provide care for complications without any compensation.*

Economic Impact on High-Risk Specialties

The CMS policy of nonpayment for care of surgical complications has a significant impact in high-risk specialties, such as vascular surgery, cardiovascular surgery, neurosurgery, and orthopedics.

This policy, combined with underlying low reimbursement rates, places significant economic pressure on these physicians to limit the number of new Medicare patients they will accept into their practice, or to not accept them into their practices at all.

Barriers to Correcting the CMS' Non-compliant Treatment of Modifier 24

If Medicare wishes to include care for complications in the "surgical package," then the RVUs for surgical services should be increased to account for this change in policy.

Unfortunately, there is a political problem with this proposal. As a result of the Balanced Budget Amendment requirement for budget neutrality in the Medicare system, any increase in RVUs for all surgical procedures will necessarily have to be offset by either a decrease in RVUs for E/M services or a global decrease in the conversion factor. The net economic effect of such a change would be zero. Therefore, the result of this non-compliant Medicare policy for physicians has been a permanent elimination of payment for the care of surgical complications.

The second category of "disconnects" due to Medicare national payment rules and policies concerns nonpayment for some procedures or services for which the global period concept does not apply (ie, codes designated as XXX for the global period). Although this policy denies payment regardless of whether the services in question are submitted alone or with another service, it is most obvious when physicians submit these codes for care on the same date as an E/M visit. For example, Medicare provides no reimbursement for the physician performing a venipuncture (CPT code 36415).

The RBRVS publication does not particularly draw attention to this nonpayment policy; it simply fails to list these codes at all. A Web site reference on the Correct Coding Initiative quotes this policy as follows[5]:

X = Statutory Exclusion. These codes represent an item or service that is not in the statutory definition of 'physician services' for fee schedule payment purposes. No RVUs or payment amounts are shown for these codes, and no payment may be made under the physician fee schedule. (Examples are ambulance services and selected diagnostic laboratory services.)

Critique of Medicare Noncompliant Practices

Since Medicare requires use of CPT codes for claims submission, reports payments on explanation of benefits (EOB) forms by using CPT codes, and requires physicians to follow CPT coding system compliance concepts, most physicians are unaware that Medicare has policies that override some CPT coding system guidelines and deny payments. Further complicating this situation is the fact that Medicare has not made it clear whether physicians have the right to bill patients for these "noncovered services" after providing an advance beneficiary notice.

It is critical for physicians to understand this coding and compliance disparity and to educate themselves (and their administrative staff) to identify instances of nonpayment for services provided to their patients. With this knowledge, physicians should be able to make informed decisions about how to react to these circumstances. Although there may be no recourse other than to provide free care for postoperative complications, there should be alternatives for the noncovered XXX services (such as sending the patient to the laboratory rather than performing the venipuncture).

Assessment of Medicare Nonpayment Policies

Medicare is a national health care system that provides care for patients aged 65 and over. Funding is provided for this system through Medicare taxes. These administrative policies regarding nonpayment of physicians' services, all of which have practice expense and liability insurance expense components, can be considered an additional tax on physicians toward the funding of this system.

Commercial Insurance Companies and E/M Modifiers

Commercial insurers require physicians to submit their claims with CPT codes. They indicate their payments on EOBs, which also use CPT codes. They provide information about reimbursement schedules by using CPT codes. Nevertheless, often they do not follow CPT coding system guidelines and principles when the indicated care involves more than one service on the same date.

The range of noncompliant insurer practices related to modifiers 24, 25, and 57 includes the following:

■   Some insurers program their claims adjudication software to ignore some or all modifiers. Under these circumstances, only one service will be paid on a given date, regardless of CPT coding system compliance principles and physician effort and expense.

■   Some insurers that do recognize modifiers in general have also programmed elaborate edits that deny payment for multiple code combinations, even when properly submitted with modifiers.

■   Some insurers do not follow the global period exceptions of the CPT code set.

■   Some insurers treat selected codes that have an XXX global designation (ie, the global concept does not apply) as if they had a zero-day global period. As a result, when a physician submits an E/M code and a procedure code with the XXX designation on the same date, the insurer will treat the E/M code as if it were a component of the procedure and deny payment.

In their attempt to "justify" these improper nonpayments, the insurers' EOBs include remarks, in their own terminology, that postulate various relationships between the two services (eg, they frequently describe one service as being "incidental to" another). However, these descriptions and proposed relationships that are used to justify denial of payment are commonly noncompliant, directly conflicting with CPT coding guidelines. These remarks also do not inform physicians that the insurer's bundling of the services and denial of payment are not in compliance with the CPT coding system. On the other hand, physicians commonly believe (erroneously) that the insurers are actually providing a CPT-based explanation for their nonpayment practices. Even when physicians do recognize these errors, appeals do not change these noncompliant policies.

Critique of Commercial Insurer Noncompliant Practices

As noted at the beginning of this chapter, the design of the CPT and RBRVS systems infer that every medical service performed should be compensated once, but only once.

The modifier system provides a means for physicians to submit claims when they provide nonrelated medical services within the global period of another service. This system encourages medical efficiency and patient convenience.

Insurers require physicians to use the E/M coding system, and they rely on physicians to submit claims in compliance with that system. Their knowing violation of the CPT coding system relationships and modifiers places an unjustifiable financial burden on physicians. This directly benefits commercial insurers by improperly causing doctors to provide free services for the care insurers should cover. Further, the negative economic impact of this insurer strategy is a direct disincentive for efficient quality care.

It is critical for physicians to understand this coding and compliance disparity by commercial insurers. It is also mandatory for them to educate themselves and their administrative staff to identify instances of improper nonpayment for services provided to their patients. With this knowledge, physicians should be able to make informed decisions about how to react to these circumstances. Possible options for addressing this problem are discussed in the accompanying sidebar.

Possible Physician Responses to Noncompliant Insurer Practices Regarding Modifiers

My review of CPT coding system principles has led me to infer a unifying principle regarding proper submission of codes for reimbursement.

This coding concept is based on the interpretation that, at its core, *CPT coding system principles provide that every service should be submitted (for reimbursement) once, but no service should be submitted (for reimbursement) more than once.* This reflects our previous representation that E/M care should not be coded separately when it is a recognized *component* of another service, but it should be coded separately when the E/M care provided exceeds the level of care included in the second service. It similarly reflects the RBRVS analysis that E/M care should not be coded separately when the RVUs for that care have been calculated into the value of another service, and it should be coded separately when they have not.

When only physicians follow these rules, and the organizations providing reimbursement do not, the inequity and injustice disrupt not only the credibility of insurers, but also the quality of our health care system. Physicians do have several options to respond to these insurer economic tactics, other than providing free care as a donation to commercial insurers.

1. Physicians can file appeals.

   ■ Unfortunately, these frequently fail. Even when appeal of one case succeeds, it does not change insurer payment policies, and the same nonpayment appeal will have to

continued

be filed over and over again, ad infinitum. Furthermore, the administrative costs of appeal generally far exceed the yield for each individual case. The administrative burden also demands more personnel, requires more space, and generally disrupts smooth billing procedures.

2. Physicians can explain the dilemma to their patients and ask that they file a complaint with the insurance carrier.
   - Unfortunately, the carrier will usually send a letter to the patient simply stating its (nonpayment) policy and informing the patient that the physician must provide this care anyway.

3. Physicians can identify which insurers are noncompliantly denying payment, and the combinations of services they are noncompliantly "bundling" together. They can simply not schedule those combinations for patients insured with the identified carriers.
   - The downside to this approach is that it may be quite challenging, costly, and time consuming to determine which noncompliant policies apply to each insurer and coordinate scheduling accordingly.
   - This issue is even more complex, because each insurer commonly has multiple policies, each of which is individualized to each employer they insure or administer.
   - The challenge increases as insurers regularly add new nonpayment policies and modify old ones.

4. Physicians can elect to provide only one service per visit, when that is the only care for which the noncompliant insurers will consistently *authorize* payment. That is, when insurers are bundling E/M services into procedure services on the same date of care, despite proper submission with modifiers, physicians have the option to perform the extraordinary E/M care on a different date from the date of the procedure. This ensures that they will receive reimbursement for the care they provide.
   - When my own three-physician office was forced to adopt this policy because of high frequency of improper nonpayments, our number of appeals of noncompliant payment denials fell from more than 70 per month to 2 per month.
   - In dealing with patients, we advised that we would schedule a separate appointment to address the unrelated issue (the current appointment has sufficient time only for the scheduled care).

For example, a common annoying situation occurs when patients who have scheduled allergy immunizations arrive at the physician's office with an additional medical problem unrelated to their allergy care. Allergy immunotherapy (eg, CPT code 95117) has a zero-day global period, thereby including E/M care related to the patients' allergies. However, when the physician provides E/M care for an unrelated problem, CPT and RBRVS both indicate submitting for the E/M service with modifier 25 (in addition to submitting the 95117 code for allergy treatment). When the insurer's automated claims processing denies the E/M service despite the modifier, the physician has just donated significant funds to the insurer's bottom line. The alternative is to politely inform the patient that the insurer refuses to authorize physicians to provide both the allergy treatment and care for the patient's new problem on the same day. The physician determines with the patient which care he or she would prefer today and schedules the patient to return for another appointment to address the second problem.

Is this a reasonable solution? Of course not. It upsets both the physician and the patient. It violates optimal care and it violates common sense. In addition, the CPT coding system provides for physicians to give this care to their patients and receive appropriate reimbursement. Insurers have violated the letter and the spirit of the CPT coding system, making this unreasonable solution a necessary option.

SUMMARY

The compliant use of modifiers is critical for physicians requesting appropriate reimbursement for E/M services under certain specified circumstances. Physicians need to understand and follow the CPT coding system principles that govern coding when E/M services are provided either on the same day as a procedure, or during the global period of a procedure. The CPT codebook describes the modifiers that are submitted with an E/M code when a physician provides E/M services that exceed the level of E/M care included in a procedure's "surgical package."

The CPT coding system's relatively straightforward system of modifiers that can be used with E/M codes is designed to encourage efficient and convenient care to patients, while ensuring appropriate reimbursement to physicians for the services they provide. To accomplish this, however, physicians and insurers must accept and implement the same set of rules. Unfortunately, this is currently not the case. Many insurers employ claims processing software specifically designed to circumvent the CPT principles governing compliant use of modifiers. This noncompliant policy has created disincentives to efficient and cost-effective health care, while also causing significant inconsistency, confusion, and mistrust in our health care environment. As a consequence, physicians must develop awareness of these coding and reimbursement problems, so that they can consider their most reasonable options for dealing with this predicament.

Physicians, patients, and elected officials should all acknowledge the benefits of holding Medicare carriers and commercial insurers responsible for following the same CPT guidelines as physicians, and they should advocate for legislation to achieve this goal.

References

1. American Medical Association. *Current Procedural Terminology CPT® 2008*. Chicago, IL: American Medical Association; 2007.

2. Gallagher P, ed. *Medicare RBRVS: The Physicians' Guide*. Chicago, IL: American Medical Association; 2004.

3. Health Care Financing Administration. *Documentation Guidelines for Evaluation and Management Services*. Chicago, IL: American Medical Association; 1997.

4. Jacobellis v Ohio, 378 US 184 (1964).

5. CodingToday Web site. http://www.codingtoday.com. Accessed July 10, 2008.

E/M Enhancements and Health Care Evolution

Because evaluation and management (E/M) services are a vital component of quality health care, it is important to examine the implications of E/M care in both our current and future health care environments.

WHERE ARE WE NOW AND WHERE ARE WE GOING?

The traditional formats of written and dictated medical records are currently "under fire" over issues including illegibility, noncompliance, and lack of interoperability and interconnectivity within the health care system. Further, these traditional formats do not adequately access the vast potential for electronic compilation and sharing of clinical data or for the provision of clinical decision support at the point of care.

The current generation of electronic health records is in the process of transformation and evolution. Some of the problems with the existing software systems include the lack of E/M compliance, documentation limitations that do not allow descriptions that distinguish each unique patient illness and each visit, inefficient data entry, and interference with patient-physician communications and relationships.

An insightful analysis of the issues with both conventional and electronic medical records appeared in a February 2005 article in the *New York Times*.[1] The author, Dr Abigail Zuger, matched different medical record formats (paper vs electronic) with the ages of the physicians using them. She posed this provocative question in her title: "When Is a Doctor Too Old? Or Too Young?" The central theme of her article is described below:

> The old doctor stored important details about patients in memory, and nowhere else. The doctor's hesitantly typed notes recording office visits were brief and old-fashioned—a few sentences at most, difficult for anyone else to interpret.
>
> The young doctor remembered little about each patient from visit to visit, but typed volumes, and was a big fan of medical software that supplies preformed phrases, sentences and paragraphs—the results of an entire physical exam, for instance—at the click of the mouse. Sometimes the mouse clicked just a little too quickly and erroneous information crept into the charts.
>
> Insurance reviewers occasionally confused the old doctor's terse notes with incompetence. Patients occasionally complained bitterly about the young doctor, deploring that habit of pounding the computer keyboard for the duration of their visit and never once looking them in the eye. Both doctors, learning of these misunderstandings, were mortified and furious. Colleagues who had to wade through charts belonging to either one just tore their hair.

More often than not, the (possibly exaggerated) characterizations of Dr Old with his typed (or written or dictated) records, and Dr Young with his laptop, are frighteningly, and sadly, right on target. However, in reality, Dr Zuger's descriptions of these problems apply to the two medical record technologies that shape these patient visits more appropriately than they apply to the age of physicians. In reality, providing Dr Young (or a middle-aged "Dr Middle") with a *conventional* paper record results in the same scenario just described for Dr Old. Similarly, equipping Dr Old (or Dr Middle) with a laptop, and charging him with the task of clicking the mouse and pounding the keys while attempting to obtain valuable information from (and to communicate with) his or her patients, leads to the identical image portrayed for Dr Young.

Dr Zuger has insightfully articulated the inability of both of our existing medical record systems to satisfy our requirements for quality care, compliant documentation, patient caring, usability, efficiency, and physician satisfaction. However, it may be that she has placed her emphasis on the wrong part of this picture. The cause of the problems described is not the age of the physicians; it is the inadequacy of the medical record tools and methodology the physicians are employing. As the age of electronic records evolves, we need to recognize and remedy the physician and patient-related concerns highlighted in Dr Zuger's article, as well as those that were discussed in Chapter 23.

Practical E/M concepts address many of the design and data entry shortcomings that are intrinsic to both of these medical record systems, regardless of the age of the physicians. While this approach succeeds in solving many of the medical record problems we have discussed, it also introduces a new set of challenges:

- How do we help physicians incorporate the methodology of Practical E/M and the tools of the intelligent medical record (IMR) into their practices in all medical record formats?

- How early in physicians' careers should we introduce Practical E/M and the IMR into the physician's toolbox?

- In what ways can we further enhance E/M coding and the *Documentation Guidelines for Evaluation and Management Services*[2] to promote quality health care?

- Can we identify the external pressures on the health care system that negatively affect quality patient care? Once identified, how can physicians and society address them?

The remaining sections of this chapter evaluate these challenges and discuss options for addressing them. Hopefully, consideration of these options will stimulate thoughtful discussion, lead to meaningful action, and result in the adoption of a new approach that assists physicians and significantly improves the overall quality of medical records, patient care, and the health care system itself.

TRAINING PHYSICIANS AND AUDITORS

In 1992, the Health Care Financing Administration (the predecessor of the Centers for Medicare and Medicaid Services [CMS]) assumed the responsibility of training physicians and auditors in how to use the newly introduced E/M coding system. The organization implemented an extensive and well-intended training effort. However, the subsequent audits of physician records proved the need for additional "documentation guidelines" to complete the initial system. Although these entered the system in 1995 and 1997, with additional training for physicians as well, experience shows that we now need to teach a modified and usable approach and provide compliant medical record tools in order for physicians to implement an effective E/M coding and documentation system in their medical practices.

There appear to be positive incentives for all parties to encourage adoption of the Practical E/M approach. From the physicians' perspective, employing this system offers a reasonable probability of increased productivity, while ensuring compliance, efficiency, and quality care. There are also significant incentives for adoption by CMS and private insurers. Since experience indicates that improved quality of care increases medical cost-effectiveness, there should be a powerful motivation for CMS and commercial insurers to provide training and tools for practicing physicians. It is likely that an updated training protocol for physicians and auditors, sponsored by CMS (and possibly supported by insurers), would prove beneficial to all parties in our health care system, including patients.

A coordinated training effort will enable auditors to acquire the skills and tools they need to conduct educational audits, which will allow them to positively reinforce the E/M training provided for physicians. At the same time, this would be an opportunity to standardize audit methodology and ensure the use of compliant auditing tools. This training will correct the current problem of auditors employing a variety of audit tools that are not compliant with the Current Procedural Terminology (CPT®) coding system and that have not been standardized or approved by the American Medical Association or published for physicians by CMS. The overall effects of this type of program for auditing should be the establishment of reliable E/M audit methodology and consistency in the content of audit reports, resulting in increased credibility for the entire process.

TRAINING MEDICAL STUDENTS AND RESIDENTS

At what stage of their medical careers should physicians be introduced to the E/M concepts and tools they are required to use for the rest of their careers, to achieve compliance, efficiency, productivity, usability, and (most importantly) quality of care? In Chapter 3 we pointed out that, for most medical students, their introduction to the history and physical (H&P) early in their medical school education emphasizes the importance of the medical record in general and the comprehensive medical history in particular. This is the ideal time to teach young physicians Practical E/M methodology, including the concepts of the role of the nature of presenting problem (NPP) and the principles of E/M documentation and compliance. It is also the right time to provide students with IMR tools that will increase their efficiency of care while guiding and assisting their evaluation of patients and medical record documentation.

To accomplish these goals, we first need to educate our medical educators in the principles of Practical E/M. The E/M coding system was not brought into medical schools and residency programs when it was introduced in 1992. As a result, we lost the opportunity to educate young physicians in understanding and using the E/M coding system. Also, we cannot just teach medical record principles in the second year of medical school without follow-up education and monitoring. Physician educators trained in E/M documentation and knowledgeable in the relationships between comprehensive history, clinical diagnosis, and medical record compliance must monitor these developing skills throughout medical school and residency. This will provide young physicians with the educational environment to complete their formal training equipped and comfortable with quality medical record tools and E/M compliance methodology. The addition of Practical E/M concepts and tools to medical school and residency training is a logical extension of the fact that the E/M system is a codification of the medical care process taught to students and exemplified in the standard reference text, the "Bates' Guide to the Physical Examination and History Taking" (as discussed in Chapter 1). Practical E/M complements the customary teaching process by providing medical record tools that add efficiency, usability, and compliant documentation to the optimal diagnostic process physicians learn, allowing them to implement these principles effectively in the practice of medicine.

Such an educational program should remedy the problem, which was also noted in Chapter 3, that physicians currently entering practice after residency training generally have no significant training in E/M compliance. They do not sufficiently understand the vocabulary or requirements of documentation and coding, and they have little insight into the close relationship between quality of care, E/M compliance, office efficiency, the medicolegal environment, and their medical records. They enter their medical practice like either Dr Old or Dr Young from the *New York Times* article, without a functional, usable, and compliant medical record system to help them with the management of their patients in practice.

Assessment of Current Physician Training in E/M

What happens to documentation and coding in training today? My surveys of the educational environment demonstrate that E/M coding is barely, if ever, mentioned during medical school or residency. In general, the teaching of medical record documentation begins with an emphasis on recording a comprehensive H&P. The introduction to medical decision making (MDM) is limited to documentation of impressions, recommendations, data reviewed, and data ordered. There is no discussion about the necessity of documenting the level of risk of the presenting problem(s), risk of diagnostic tests, and risk of management options. There is also no consideration of the concept of compliance and the role of medical necessity in gauging appropriate levels of care. Finally, medical record tools designed to facilitate documentation are not considered.

Attention to the medical record decreases in the later years of medical school, and it essentially vanishes during residency. As the time pressures and work burdens on residents increase, they commonly respond by introducing shortcuts to the medical history: paring down the family history, shortening the social history, limiting the review of systems (ROS), and narrowing the focus of the history of the present illness. They simply do not have time to ask all the questions and write all the answers. Since residency training programs have not introduced tools for efficient documentation into resident education, the "system" trains them to conclude that their only recourse is to move toward a problem-focused history. For the same reasons, the physical examination and MDM become similarly compromised. Optimal care and documentation are further undermined by the fact that during their training, very few of the students' and residents' physician role models have adequate time or tools to perform and document at the recommended level. By the end of residency, the ideals of using the comprehensive H&P as a powerful diagnostic tool have generally been pushed aside and lost.

The basic premise that a high-quality H&P is still the most powerful diagnostic arrow in a physician's medical quiver is still being emphasized to medical students early in their clinical training. What these students do not learn, however, is how to obtain and document this high-quality H&P in a realistic health care setting. In the real world, physicians do not have even one-quarter of the amount of time required to conduct a high-quality H&P as it is taught in medical school using blank sheets of paper. Practical E/M methodology and IMR templates can help answer this challenge for medical students and residents. They can teach student physicians how to select appropriate levels of care based on the severity of their patients' medical problems, how to satisfy the CPT coding system requirements for providing that extent of care, and how to efficiently and effectively record that care. Providing these tools to students from the inception of training in clinical medicine is like teaching a second language in early childhood—when the language of coding and documentation is taught early in their training, medical students will develop "fluency" in this language. This will enable them to easily fulfill the goal of using the medical record for quality care, efficiency, and compliance. They will also be equipped with the ability to provide and document this caliber of care throughout the rest of their medical careers.

Some nostalgic critics might long for the "days of the giants," when obtaining and writing out complete H&Ps on blank paper took 45 to 60 minutes. While some of this time was devoted to patient care, an inordinate amount of it was spent performing clerical tasks: writing long lists of routinely asked questions and lists of the names of body areas examined. This inefficient protocol takes away from meaningful patient interaction and ultimately leads, as noted above, to physicians elimination portions of their care and performing problem-focused H&Ps. Residents and practicing physicians can no longer afford to invest the time required to complete these nonproductive chores, which would demand several hours per day. Students and residents do not learn how to ask "magic questions" that will help them to make diagnoses, or master the "art of medicine," through memorizing lists of questions and writing prolonged long-hand documentation. They acquire these skills by learning how to process and analyze the preliminary patient information and by figuring out what to ask next. Many of the H&P concepts traditionally employed in medical teaching programs continue to have high merit in training physicians today. However, the medical record documentation practices of those "golden old days" need to be retired, so that we can train students in how to use the principles and tools that they will require to meet the demands, standards, and challenges they will face in the current time-constrained and economically pressured environment of medical practice.

Adding E/M efficiency tools to the curriculum can add secondary benefits for the educational environment as well. Currently, all too often we send our medical students and residents home physically and mentally exhausted, barely able to complete their workload and unable to do much more than wolf down a veggie burger and collapse. Enthusiasm and time for reading and research about their patients' medical conditions are frequently victims of this schedule. Consider the benefits for quality of medical education, where the residents save two hours or more of "scut work" each day, by virtue of having an IMR that assists them with their documentation and patient care. Freed from unproductive clerical drudgery, they can retain the excitement of learning something new every day. They will have added time to look up information about the most interesting and unusual cases they cared for during the day. There can even be time to share with family and friends, and still get enough sleep to function well the next day. All of these changes benefit both patient care and the students' or residents' learning process.

FINE-TUNING E/M CODING AND THE *DOCUMENTATION GUIDELINES*

Years of working with physicians on the positive features of the E/M documentation and coding process have also revealed areas where we should consider further refining and enhancing this system. These suggestions fall into several categories. The first two propose clarification or quantification of several qualitative descriptors remaining in the E/M system. The next recommends additional approved single-organ-system examination templates for physicians in different specialties. The final proposal considers the probability that overall population health care could be improved by using input from multiple specialties to compile a basic ROS template.

Clarification of NPP Midlevel Definitions

In Chapter 5 we discussed the two "midlevel" descriptions of NPP, "low to moderate" and "moderate to high." While these terms lack a specific written definition in the CPT codebook, they appear in the descriptors of numerous E/M services. Fortunately, this challenge has been reasonably addressed by the clinical examples found in Appendix C of the CPT codebook.[3] For example, the clinical examples reported for codes 99204 and 99205 correlate with the "moderate to high" NPP associated with these codes.

However, it could also help physicians' understanding of this critical coding factor to add written definitions of these midlevel descriptions to the Guidelines section of E/M Services in the CPT codebook, as we suggested in Chapter 5.

Adoption of Documentation Guidelines for MDM

Chapter 5 also introduced the challenge associated with the use of qualitative descriptions for several elements of MDM: *number* of possible diagnoses, *number* of treatment options, and *amount* of data ordered or reviewed. The CPT coding system offers four degrees of "number": (1) minimal, (2) limited, (3) multiple, and (4) extensive. It also provides four degrees of "amount": (1) minimal or none, (2) limited, (3) moderate, and (4) extensive. It would be extremely helpful, for both physicians and auditors, for the *Documentation Guidelines* to introduce a new MDM guideline that assigns quantitative values to these qualitative terms. We suggest that it is reasonable to assign 1 as the number (or amount) indicated by the term *minimal*, 2 as the number (or amount) indicated by the term *limited*, 3 as the number (or amount) indicated by the terms *multiple* and *moderate*, and 4 or more as the number (or amount) indicated by the term *extensive*.

Refinements for the Single-Organ-System Examinations

Physicians would benefit from a constructive review and update of all the single-organ-system examinations published in the 1997 edition of the *Documentation Guidelines*.[2] Some of the examination elements included in the boxes with unshaded borders seem inappropriate to most specialists in the fields represented by these examinations. For example, examination of the neck and thyroid gland do not seem relevant to a urologist performing a genitourinary examination. In the interest of maintaining the credibility and integrity of the single-organ-system examinations, the relevant specialty societies should be allowed to reconsider the appropriateness of each of the existing requirements, based on the current nature of their specialty and the years of experience their members have had with these guidelines.

Even more critical is physicians' need for more specialty-specific examinations. Although it is usually possible to configure a general multisystem examination to create an acceptable template for physicians in most specialties, this solution is not optimal. The introduction of additional, well-designed single-organ-system examinations would be more appropriate and extremely helpful for physicians in a variety of specialties and perhaps subspecialties as well.

Creation of a Core ROS Template Through Specialty Society Input

It may be worthwhile to consider the possibility of asking specialty societies to suggest key symptoms that they believe are most relevant as screening questions in their areas of expertise. The suggestions from the different specialties could then be compiled into a basic, standardized ROS that could be included in every physician's initial visit template. Each physician would then enhance this basic template by adding questions relevant to his or her specialty and personal preferences. The common foundation would ensure that all initial patient visits would include a comprehensive screening questionnaire for important medical issues related to most clinical specialties.

EXTERNAL PRESSURES OF THE HEALTH CARE SYSTEM ON E/M AND QUALITY OF CARE

We have focused our attention on an approach to E/M services that integrates compliant documentation and coding into a process that helps physicians provide quality care for their patients. While this patient-physician relationship should be the central concern of our health care system, scientific, technological, financial, legal, and political interests are also exerting significant influences on this relationship, and on physicians' ability to deliver quality health care.

Extensive evaluation of the effects of these external forces on our health care system is currently taking place among economists, the office of the national coordinator for health information technology, politicians, public health policy think tanks, insurers, CMS, medical societies, and physicians. A critical focus of current discussions is the concept that the "alignment of incentives" of all the organizations participating in our health care system will be the most effective way to achieve the goals of improved quality, increased patient safety, reduction of medical errors, and optimal cost effectiveness. Let's use this point of view to evaluate the multiple influences on the quality of patient care from the E/M perspective, and then consider changes that could improve this quality.

Defining the Incentives

All those using the expression "aligning the incentives" need to define both the target we are aligning to hit and the incentives we are attempting to bring into that alignment. The target, or center of focus, certainly should be quality of care, and access to it, for all patients. From a physician's perspective, some of the prominent incentives that impact on a physicians' ability to provide quality care include the following:

- adequate reimbursement,
- time and efficiency,
- compliance issues,
- quality and enjoyment of the task,
- administrative hurdles,
- emotional hurdles,
- physician satisfaction, and
- patient satisfaction.

IMR Contributions to Aligning Physician Incentives

Intelligent medical records have evolved both conceptually and pragmatically over the last 13 years by attempting to address the existing positive and negative influences of many of these incentives, while maintaining the goal of helping physicians provide quality care. The first priority addressed was *compliance,* which has been structured into the IMR through the combination of including all elements of care and assessment required by the CPT coding system guidelines and the *Documentation Guidelines,* and by the addition of compliant documentation prompts. *Optimal efficiency* is also designed into the templates by a combination of features:

- Different interfaces (graphic and narrative) are matched to each task of documentation for optimal efficiency.
- Facilitation of data entry by personnel other than the physician provides a comprehensive history for each visit with a minimum investment of physician time.
- Options for data input are available through different formats, including hybrids.

In addition, for many physicians, the benefits of optimal care, compliance, and efficiency also result in a positive influence on *reimbursement*. The quality of care that is the central feature and goal of the IMR contributes to *patient satisfaction* with their clinical results, while minimization of data entry tasks enhances the *enjoyment of the task* and *physician satisfaction*. In summary, Practical E/M, combined with the IMR, strives to align six of these eight listed physician incentives with the target of quality care.

Insurers and Physician Incentives

Medical insurance companies, CMS, and liability insurance companies all exert powerful influences on the health care system. Their central focus on meeting their own economic priorities generates significant incentives and disincentives that can interfere with the ability of physicians to provide patients with access to cost-effective, quality health care. Evaluation of the effects of these nonaligned incentives also compels us to consider their long-term consequences for the health care system.

Practical E/M maintains that the integration of a high-quality medical H&P with care and documentation that is appropriate for the severity of each patient's illness is an extremely valuable and reliable diagnostic tool in the medical armamentarium. It is also a proven path to quality care, which is also often the most cost-effective medical care. Therefore, it *should be* in the best interest of insurers to remove inappropriate financial disincentives that interfere with physicians' ability to perform high-quality E/M services.

Medicare and Compliance Disincentives

While CMS strongly advocates for compliant documentation and coding practices by physicians, it has permitted some Medicare carriers to employ non-compliant E/M auditing tools and to broadcast related non-compliant documentation practices in their publications and on their websites. Use of these improper tools can result in audit results by carriers and coding habits by physicians that conflict with the established guidelines of the CPT codebook and the *Documentation Guidelines*. In addition, because of the relationship of compliant E/M documentation with quality care principles, the use of non-compliant tools can also negatively impact patient care. It is strongly recommended that CMS insist that its carriers use only compliant E/M tools and train their auditors to use them effectively, in order to maintain its credibility with physicians, quality care advocates, and legislators.

Medicare and Reimbursement Disincentives

We can actually examine whether Medicare financial incentives are aligned to support quality E/M care. This review is based on the typical time for individual E/M services reported in the CPT guidelines,[2] relative value units (RVUs) assigned for E/M services in the Resource-Based Relative Value Scale (RBRVS) system,[4] the current Medicare national conversion rate,[5,6,7] and actual current (approximate) medical practice expense costs and liability insurance costs per physician per hour.

As shown in Table 27.1, calculations based on the 2008 Medicare RBRVS and national conversion factor demonstrate a considerable financial disincentive to providing the typical amount of time recommended by the CPT codebook for E/M services. Based on a very conservative estimate of $250 per hour per physician practice expense costs (which does not include any payment for physician salary), Medicare payments cover approximately *11.1 minutes* of care for a patient whose initial outpatient visit is appropriately coded as 99203; this is a service that the CPT codebook descriptors indicate typically warrants *30 minutes* of face-to-face time. Similar calculations for an outpatient established patient visit coded as 99213, which is the most common E/M service, reveal that Medicare payments cover approximately *6.9 minutes* of care for a service that the CPT descriptors identify as typically involving *15 minutes* of face-to-face time. It is clear from Table 27.1 that the RBRVS system, with Medicare's current conversion factor, is reimbursing physicians for no more than 30% to 40% of the time of care indicated by the CPT coding system guidelines as being typical for the patients' NPP.

TABLE 27.1

Time Funded for E/M Under 2008 Medicare RBRVS and Conversion Factor (Real Expense, $250/Hour). This table shows the typical time assigned by the CPT descriptors for each of the listed E/M codes, and it multiplies this time by the conservative hypothetical hourly overhead cost of $250 per hour to show the physician's cost of providing this amount of care. The next two columns show the RBRVS system's RVUs for each service and how much this pays the physician for expenses based on the CMS national conversion rate.[*] The final column shows how many minutes of overhead expense are in reality covered by this level of payment.

E/M Code	Typical Time, per CPT	Physician Expense	RVUs for PLI[†] and Expenses	Amount Paid for Expenses	Time Paid by Fee Schedule
99203	30 minutes	$125	1.21	$46.06	11.1 minutes
99204	45 minutes	$188	1.61	$61.32	14.7 minutes
99213	15 minutes	$63	0.76	$28.95	6.9 minutes
99214	25 minutes	$104	1.11	$42.28	10.2 minutes
99243	40 minutes	$167	1.55	$59.03	14.1 minutes
99244	60 minutes	$250	2.04	$77.70	18.6 minutes

[*] The early 2008 Medicare conversion rate was $38.0870. At the time of this writing, a 10.6% reduction scheduled to take effect on July 1, 2008, was halted by last-minute legislation and a Congressional override of a Presidential veto, resulting in continuation of the exiting 0.5% increase in the rate for the remainder of 2008 and an additional 1.1% increase to be in effect throughout 2009.[*] This calculates to a conversion rate of approximately $38.467 for 2009. Unfortunately, medical practice overhead costs continue to rise at 5% - 7% per year which results in even less time for visits being paid by the fee schedule.[8]

[†] Practice Liability insurance.

Viewing these figures from another perspective reveals that if a physician does provide the amount of time recommended for each service by CPT coding system guidelines, the *total reimbursement* from Medicare will still be insufficient to cover physicians' actual overhead expenses (with no consideration of a salary for the physician). Clearly, this is not alignment of incentives. On the contrary, it indicates that the current Medicare conversion rate provides a powerful financial disincentive to providing the time indicated for quality medical care, and therefore also a significant financial disincentive to achieving cost-effective medical care.

Commercial Insurers and Reimbursement Disincentives

We also know that, in general, reimbursements by commercial insurers range from 20% below Medicare rates to 10% above Medicare rates. They accomplish this by paying on the basis of a multiple of the Medicare conversion rate, which is then applied to the RVUs for each CPT code in the RBRVS schedule. Therefore, the *financial disincentives* to quality care from commercial carriers parallel those from Medicare.

Higher Code Levels vs Appropriate Reimbursement

Under the economic strains of current Medicare and commercial insurer underpayment, physicians commonly ask how they can bill more high-level E/M codes. My response is to ask whether they would be asking this question if they were being reimbursed *appropriate* amounts (based on an *accurate* resource-based payment system) for medically indicated level 2 and level 3 services, suggesting payment levels approximately three times the amount they currently receive. Their inevitable reply is that such correct payment would resolve their coding level issues.

"Payment Policies"

As discussed in Chapter 26, Medicare and private insurers have adopted a variety of payment policies that contradict the CPT coding system guidelines for properly submitting claims for E/M services and procedure services on the same date. While Medicare has a small number of such edits, commercial insurers have a significant number of claims editing policies that either fail to recognize modifiers submitted with E/M codes or override the modifiers and deny payment for either the E/M service or the procedure when both are correctly submitted for the same date. These policies put most of our listed incentives out of alignment with our target of cost-effective quality care, including:

■ reimbursement,
■ efficiency,
■ compliance issues,
■ administrative hurdles,
■ enjoyment of task,
■ physician satisfaction, and
■ patient satisfaction.

Furthermore, these policies amplify physician frustration because they conflict with the integrity of the CPT coding system, and they financially penalize physicians who follow compliant coding practices. As a result, they severely disrupt compliance incentives and destroy insurer credibility, because when physicians are coding in compliance with CPT coding system guidelines, they expect to be treated compliantly by Medicare and insurers.

All physicians would agree that insurers must eliminate these disincentives to achieve uniformity, fairness, and compliance, and to encourage medically indicated levels of quality E/M care. Also, from a financial incentive perspective, insurers should have every reason to do so when they accept the premise that, in the long run, not only is promoting quality medical care their obligation to patients, it is also the most cost-effective medical care.

Bringing Insurer Incentives Into Alignment

Two basic policy changes by Medicare and commercial insurers would lead to alignment of these eight incentives with the goal of quality health care:

- Claims editing software should be compliant with CPT coding system rules and guidelines. Basically, all parties in the health care system need to be "playing by the same rules" and applying the same values.

- The RBRVS system should be reconfigured to be a true resource-based value scale system ("RBVS," removing the concept of "relative"). That is, the system should perform the way physicians and legislators actually envisioned it when its enabling legislation passed in 1989. To accomplish this, at a minimum, the conversion factor needs to be sufficiently increased to cover the actual practice expense costs, liability insurance costs, and appropriate work value for each CPT-coded service.

The Impact of the RBRVS

The term *relative* in RBRVS is the feature that permits the conversion factor (and reimbursements) to be lowered to levels below (or far below) actual medical costs. The system permits this as long as the *relative* degree of reduction is the same for every CPT code, and therefore the same for every physician. My analysis of the overall effect of this approach surmises that it is the equivalent of ensuring that all parts of the Titanic sink at the same time (rather than the bow going down first).

Reducing the conversion rates to their current levels, where payments provide no net reimbursement to physicians for the level of care indicated and are often insufficient to even cover practice expenses, poses a great danger to our patients and to the integrity of our health care system. When he was Surgeon General, Dr C. Everett Koop offered the insight that there are three critical factors in the health care equation—access, quality of care, and cost control. He concluded that we could have any two out of the three. Unfortunately, Dr Koop did not contemplate what happens when payments to physicians are reduced to levels insufficient to cover overhead costs. However, we do have a 40-year experience with that model; it is called Medicaid. When reimbursements fall this low, *we lose all three* of the critical factors in Dr Koop's equation. Quality deteriorates, access becomes more difficult, and health care costs actually increase, because by the time patients actually enter the system (usually through the emergency department), they are so sick that the cost of their medical care is a multiple of what it should have been.

I call this process "Medicaidization." I believe our Medicare system and our managed care reimbursement system have both already crossed over this threshold, and the deterioration will continue to accelerate because legislated increases in the conversion factor are less than the increases in medical practice expense costs. As always, minimal Medicare payment increases will likely be mimicked by similarly minimal changes in commercial insurer reimbursement rates. Physicians face the dilemma of being forced to accept reimbursements that are too low to cover their costs while unwillingly giving charity to insurers, who make huge profits.

Physicians are left with few other choices, all of which involve some degree of practicing medicine or earning income outside our established health care environment. In its most extreme form, areas of the country are experiencing the phenomenon of significant numbers of physicians refusing to participate with Medicare and refusing to sign insurance company contracts, due to insufficient reimbursement schedules. This degree of alienation is predictable under "Medicaidization," though to the detriment of physicians, patients, and the health care system as a whole.

Liability Insurance

Medical liability insurance offers the final complicating factor in the nonalignment of incentives in our present reimbursement system. The number and severity of disincentives associated with this cost requirement is almost overwhelming. The first impact is *financial*. When physicians' premiums for this insurance increase, the

RBRVS system has not provided any compensatory increases in payments, despite the fact that the cost of liability insurance is one of the three components of the RBRVS system. The liability insurance crisis also introduces potent *emotional hurdles* for physicians and disincentives for *physician satisfaction* and *enjoyment* of their medical practice.

Examples of Liability Insurance Costs Compared to Health Insurer Reimbursements

The economics of liability insurance cost vs reimbursements are beyond critical in the highest-risk specialties. In Connecticut, an obstetrician who performs 50 routine obstetrical deliveries per year (CPT code 59400) pays between $1,500 and $2,500 per delivery just for the liability insurance to cover that care. The RBRVS system assigns only 5.5 RVUs per delivery, which translates to approximately $209, to pay for the cost of this liability insurance. In fact, the entire delivery (including prepartum and postpartum care) is valued at only 47.01 RVUs, which provides a total of approximately $1,800 per delivery. Even the total payment is generally inadequate to cover the per-case cost of the premium, without consideration of other practice expenses. The strongest financial incentive this situation provides obstetricians is to stop performing obstetrical care and drastically reduce their liability insurance premiums. Sadly, many practitioners have been forced to make this choice.

Although the numbers are not as dramatic, general surgeons pay approximately $100 to $200 in liability premiums per operation (depending on the number of operations they perform per year). The RBRVS system allows 0.40 RVU per endoscopic gallbladder removal, which translates to approximately $16, to pay for the cost of liability insurance. The incentives for surgeons in this predicament are either to discontinue performing surgery, or to cease participating with Medicare and private insurers who so severely undervalue their payments.

The conditions of our medicolegal crisis are also disruptive to quality of patient care. Since the results in medicolegal cases in reality seem to center around patients' health outcomes rather than whether physicians practiced within the standard of care, there has developed a strong incentive for what is labeled "defensive medicine." This is the ordering of nonessential laboratory tests and radiology examinations on the basis of protecting against an adverse legal outcome, rather than on the basis of medical indications. Ironically, this situation actually pits one insurance philosophy against another. While Medicare and health care insurers want the physician to do only what *should* be done, liability insurers provide this powerful incentive for the physician to do everything that *could* be done. This leads to increased ordering of, and reliance on, sophisticated medical tests and imaging, usually at the expense of spending sufficient time performing a thorough H&P.

SUMMARY

There is longstanding motivation for physicians to have a usable and functional approach to the E/M coding system. A recent CMS report concluded by "asking the [American Medical Association] to collaborate on a new effort to give physicians and carriers better guidance on E&M codes accuracy."[5] That report also cited "the importance of billing correctly to avoid upcoding and undercoding."[5]

Practical E/M offers an effective solution by addressing the need for a compliant, usable, and functional approach to E/M documentation and coding. The importance of training physicians was also considered in the CMS report, which stated, "The authors of the Medicare report acknowledge that simply implementing better education for physicians on the guidelines that exist today might be a good place to start."[5] With the effective concepts presented in this volume, we propose a new educational program to train both physicians and auditors in Practical E/M methodology, so that all parties are able to use the system consistently, effectively, and correctly.

However, this renewed training effort should correct a flaw of earlier E/M educational efforts by bringing this training into medical school and residency training programs as well. Efficient and compliant documentation and coding principles and IMR tools should be taught to medical students and residents as an integral component of an effective H&P. This should help them promote quality care, enhance the medical training experience, and enable physicians to enter practice equipped to deal with E/M documentation and coding requirements.

At the same time, we suggest that there are benefits to refining and strengthening the current E/M protocols to make the system work as well as possible for physicians.

Finally, E/M care is a central component of the provision of quality health care. However, it does not exist in a vacuum. As we strive to make this aspect of medical care function effectively, we must similarly address and correct the political and economic forces that are creating adverse incentives to quality health care, and we must move to correct them for the well-being of our entire health care system.

References

1. Zuger A. When is a doctor too old? Or too young? *New York Times*. February 8, 2005:F5.

2. Health Care Financing Administration. *Documentation Guidelines for Evaluation and Management Services*. Chicago, IL: American Medical Association; 1997.

3. American Medical Association. *Current Procedural Terminology CPT® 2008*. Chicago, IL: American Medical Association; 2007.

4. Gallagher P, ed. *Medicare RBRVS: The Physicians' Guide*. Chicago, IL: American Medical Association; 2004.

5. Glendinning D. Medicare zeroes in on E&M coding as key source of payment mistakes. *American Medical News*. January 3/10, 2005:1

6. American Medical Association. *Medicare RBRVS 2008: The Physicians' Guide*. Chicago, IL: American Medical Association; 2008.

7. American Medical Association. The RBRVS and the AMA Specialty Society RVS Update Committee (RUC) Process 2008. www.gastro.org/user-assets/Documents/03_Practice_Management/RUC_Process_2008.ppt. Accessed May 19, 2008.

8. Nicole Gaouette, *Los Angeles Times*, "Congress Overrides Bush Veto on Medicare Bill, http://www.latimes.com/features/health/medicine/la-na-medicare16-2008jul16,0,7928843.story, accessed July 18, 2008.

Examples of Different Types of NPP With the Appropriate Level of Care and Extent of Documentation

SAMPLE NPP SEVERITY SEQUENCE

We can examine how the practical evaluation and management (E/M) process works in conjunction with an intelligent medical record (IMR) during patient care by looking at a series of summary profiles for patients who might present to the physician with the same chief complaint. These examples illustrate how the details of the history of present illness (HPI) initially distinguish the cases and enable the physician to identify a reasonable type (severity) of the nature of presenting problem (NPP) and indicated level of care, following the Current Procedural Terminology (CPT®) coding system guidelines.[1]

Comparing sample profiles for patients with the same chief complaint, but with progressively more complex HPIs and more significant examination findings, demonstrates how the practical E/M process works during patient care. In these illustrations, the severity of illness and the extent of care and documentation will progress from a level 2 initial outpatient visit, step by step through a level 5 visit. These charts highlight the interplay between medical history, NPP, level of care selected, modification introduced by examination findings, and the care provided and documented in the medical record.

Tables A.1 through A.4 organize the narrative portions of completed IMRs for patients presenting with a chief complaint of "simple" nasal congestion, a symptom commonly encountered by physicians in many different specialties. The columns in each table show the significant findings and interpretations in the normal sequence of providing care: completing the medical history, identifying the NPP and appropriate level of care, performing the examination, and completing the medical decision making (MDM) (impressions, treatment options, and highest of the three levels of risk).

To allow the illustrations to focus on these critical relationships in the most direct manner possible, in each sample case we will make the following assumptions:

- Each IMR form has documentation (as recommended) of a complete past, family, and social history (PFSH) and a complete review of systems (ROS). For these examples, it is assumed that the PFSH and ROS contribute no significant positive medical history.

- The physician has obtained and documented a true medical history (ie, a chronological description of the course of the illness) that includes at least four of the eight elements of the HPI. This fact, combined with the previous assumption, creates a "comprehensive" medical history in every case.

■ There are no significant abnormal findings on the physical examination, other than those pertaining to the HPI, which are listed in the table.

In the four illustrations, the HPI shown in column 1 suggests the type (severity) of NPP. Column 2 reports the physician's selection of an appropriate type of NPP and the corresponding appropriate level of care for this NPP (the physician would identify this selection from the IMR's documentation prompts, which are derived from the CPT codebook[1]). Column 3 shows the extent of physical examination performed and the significant findings that would be documented in the narrative section of the exam. Columns 4, 5, and 6 list the MDM performed and documented to equal or exceed the recommendations of the CPT coding system. The overall result for each sample patient is a level of care (and CPT code) that is appropriate for each patient's illness, combined with compliant coding and documentation.

TABLE A.1

Sample of Practical E/M Approach for Initial Visit of Patient With 99202 Level Upper Respiratory Illness

History	NPP/Level of Care	Physical Examination	Impressions	Treatment Options	Risk of Presenting Problem
Four days ago, the patient had onset of mild pain in the back of the throat. Two days ago, pain subsided but severe persistent bilateral nasal congestion developed. Clear discharge, with small amount of yellow, in AM only. No headache. No past history of sinusitis. No smoke exposure. No over-the-counter (OTC) nasal medications.	**NPP** = Low to Moderate (physician draws a circle around both classifications in the medical record) **Level of care** = 99202 (as indicated by CPT codebook[1] descriptions for NPP)	Detailed ENT examination performed and documented[2] in graphic section of IMR Narrative section states: *Nose: Bilateral turbinate congestion. Clear discharge bilaterally. Following (decongestant) spray, patent airway bilaterally, without lesions. Nasal septum straight.*	1. Viral upper respiratory infection. 2. No evidence of bacterial infection at this time.	1. Reassure, OTC decongestant and ibuprofen, steam. 2. Call if symptoms persist > 7 days, or persisting purulent discharge, or significant headache develops.	Low

Commentary: This history strongly suggests that the patient has a viral upper respiratory infection. The physician sets the NPP and level of care appropriately. The examination demonstrates no findings to the contrary (detailed examination exceeds requirement for level of care; performed at physician's choice for quality of care). The MDM for this type of service and level of care requires only one diagnosis and lowest level of risk. The physician treats the patient symptomatically, provides reassurance, and provides written information for future self-care (the information sheet discusses cause of the illness, how the patient should self-treat, and circumstances that would indicate a call to a physician for help, such as prolonged symptoms, persisting purulent discharge, or severe headache).

TABLE A.2

Sample of Practical E/M Approach for Initial Visit of Patient With 99203 Level Upper Respiratory Illness

History	NPP/Level of Care	Physical Examination	Impressions	Treatment Options	Risk of Presenting Problem
Three weeks ago, patient had onset of mild posterior throat pain. Two days later, the pain subsided, but the patient developed severe bilateral nasal congestion with clear nasal discharge. Two weeks ago, the patient noted bilateral yellow and green discharge, R>L. Intermittent right frontal headache for last 10 days, relieved with ibuprofen. Similar episodes occur once every 1 or 2 years, always respond to antibiotics. The patient normally breathes well through both nostrils. No smoke exposure. No OTC nasal meds.	**NPP** = moderate **Level of care** = 99203 (indicated by CPT codebook[1] descriptions for NPP)	Detailed ENT examination performed and documented[2] in graphic section Narrative section states: *Nose: Bilateral congestion. Purulent discharge bilaterally, R>L. Following decongestant spray, moderate nasal septal deviation to the right with patent airway bilaterally. No polyps.*	1. Acute bacterial sinusitis 2. Possible underlying chronic sinusitis 3. Mild septal deviation to right (asymptomatic)	1. Amoxicillin, 500 mg three times daily (tid) × 10 days, OTC decongestant and ibuprofen, steam, room humidifier; recheck in 2 wks 2. Patient advised; recheck septum after infection resolved ——— **Data ordered:** Probable screening computed tomography (CT) of sinuses 6 wks after symptoms resolve	Moderate

Commentary: The history strongly suggests that the patient has an acute bacterial sinus infection, probably bilateral and worse on the right side. The history of recurring problems also suggests the possibility of a chronic underlying problem. The physician sets the NPP and level of care appropriately. The examination demonstrates findings compatible with the probable diagnosis and the indicated level of care. This level of care calls for at least two impressions or treatment recommendations; in this example, this minimum is exceeded by the details of the impressions section, written by the physician to provide a blueprint for future care.

TABLE A.3

Sample of Practical E/M Approach for Initial Visit of Patient With 99204 Level Upper Respiratory Illness

History	NPP/Level of Care	Physical Examination	Impressions	Treatment Options	Risk of Presenting Problem
18-month history of progressively increasing bilateral nasal congestion. The patient now mouth breathes most of the time. Occasional clear nasal discharge. Some sneezing fits. Episodes of purulent discharge and cheek pain, diagnosed as sinusitis and treated by primary physician with antibiotics; these relieve discharge and pain but not congestion. No relief from OTC decongestants or nasal sprays. Mild improvement on antihistamines. No epistaxis.	**NPP** = moderate to high **Level of care** = 99204 (indicated by CPT codebook[1] descriptions for NPP)	Comprehensive ear, nose, and throat (ENT) examination performed and documented[2] in graphic section Narrative section states: *Nose: Severe bilateral congestion. Moderate polyps on right; polyps fill left nasal cavity. Small amount of purulent discharge bilaterally. Following decongestant spray, septum straight anterior; cannot visualize posterior nasal cavity due to polyps.*	1. Bilateral nasal polyposis; L>R 2. Probable bilateral chronic sinusitis 3. Possible allergic rhinitis 4. Doubt inverted papilloma	1. Sinus protocol: Augmentin, 500 mg tid × 2 wks; Ceftin × 2 wks; Levoquin × 2 wks 2. Intranasal steroid spray 3. Return in 2 wks with nasal endoscopy 4. Possible future allergy treatment 5. Possible future endoscopic sinus surgery ——— **Data ordered:** 1. Screening allergy testing. 2. CT of sinuses 4–6 wks after completing antibiotic protocol.	Moderate to high

Commentary: The history strongly suggests that the patient has chronic bilateral sinus pathology. The physician sets the NPP and level of care appropriately. The examination demonstrates findings of nasal polyps and confirms the probable diagnosis and level of care. This level of care calls for at least three impressions or treatment recommendations; in this example, this minimum is exceeded by the details of both impressions and treatment options, written by the physician to provide a blueprint for future care.

TABLE A.4

Sample of Practical E/M Approach for Initial Visit of Patient With 99205 Level Upper Respiratory Illness

History	NPP/Level of Care	Physical Examination	Impressions	Treatment Options	Risk of Presenting Problem
Four-month history of progressively increasing left-sided nasal congestion. Intermittent clear nasal discharge, occasionally blood tinged. Intermittent mild aching pain in left periorbital area, not relieved with OTC ibuprofen or acetaminophen. No purulent discharge, sneezing fits, or watery eyes. No previous history of nasal or sinus disease. No smoke exposure. No OTC nasal medications.	Initial assessment: **NPP** = moderate to high **Level of care** = 99204 or possibly 99205 (indicated by CPT codebook[1] descriptions for NPP) ——— After findings on the physical examination, change to: **NPP** = high **Level of care** = 99205 (indicated by CPT codebook[1] descriptions for NPP)	Comprehensive ENT examination performed and documented[2] in graphic section Narrative section states: *Nose: Left-sided turbinate edema with mild crusting and discharge in middle meatus. Following topical spray, crust cleaned, revealing irregular lesion in middle meatus; granular and firm to palpation with suction. No polyps. Septum straight, right airway patent without lesions or discharge.*	1. Lesion left middle meatus 2. Probable inverted papilloma* 3. Possible carcinoma 4. Probable involvement of left ethmoid sinus, possible involvement of other left sinuses 5. Possible orbital involvement 6. No evidence of right-sided pathology *An invasive local or regional neoplasm that does not metastasize.	1. Augmentin, 500 mg tid × 2 wks 2. Intranasal steroid spray 3. Return in 3 wks for nasal endoscopy and biopsy; review CT scan here 4. Probable future nasal and/or sinus surgery, depending on pathology 5. Possible added radiation if carcinoma ——— **Data ordered:** 1. CT of sinuses in 2 wks 2. Future chest x-ray if findings show malignancy	High

Commentary: The history suggests that the patient has unilateral nasal or sinus pathology. The physician sets the NPP and level of care appropriately at level 4. However, the examination demonstrates findings suggestive of probable neoplasm, with the possibility of locally aggressive or malignant potential. This leads the physician to modify the probable diagnoses, NPP, and level of care (changed to level 5). This revised level of care calls for at least four impressions or treatment recommendations; this minimum requirement is appropriately met, and exceeded, by the details of both impressions and treatment options, written by the physician to provide a blueprint for future care.

WHY AN EXAMPLE FOR LEVEL 1 CARE IS NOT INCLUDED

For a physician following the CPT coding guidelines and the Practical E/M approach for achieving quality care, the level of care should appropriately exceed level 1 for every encounter. This results logically from the design and goals of Practical E/M, which require that the medical record include:

- **Medical history.** For purposes of quality medical care, a comprehensive history is performed and documented for every visit; this is sufficient to support every level of E/M care.

- **Physical examination.** For every initial visit, the physical examination may reasonably and appropriately encompass care that is at least "expanded problem focused" (ie, six or more examination elements). For established visits, even problem-focused examination by the physician supports level 2.

- **MDM.** For initial visits and established visits, the lowest level of complexity of MDM ("straightforward") supports level 2 care.

Quality Care Indications for Expanded Problem-Focused Exam for Initial Visits

On the basis of quality care, practical E/M recommends that an expanded problem-focused examination is medically indicated during initial patient visits. For physicians involved with overall general patient health, an initial evaluation offers the opportunity to appropriately perform reasonable baseline medical assessments of each patient, such as vital signs, patient's general appearance, and status of the heart, lungs, abdomen, and extremities. Documenting the findings of these reasonable exam elements invariably results in an expanded problem-focused or detailed examination.

Similarly, for physicians who employ a single-organ-system examination, there are sufficient specialty-related areas warranting baseline examination to indicate the appropriateness of an expanded problem-focused exam during an initial visit. As an example, for an otolaryngologist, regardless of the patient's chief complaint, it is reasonable and within the standard of quality care to examine (and document) each new patient's vital signs, general appearance, facial strength and tone, facial and scalp appearance, external ears and nose, tympanic membranes, general hearing level, nasal passages, lips, teeth, gums, oral cavity, pharynx, voice quality, salivary glands, neck, and thyroid gland. Quality medical care indicates that a thorough head and neck examination can lead to the discovery of significant asymptomatic pathology, eg, small tympanic perforation, unilateral hearing loss, nasal polyp or inverted papilloma, oral or throat cancer, thyroid mass, salivary gland mass, or adenopathy.

References

1. American Medical Association. *Current Procedural Terminology CPT® 2008*. Chicago, IL: American Medical Association; 2007.

2. Health Care Financing Administration. *Documentation Guidelines for Evaluation and Management Services*. Chicago, IL: American Medical Association; 1997.

Sample Consultation Templates

In keeping with the goal of being "practical" with coding and documentation, following are reasonable suggestions for consultation reports that are compliant, effective, and reasonably efficient.

The conventional consultation letter generally begins with a synopsis of the medical history, then describes the physical examination, and concludes with the physician's impressions and recommendations. However, this traditional structure is not compatible with the realities of how most physicians prefer to review consultation letters. Ideally, physicians who requested a consultation:

- prefer to receive consultation letters very promptly,
- do not have time in their schedule to read and digest a several-page expository dialogue about the patient, and
- generally skip the history and examination findings to read the section reporting the consultant's impressions and recommendations.

To accommodate these realities, we suggest using a relatively brief letter with the reader-friendly organization described in this appendix. The report begins with a listing of the consultant's impressions and recommendations. It then briefly reviews pertinent findings in the patient's medical history and physical examination.

Whether the physician types his or her own consultation letters on a word processor or dictates to a transcription service, using a template that is preformatted with all the headings and introductory linking phrases saves time, effort, and transcription costs.

Figure B.1 illustrates a sample fax template for an efficient consultation letter, which the physician can complete on a word processor and fax immediately to the referring physician. The physician completes all the "xxxxx" demographics, fills in the blank clinical areas, and prints the form.

Figure B.2 presents a similar template with a more narrative design, which a transcriptionist can preload into a word processor. With this template, the consultant physician dictates only the sections in italics. The preloaded nonitalicized portions link the thoughts into an intelligible consultation letter that is patient-specific, thorough, effective, brief, and to the point. This same template can be formatted to merge the corresponding portions of the H&P for physicians who dictate the narrative sections. It can similarly be incorporated into an electronic health record to merge the appropriate narrative portions of the electronic H&P documented during a consultation visit into an original consultation letter.

Both of these model forms can, of course, be further modified or customized to meet each physician's own preferences.

F I G U R E B.1

Sample Consultation Fax Template for Word Processor
The recommendation section can include management options and data ordered. The primary symptoms section records the HPI. The secondary symptoms section includes significant narrative explanations of positive ROS responses.

XYZ Medical Specialists

Physicians
Donald D. Doctor, MD
Elizabeth S. Smith, MD

Nurse Practitioner
Flo Nightingale, APRN

Staff Nurses
Mary Mxxxxxxxxx
Alice Axxxxxxxxx

THIS MATERIAL IS STRICTLY CONFIDENTIAL. ALL PERSONS ARE ADVISED THAT THEY MAY BE PROSECUTED UNDER FEDERAL AND STATE LAW FOR SHARING THIS INFORMATION WITH UNAUTHORIZED INDIVIDUALS.

FACSIMILE CONSULTATION SHEET

To: *xxxxxx, MD*	Tel: *xxxxxx*	Fax: *xxxxxx*

From: ☐ Donald D. Doctor, MD ☐ Elizabeth S. Smith, MD ☐ Flo Nightingale, APRN	(203) 222-3332 Telephone (203) 222-4444 Facsimile

Patient name:	*xxxxxx*
Date:	*xxxxxx*

Diagnoses: 1)

                       2)

                       3)

Recommendations: 1)

                       2)

                       3)

History and physical examination indicate:

   Primary Symptoms:

   Secondary Symptoms:

   Examination Findings:

Thank you for requesting a consultation on this patient. My impressions and recommendations are listed above. I have advised follow-up in our office in:

If further evaluation reveals pertinent information, I will keep you informed. Thank you for requesting that I participate in this patient's care.

Regards,

FIGURE B.2

Sample Consultation Template for Transcription
The recommendations section can include management options and data ordered. The primary symptoms section records the HPI. The secondary symptoms section includes narrative explanations of positive ROS responses.

Date

Physician name, MD

Address

Address

Re: *Patient name*

Diagnoses: 1)

2)

3)

4)

Recommendations: 1)

2)

3)

4)

Dear *physician's name*

At your request, today I had the opportunity to evaluate *patient's name*, a *age*-year-old patient who arrives with the following primary concern(s): *Listing of primary symptoms*

Additional review of the patient's medical history and review of symptoms also indicates the following additional significant areas of difficulty:

Listing of significant secondary symptoms

Relevant findings on physical examination and relevant testing include:

Listing of significant examination and laboratory findings

I have reviewed today's findings with the patient. The symptoms and findings are compatible with the diagnoses listed above. Appropriate recommendations at this time are also listed above. I *have (or have not)* advised follow-up in *(our, your)* office in *number* weeks. Thank you for asking me to evaluate this patient.

Sincerely,

Physician's Name, MD

Automated Downcoding and External E/M Audits

NONCOMPLIANT E/M DOWNCODING PRACTICES

Chapter 24 examined the following two external evaluation and management (E/M) chart audit protocols, both of which are based on the actual review of physicians' medical records:

- the conventional approach, which calculates an E/M code solely on the basis of the three key components and compares this calculated code to the code submitted; and
- the Practical E/M audit approach, which makes an initial determination of the appropriate level of care (ie, E/M code) on the basis of the nature of presenting problem (NPP). It then determines whether the submitted code was appropriate for this NPP, followed by a conventional evaluation of the three key components to determine whether the care documented meets or exceeds the Current Procedural Terminology (CPT®) coding system requirements for the selected level of care.

In contrast to these formally conducted E/M audits, many commercial insurance carriers have installed software that automatically downcodes claims for E/M services according to a variety of mathematical assumptions, without ever reviewing actual patient records. Insurers offer rationalizations for the use of these downcoding functions that range from statistical probabilities of physicians submitting codes at various levels to attempts at associating levels of care with specific diagnosis codes.

The mathematical assumptions applied in all of these systems are in fact, invalid, as will be discussed in some detail later in this appendix. The most significant criticism of automated downcoding systems, however, is that they are 100% noncompliant with the CPT coding system guidelines[1] and with the *Documentation Guidelines for Evaluation and Management Services*.[2] Both of these publications base the correct determination of the documentation and coding solely on the seven components of E/M services ("history, examination, medical decision making, counseling, coordination of care, nature of presenting problem, and time"[1]). The only way to assess these seven components is through actual review of the medical record. Neither of these publications includes any consideration of statistical probabilities or correlations between diagnosis codes and levels of care when establishing the standard for E/M documentation and coding. Although commercial insurers have also attempted to rationalize the use of these automated systems on the basis of audit results, the sole reason for noncompliant automated downcoding appears to be insurers' economic benefit from reducing physician reimbursement.

AUDITS AND AUTOMATED DOWNCODING BASED ON A "BELL CURVE"

A number of organizations have compiled statistical analyses of the frequency with which individual physicians submit different levels of E/M codes. When these statistics are plotted with the progressively increasing levels of E/M codes on the *x*-axis and the number of claims (for each code level) on the *y*-axis, the resultant graph generally has an appearance similar to that of a classic bell curve. For types of service with five code levels, level 3 services are the most frequently submitted. Level 2 and level 4 services are submitted with a significantly lower frequency, and level 1 and level 5 services are submitted least frequently. These statistics are compiled by type of service, generally examining the most frequently performed E/M services, including initial and established outpatient visits, initial hospital care (ie, admissions), and subsequent hospital care. Bell curve statistics are also often subcategorized according to medical specialties.

These statistical studies were produced with the declared purpose of establishing a "baseline" probability of a physician submitting various levels of E/M codes. The two original rationalizations for compiling and considering these statistics were the following:

- Reviewing the statistics would enable physicians to compare the frequency of their E/M code submission with that of their peers.

- Insurers could employ the statistics for a comparative baseline that would enable them to evaluate "coding patterns" for individual physicians. Such reviews could hypothetically permit insurers to identify "outliers," or physicians whose frequency of submitted E/M code levels falls outside the expectations indicated by the bell curve. The insurers could then have the option to conduct formal documentation and coding reviews (ie, compliance audits) of medical records of the selected outlier physicians.

These two rationalizations are completely flawed from a statistical perspective, as discussed later in this appendix. However, they are not out of compliance with CPT coding system principles. This is because these original intentions are only to select charts to be properly reviewed, not to implement automatic downcoding.

Unfortunately, some commercial insurers have adopted automated software that applies this process improperly. Rather than identifying "outliers" and reviewing selected charts, this claims processing software automatically downcodes higher-level E/M services solely on the basis of the frequency expectations of the bell curve statistics. This downcoding occurs without any review of medical record documentation; it is therefore noncompliant.

Commercial Insurers Review Outliers Only on One Side of the Bell Curve

Historically, commercial insurers have chosen to review only those outliers who submit an increased frequency of high-level codes; they have ignored physicians who have a higher frequency of submitting claims for low levels of care. This fact spotlights the reality that insurers' interests are entirely focused on their own economics, not on quality of patient care.

Critique of Bell Curve Statistics for E/M Coding

There are multiple flaws, both conceptually and statistically, in the application of the bell curve model to the frequency of E/M code submissions. First, the classic mathematical bell curve is designed to review single test scores from each individual in a large population. By definition, these scores are then normally distributed, with 68%

of individuals falling within one standard deviation of the mean test score, 95% falling within two standard deviations, and 99% falling within three standard deviations. This statistical approach is neither designed for, nor appropriate for, studying data that derives from each individual having multiple "scores" (ie, a large number of claims for each physician to ascertain frequency of five different E/M levels). Another criticism of using this approach is that some statisticians have applied data collected from geographic regions that are not representative of the regions being evaluated. For example, some bell curve publications apply rural-based claims experience to all physicians, including those who practice in metropolitan environments.

However, the greatest objection to the bell curve approach is that the statistics used to compile these bell curves are based on severely flawed data: the E/M code levels submitted by physicians whose charts have not been audited to assess the accuracy of their E/M coding and documentation. As noted in Chapter 4, actual audits that compare the E/M code submitted with the code calculated on the basis of the actual care delivered, documented, and medically indicated demonstrate an inaccuracy rate varying from 30% to 85% for the codes submitted. Any statistical study based on data with this degree of inaccuracy is corrupted beyond reliability. It is a classic example of "garbage in, garbage out," in which flawed data invalidates statistical results and conclusions.

AUTOMATED DOWNCODING BASED ON DIAGNOSIS CODE PATTERNS

Some private insurers employ claims editing software that automatically reduces code levels for E/M services when they are submitted with a variety of *International Classification of Diseases, Ninth Revision* (ICD-9)[3] diagnosis codes. This type of software employs a database that relies on a statistical probability (ie, the "pattern") of various diagnosis codes being associated with the higher-level E/M services. In cases where the probability of a given diagnosis being submitted with a level 4 or level 5 E/M code is relatively low, the insurer's software will automatically downcode the submitted E/M service. This is done without any review of the medical record. The physician's only recourse is to appeal the downcoding, likely requiring submission of a copy of the medical record and requesting individual review.

Critique of Downcoding Based on Diagnosis Code Patterns

This form of automated downcoding is also built on several defective theories. As demonstrated in the review of automated bell curve downcoding, the underlying statistics used to justify automated downcoding are based on E/M codes submitted by a random sample of physicians whose charts have not been audited. Because physician E/M coding is frequently inaccurate, the database for this software program is also built on faulty data. Further, there is no recognized or authoritative reference correlating various ICD-9 diagnosis codes with levels of illness severity, NPP, or "appropriate" E/M code levels. Most diagnoses can present with a wide range of severities and varying types of NPP. Compliant coding and auditing relate the E/M code level to the NPP, not to the diagnosis. (For example, even a viral respiratory infection that has low morbidity for healthy individuals can be associated with a significant risk of morbidity in a patient who is severely immunocompromised.) These software programs are not compliant with CPT coding guidelines for E/M services, and they severely penalize physicians who are appropriately providing and documenting high-level, high-quality care to patients who present with a moderate or high NPP.

Guilty Until Proven Innocent

Compliant reimbursement requires payment of claims submitted unless actual documentation review proves inappropriate coding. Both forms of statistically automated downcoding operate in a perverse environment of automatically reducing payments and forcing physicians to expend significant time and money to file appeals to receive the payment to which they are entitled. Further, many insurers' audits are suspect since most do not send formal audit reports back to the physicians, and many fail to employ certified coders with E/M auditing expertise.

RISKS IN EXTERNAL E/M AUDITS

Chapter 24 reviewed conventional E/M audits conducted by Medicare and insurers. For physicians facing such an audit, concerns include the following:

- What are the qualifications of the individual or organization performing the audit? Have they been certified? Have their audits been audited for compliance, accuracy, and consistency?

- Is the auditor employing compliant audit standards, or is he or she using "short-cut" mathematical formulas that are not compliant with CPT coding guidelines and the *Documentation Guidelines*?

- If the auditor is a hired contractor, has the insurer's contract offered financial incentives to encourage downcoding (eg, by paying the auditor solely on the basis of a percentage of the amount of funds confiscated as a result of the audits)?

- Have the results of an audit been extrapolated from a relatively small number of medical charts to a large number of claims submitted?

- What is the possibility of being penalized? Governmental organizations that perform E/M audits have the authority to extrapolate and also to implement penalties for fraud when they judge that there is a persistent pattern of significant improper coding. Penalties are permitted for up to $11,000 per chart when there is determined to be fraud. (This can occur even if the identified persistent pattern of improper coding was unintentional and/or resulted from ignorance on the part of the physician.)

POSSIBLE PHYSICIAN RESPONSES TO AUTOMATED DOWNCODING

Automated downcoding is a noncompliant practice. Fortunately, the prevalence of this practice should be declining, because most of the settlements in the physician class-action lawsuits against private insurers have included an agreement to prohibit automated downcoding of E/M services. However, some of those settlement agreements have already expired, and those insurers are no longer restricted from these noncompliant practices. Physicians are advised to make their administrative staffs aware of this noncompliant downcoding practice, so that when they review insurer explanation of benefit forms they can identify any instances of automated E/M downcoding and determine how to address the problem. If these practices are discovered, we recommend that physicians contact their state medical society to ask for their assistance in addressing the problem and using all possible means to compel insurers to end this noncompliant practice.

Medical practices may also choose to respond directly. In all cases where E/M claims have been downcoded, we recommend that the appropriate initial response is for the administrator and physician to review the medical record(s) in question and to determine whether it appropriately supports both the medical necessity (ie, NPP) and the documented level of care required for the submitted code. When the practice does not have a qualified reviewer, an outside compliance consultant should be asked to perform the review.

The Extent of an Internal E/M Compliance Review

My experience in reviewing physician E/M medical records is that a review of no more than five initial visit charts and five established visit charts (that had been submitted with various code levels) provides a sufficient basis for an effective overall assessment by a qualified auditor. The internal audit should provide the physician with a realistic appraisal of whether the records reviewed fulfill the requirements of medical necessity, and whether the records are generally overcoded, undercoded, underdocumented, or correctly coded.

This information should help the physician and his or her advisors determine a reasonable course of action, following some or all of the five steps listed later in this appendix for dealing with automated downcoding or with a formal external audit. Whichever course of action the physician chooses, it should include the implementation, if required, of compliant E/M practices for the future.

For cases in which the audit reveals that the physician's documentation and coding are appropriate, the medical practice should appeal the downcoding. If the insurer requests to review the medical record, the physician should provide a copy of the record and should point out the need for the insurer to provide a copy of the detailed audit report of each individual chart, so that the physician may evaluate whether the audit was performed in compliance with CPT coding guidelines. Then, if the insurer's audit appears to be flawed, the physician may also request an external appeal, depending on the terms of the contract with the insurer.

If, on the other hand, the practice determines that the E/M codes submitted are not supported by the documentation in the medical record, it is inadvisable to request that the insurer perform a formal chart audit. This conclusion should instead prompt the physician to consider bringing the practice's E/M documentation and coding into compliance, so that in the future the practice can appeal automated downcoding.

POSSIBLE PHYSICIAN RESPONSES TO A FORMAL EXTERNAL AUDIT

There are multiple potential responses to requests for medical records by Medicare or a private insurer for the purpose of a formal audit. How a physician should react to an inquiry will depend on the circumstances, including whether the physician's own internal audit of the records in question reveals a compliance problem.

In general, we recommend seeking professional advice from one or more of the sources listed below prior to submitting records for review. The state medical society and/or the other resources should help guide the most appropriate course of action. The range of responses to a request for review of medical records can include some or all of the following:

- Perform a reliable review, or formal audit, of the charts in question. This should be conducted by a qualified professional, who may be either a member of the practice's staff or a qualified consultant.
- Contact the state medical society for assistance, including recommendations for consultants and/or attorneys with expertise in dealing with insurer audits.

- Contact a qualified consultant.
- Contact an experienced health care attorney.
- Institute compliant E/M documentation and coding practices as soon as possible.

PHYSICIANS WITH COMPLIANT E/M RECORDS

Physicians who correctly follow Practical E/M methodology and employ intelligent medical record documentation templates should have a very high probability of success in the event of an external audit. Their charts should encounter no objections from auditors using methodology compliant with the CPT coding system guidelines, regardless of whether they employ conventional audits or Practical E/M audits. The codes submitted should satisfy the criteria of medical necessity, and the medical record documentation should always support the selected E/M code.

We also recommend that these physicians request copies of the formal report generated for every chart audited. This will permit an audit of the audit, enabling the physician to determine whether the auditor has employed noncompliant practices. If a physician does encounter an improperly performed audit, the responses can include the following:

- Documenting the errors in the noncompliant audit and filing a request for an impartial external review.
- Obtaining assistance from the state medical society, including guidance on the advisability of further assistance from an outside compliance consultant and/or health care attorney.

SUMMARY

Insurers have employed both noncompliant automated downcoding practices and financially punitive audits of medical records. All of these efforts by insurers result in reduced payments to physicians for E/M services. Physicians' responses to such practices should include assessment of the records in question, seeking assistance from the state medical society and qualified professionals, and making a concerted effort to ensure E/M compliance in the future.

As discussed in Chapters 24 and 27, proper reimbursement for indicated levels of E/M services is essential for the delivery of quality health care. Insurers should remove the perverse incentives created by automated downcoding, and they should also ensure that their E/M audits are educational and constructive for physicians.

References

1.   American Medical Association. *Current Procedural Terminology CPT® 2008*. Chicago, IL: American Medical Association; 2007.

2.   Health Care Financing Administration. *Documentation Guidelines for Evaluation and Management Services*. Chicago, IL: American Medical Association; 1997.

3.   *International Classification of Diseases, Ninth Revision*. Chicago, IL: American Medical Association; 2007.

Sample IMR Forms

On the following pages are two sample intelligent medical record (IMR) forms, which are provided for reference while you are reading about Practical Evaluation and Management (E/M). Most readers will find it helpful to have a photocopy of these forms, or printouts of forms from the accompanying CD-ROM, in hand while reading the text. For both clinicians and administrators, having a complete form in view not only helps achieve an understanding of Practical E/M principles, but also facilitates an appreciation of how to apply the Practical E/M approach while actually providing patient care.

These forms could be used (or modified and used) by a family practitioner or by an internist who elects to use a general multisystem physical examination template. A practice's initial visit and established visit forms will have identical sections for history of present illness, physical exam, medical decision making, and nature of presenting problem. The first sample IMR template shown is the initial outpatient visit (and consultation) form. The second sample template is the established outpatient visit form (which can also be used for consultations under appropriate circumstances, which are described in Chapter 9).

The physical examination section of these sample forms includes preprinted check boxes related to all 14 organ systems presented in the *Documentation Guidelines for Evaluation and Management Services*[1] for the multisystem exam. Due to the large number of other elements included in the general multi-system examination, the male and female genitourinary examinations and part of the musculoskeletal examination are located on a supplemental page (page 5 of the initial visit and page 3 of the established visit forms). As described in Chapter 15, physicians can partially modify the design of the general multisystem examination for their own personal IMR forms.

Following Practical E/M principles that emphasize the role of medical history in facilitating quality medical care, the design of the initial visit form includes documentation of a significantly greater amount of medical history information than the Current Procedural Terminology (CPT®)[2] coding system guidelines require to satisfy the minimum requirements for a "complete" past, family, and social history and a "complete" review of systems. While the patient completes these sections of the initial visit medical record, it is of critical importance (for both compliance and medical quality) that physicians investigate all of their patients' positive responses in these sections and document the additional medical information they uncover.

References

1. Health Care Financing Administration. *Documentation Guidelines for Evaluation and Management Services*. Chicago, IL: American Medical Association; 1997.

2. American Medical Association. *Current Procedural Terminology CPT® 2008*. Chicago, IL: American Medical Association; 2007.

Patient Name:_____   Account No._____   DOB:____/____/____

Initial Visit Form (p. 1): Please provide the following medical information to the best of your ability:

Date:	Age:	List any ALLERGIES TO MEDICATIONS:
What problems are you here for today?		

Past Medical History:
    1) Please check the "Yes" or "No" box to indicate if you have any of the following illnesses; for "Yes" answers, please explain.

	Yes	No			Yes	No	
Diabetes (Circle: type I/type II)	☐	☐	_____	Stomach or Intestinal problems	☐	☐	_____
Hypertension (high blood press)	☐	☐	_____	Allergy problems/therapy	☐	☐	_____
Thyroid problems	☐	☐	_____	Kidney problems	☐	☐	_____
Heart Disease/cholesterol probs	☐	☐	_____	Neurological problems	☐	☐	_____
Respiratory problems	☐	☐	_____	Cancer	☐	☐	_____
Bleeding disorder	☐	☐	_____	Other Medical Diagnosis	☐	☐	_____

2) Please list any operations (and dates) you have ever had (including tonsils & adenoids) :

3) **Please list any current medications (and amounts, times per day):**
    (include aspirin, antacids, vitamins, hormone replacement, birth control, herbal supplements, OTC meds including sinus/allergy/weight loss meds):

Social History:	Yes	No		Please list details below:
Do you use tobacco?	☐	☐	List type and how much:	_____
If no, did you use it previously?	☐	☐	List type and how much:	_____ **When did you quit?**
Do you drink alcohol?	☐	☐	List type and how much:	_____
Do you use recreational drugs?	☐	☐	List type and how much:	_____
What is your occupation?			_____	

Family History:
    Please check the "Yes" or "No" box to indicate whether any relatives have any of the following illnesses:
    If yes, please indicate which relative(s) have the problem.

	Yes	No	
Heart problems/murmurs	☐	☐	_____
Allergy	☐	☐	_____
Diabetes	☐	☐	_____
Cancer	☐	☐	_____
Bleeding disorder	☐	☐	_____
Anesthesia problems	☐	☐	_____

☐ See attached dictation   Reviewed by:

Date____/____/____

Patient Name:_____   Account No._____   DOB:____/____/____

Outpatient Initial Visit Form (p. 2): Please provide the following medical information to the best of your ability:

Review of Systems:

   1) Please check the "Yes" or "No" box to indicate whether you presently have any of the following symptoms:

   2) For any "yes" responses, please check the "Current" box if this symptom relates to the reason for your visit today.

		Yes	No	Current		Yes	No	Current
GENERAL	chills	☐	☐	☐	weight loss or gain	☐	☐	☐
	fatigue	☐	☐	☐	daytime sleepiness	☐	☐	☐
ALLERGY	environmental allergy	☐	☐	☐	sneezing fits	☐	☐	☐
NEURO	headache	☐	☐	☐	weakness	☐	☐	☐
	passing out	☐	☐	☐	numbness, tingling	☐	☐	☐
EYES	eye pain/pressure	☐	☐	☐	vision changes	☐	☐	☐
	watery or itchy eyes	☐	☐	☐				
ENT	hearing loss	☐	☐	☐	ear noises	☐	☐	☐
	dizziness	☐	☐	☐	lightheadedness	☐	☐	☐
	nasal congestion	☐	☐	☐	sinus pressure or pain	☐	☐	☐
	hoarseness	☐	☐	☐	problem snoring, apnea	☐	☐	☐
	throat clearing	☐	☐	☐	throat pain	☐	☐	☐
RESPIR	cough	☐	☐	☐	coughing blood	☐	☐	☐
	wheezing	☐	☐	☐	shortness of breath	☐	☐	☐
CARDIAC	chest pain	☐	☐	☐	palpitations	☐	☐	☐
	wake short of breath	☐	☐	☐	ankle swelling	☐	☐	☐
GI	difficulty swallowing	☐	☐	☐	heartburn	☐	☐	☐
	abdominal pain	☐	☐	☐	nausea/vomiting	☐	☐	☐
	bowel irregularity	☐	☐	☐	rectal bleeding	☐	☐	☐
GU	frequent urination	☐	☐	☐	painful urination	☐	☐	☐
	blood in urine	☐	☐	☐	prostate problems	☐	☐	☐
HEME/LYM	swollen glands	☐	☐	☐	sweating at night	☐	☐	☐
	bleeding problems	☐	☐	☐	easy bruising	☐	☐	☐
ENDO	feel warmer than others	☐	☐	☐	feel cooler than others	☐	☐	☐
MSK	joint aches	☐	☐	☐	muscle aches	☐	☐	☐
SKIN	rash	☐	☐	☐	hives	☐	☐	☐
	itching	☐	☐	☐	skin or hair changes	☐	☐	☐
PSYCH	depression	☐	☐	☐	anxiety or panic	☐	☐	☐

PLEASE STOP HERE   ☐ See attached dictation

Reviewed by:

Date ____/____/____

Patient States Consultation Requested By_____

Patient Name:_____

Account No._____

DOB:____/____/____

Outpatient Initial Visit Form (p. 3):

PRESENT ILLNESS	Chronology with: 1. one to three elements (level 2) 2. four to eight elements; OR status of 3 chronic or inactive conditions (level 3, 4, or 5)
	(1) duration (2) timing (3) severity; (4) location (5) quality (6) context (7) modifying factors (8) assoc. signs & symptoms

☐ See attached dictation

PHYSICAL EXAMINATION:

General Multisystem Exam

GENERAL (at least 3 measurements of vital signs)

HT___ft___in   WT_____lbs

BP sitting-standing ____/____mm Hg   BP supine ____/____mm Hg

PULSE ____/min regular - irregular   RESP ___/min   TEMP _____° (F-C)

System	Element	Description	Normal	AB		System	Element	Description	Normal	AB
GENERAL	GENERAL APPEARANCE	Stature, nutrition	☐	☐		CHEST/	BREAST INSPECTION	Symmetry, color	☐	☐
EYES	CONJUNCTIVAE & LIDS	Appearance, color	☐	☐		BREASTS	BREAST/AXILLAE PALP	Nodules, masses	☐	☐
	PUPILS & IRISES	Size, reactivity	☐	☐		GI/ABD	MASSES/TENDERNESS	Palpation	☐	☐
	OPTIC DISCS	Fundi, vessels	☐	☐			LIVER/SPLEEN	Size, tenderness	☐	☐
ENT	EARS & NOSE, EXTERNAL	Appearance	☐	☐			HERNIA EVAL	Inspection, palpation	☐	☐
	OTOSCOPY	Canals, tymp membranes	☐	☐			ANUS/RECTUM/PERIN	Appearance, palpation	☐	☐
	HEARING	Response to sound	☐	☐			STOOL, HEMACULT	Eval for blood	☐	☐
	INTERNAL NOSE	Septum, mucosa, turbs	☐	☐		LYMPH	NECK/AXILLAE/GROIN/OTHER	Adenopathy	☐	☐
	LIPS,TEETH, & GUMS	Mucosa, dentition	☐	☐			(circle areas examined; requires exam in 2 or more regions)			
	OROPHARYNX	Mucosa, tonsils, palate	☐	☐		MSKEL	GAIT & STATION	Stability & smoothness	☐	☐
NECK	MASSES & TRACHEA	Symmetry, masses	☐	☐		(partial)	DIGITS & NAILS	Color & appearance	☐	☐
	THYROID	Size, nodules	☐	☐		SKIN/	INSPECTION	Head, trunk, RUE	☐	☐
RESP	RESPIRATORY EFFORT	Inspiratory-expiratory	☐	☐		SUBCU		LUE, RLE, LLE	☐	☐
	CHEST PALPATION	Movement	☐	☐			PALPATION	Head, trunk, RUE	☐	☐
	CHEST PERCUSSION	Sound	☐	☐				LUE, RLE, LLE	☐	☐
	AUSCULTATION	Lung sounds	☐	☐		NEURO	CRANIAL NERVES	II - XII	☐	☐
CVS	HEART PALPATION	Rhythm	☐	☐			DEEP TENDON REFLEXES	Knee, ankle, Babinski	☐	☐
	HEART AUSCULTATION	Sounds	☐	☐			SENSATION	Light touch	☐	☐
	CAROTID ARTIERIES	Pulsation	☐	☐		PSYCH	JUDGEMENT & INSIGHT	Subjectively	☐	☐
	ABDOMINAL AORTA	Pulsation	☐	☐			ORIENTATION	Person, place, time	☐	☐
	FEMORAL ARTERIES	Pulsation	☐	☐			MEMORY	Recent & remote	☐	☐
	PEDAL PULSES	Pulsation	☐	☐			MOOD & AFFECT	Comments	☐	☐
	EDEMA,VARICES, LE	Appearance	☐	☐						

☐ Continued on supplemental page   ☐ See attached dictation

---

1. Problem focused = 1-5 elements (level 1) 2. Expanded = 6-11 elements (level 2) 3. Detailed = 12 or more elements [in 2 or more systems] (level 3)
4. Comprehensive = document two (or more) elements in each of nine (or more) systems (level 4 or 5)   *Optional

Date____/____/____

Patient Name:_____   Account No._____   DOB:____/____/____

Outpatient Initial Visit Form (p. 4):

MEDICAL DECISION MAKING	2 of the 3 sections (a vs a', b vs b' vs b'', c vs c' vs c'') must meet or exceed indicated level of care
DATA REVIEWED (c):	**1.** Minimal (level 2) **2.** Limited (level 3) **3.** Moderate (level 4) **4.** Extensive (level 5)

☐ X-ray/CT scan   ☐ **See attached dictation**

☐ MRI

☐ Lab/blood work

IMPRESSIONS/DIFFERENTIAL DIAGNOSES (a):   **PLANS/MANAGEMENT OPTIONS (a')**
1. Minimal (level 2) **2.** Limited (level 3) **3.** Multiple (level 4) **4.** Extensive (level 5)

1)_____   1)_____   ☐ **See attached dictation**

2)_____   2)_____

3)_____   3)_____

4)_____   4)_____

5)_____   5)_____

DATA ORDERED (c'):   **1.** Minimal or none (level 2) **2.** Limited (level 3) **3.** Moderate (level 4) **4.** Extensive (level 5)
☐   ☐   ☐   ☐

                                                                                                                   ☐ **See attached dictation**

   Information Sheets Given:

COMPLEXITY OF DATA REVIEWED OR ORDERED (c'')

	1. Minimal (level 2)	**2.** Limited (level 3)	**3.** Moderate (level 4)	**4.** Extensive (level 5)
	1. min	2. limited	3. mod	4. extensive

RISK OF COMPLICATIONS &/OR MORBIDITY OR MORTALITY (see examples in Table of Risk)

	1. Minimal (level 2)	**2.** Low (level 3)	**3.** Moderate (level 4)	**4.** High (level 5)
risk of presenting problem(s) (b):	1. min	2. low	3. mod	4. high
risk of diagnostic procedure(s) ordered or reviewed (b'):	1. min	2. low	3. mod	4. high
risk of management option(s) selected (b''):	1. min	2. low	3. mod	4. high

NATURE OF PRESENTING PROBLEM(S)

1. minor	(level 1)	Problem runs definite and prescribed course, is transient in nature, and is not likely to permanently alter health status; OR, has a good prognosis with management and compliance.
2. low	(level 1) ++	Problem in which the risk of morbidity without treatment is low; there is little no risk of mortality without treatment; full recovery without functional impairment is expected.
3. low - mod	(level 2)	Problem in which the risk of morbidity without treatment is low to moderate; there is low to moderate risk of mortality without treatment; full recovery without functional impairment is expected in most cases, with low probability of prolonged functional impairment
4. moderate	(level 3)	Problem in which the risk of morbidity without treatment is moderate; there is moderate risk of mortality without treatment; prognosis is uncertain, or there is an increased probability of prolonged functional impairment.
5. mod - high	(levels 4, 5)	Problem in which the risk of morbidity without treatment is moderate to high; there is moderate risk of mortality without treatment; uncertain prognosis or increased probability of prolonged functional impairment
6. high	(level 5)	Problem in which the risk of morbidity without treatment is high to extreme; there is moderate to high risk of mortality without treatment, or high probability of severe prolonged functional impairment.

++ For Consultation, a low NPP is equal to a level 2

Complete this section only if documented below > 50% of visit time involved counseling and/or coordinating care.

TIME: _____ minutes   ☐ > 50% of visit time involved counseling and/or coordination of care

                                                                Clinician's signature:

Date: ____/____/_____

Patient Name:_____   Account No._____   DOB:____/____/____

Outpatient Initial Visit Form (Supplement):

PHYSICAL EXAMINATION:			General Multisystem Exam (continued)			

			Normal/AB						Normal/AB
GU	SCROTAL CONTENTS	Appearance, palpation	☐ ☐	MSKEL	RT UPPER EXTREMITY	Inspec., palp., percussion	☐ ☐
MALE	PENIS	Appearance, palpation	☐ ☐			Range of motion	☐ ☐
	PROSTATE	Palpation	☐ ☐			Stability or laxity	☐ ☐
GU	EXT GENITALIA	Appearance, palpation	☐ ☐			Muscle strength & tone	☐ ☐
FEMALE	URETHRA	Inspection	☐ ☐		LT UPPER EXTREMITY	Inspec., palp., percussion	☐ ☐
(PELVIC)	BLADDER	Palpation	☐ ☐			Range of motion	☐ ☐
	CERVIS	Palpation	☐ ☐			Stability or laxity	☐ ☐
	UTERUS	Palpation	☐ ☐			Muscle strength & tone	☐ ☐
	ADNEXA/PARAMET	Palpation	☐ ☐		RT LOWER EXTREMITY	Inspec., palp., percussion	☐ ☐
MSKEL	HEAD & NECK	Inspec., palp., percussion	☐ ☐			Range of motion	☐ ☐
		Range of motion	☐ ☐			Stability or laxity	☐ ☐
		Stability or laxity	☐ ☐			Muscle strength & tone	☐ ☐
		Muscle strength & tone	☐ ☐		LT LOWER EXTREMITY	Inspec., palp., percussion	☐ ☐
	SPINE, RIBS, PELVIS	Inspec., palp., percussion	☐ ☐			Range of motion	☐ ☐
		Range of motion	☐ ☐			Stability or laxity	☐ ☐
		Stability or laxity	☐ ☐			Muscle strength & tone	☐ ☐
		Muscle strength & tone	☐ ☐			☐ See attached dictation	

_____
_____
_____
_____
_____
_____
_____
_____
_____

1. Problem focused = 1-5 elements (level 1)   2. Expanded = 6-11 elements (level 2) 3. Detailed = 12 or more elements [in 2 or more systems] (level 3)
4. Comprehensive = document two (or more) elements in each of nine (or more) systems (level 4 or 5)   *Optional

Exam Supplement

_____
_____
_____
_____
_____
_____
_____
_____
_____
_____
_____
_____
_____

Established Patient Visit Form

Patient Name:_____		Account No._____	DOB:___/___/___

Outpatient Established Visit Form (p. 1):

Date: ____/____/____	**PMH/SH/FH**	no change since last visit date: _____

Except: _____

_____

New Allergies: _____	Existing allergies: _____

Current Medications: _____

Reviewed by:

ROS   no change since last visit date: _____

Except: _____

Reviewed by:

PRESENT ILLNESS   Chronology with: 1. one to three elements (level 2 or 3) 2. four to eight elements; OR status of 3 chronic or inactive conditions (level 4 or 5)

(1) duration   (2) timing   (3) severity;   (4) location   (5) quality   (6) context   (7) modifying factors   (8) assoc. signs & symptoms

☐ See attached dictation

PHYSICAL EXAMINATION: General Multisystem Exam

GENERAL   (at least 3 measurements of vital signs)   HT___ft___in   WT_____lbs

BP sitting-standing ____/____ mm Hg   BP supine ____/____ mm Hg

PULSE ____/min regular - irregular   RESP ____/min   TEMP _____° (F-C)

			Normal/AB					Normal/AB
	GENERAL APPEARANCE	Stature, nutrition	☐	☐	**CVS**	HEART PALPATION	Rhythm	☐	☐
EYES	CONJUNCTIVAE & LIDS	Appearance, color	☐	☐		HEART AUSCULTATION	Sounds	☐	☐
	PUPILS & IRISES	Size, reactivity	☐	☐		CAROTID ARTIERIES	Pulsation	☐	☐
	OPTIC DISCS	Fundi, vessels	☐	☐		ABDOMINAL AORTA	Pulsation	☐	☐
ENT	EARS & NOSE, EXTERNAL	Appearance	☐	☐		FEMORAL ARTERIES	Pulsation	☐	☐
	OTOSCOPY	Canals, tymp membranes	☐	☐		PEDAL PULSES	Pulsation	☐	☐
	HEARING	Response to sound	☐	☐		EDEMA, VARICES, LE	Appearance, palpation	☐	☐
	INTERNAL NOSE	Septum, mucosa, turbs	☐	☐	**CHEST**	BREAST INSPECTION	Symmetry, color	☐	☐
	LIPS, TEETH & GUMS	Mucosa, dentition	☐	☐	**BREASTS**	BREAST/AXILLAE PALP	Nodules, masses	☐	☐
	OROPHARYNX	Mucosa, tonsils, palate	☐	☐	**GI/ABD**	MASSES/TENDERNESS	Palpation	☐	☐
NECK	MASSES & TRACHEA	Symmetry, masses	☐	☐		LIVER/SPLEEN	Size, tenderness	☐	☐
	THYROID	Size, nodules	☐	☐		HERNIA EVAL	Inspection, palpation	☐	☐
RESP	RESPIRATORY EFFORT	Inspiratory-expiratory	☐	☐		ANUS/RECTUM/PERIN	Appearance, palpation	☐	☐
	CHEST PALPATION	Movement	☐	☐		STOOL, HEMACULT	Eval for blood	☐	☐
	CHEST PERCUSSION	Sound	☐	☐	**LYMPH**	NECK/AXILLAE/GROIN/OTHER	Adenopathy	☐	☐
	AUSCULTATION	Lung sounds	☐	☐		(circle areas examined; requires exam in 2 or more regions)			

☐ Continued on supplemental page   ☐ See attached dictation

1. Problem focused = 1-5 elements (level 2)   2. Expanded = 6-11 elements (level 3)   3. Detailed = 12 or more elements (level 4)

4. Comprehensive = document two (or more) elements in each of nine (or more) systems (level 5)   *Optional

Date ____/____/____

Patient Name:_____   Account No._____   DOB:____/____/____

Outpatient Established Visit Form (p. 2):

MEDICAL DECISION MAKING   2 of the 3 sections (a vs a', b vs b' vs b", c vs c' vs c") must meet or exceed indicated level of care
DATA REVIEWED (c):   1. Minimal (level 2) 2. Limited (level 3) 3. Moderate (level 4) 4. Extensive (level 5)

☐ X-ray/CT scan   ☐ See attached dictation

☐ MRI

☐ Lab/blood work

IMPRESSIONS/DIFFERENTIAL DIAGNOSES (a):   **PLANS/MANAGEMENT OPTIONS (a')**
1. Minimal (level 2) 2. Limited (level 3) 3. Multiple (level 4) 4. Extensive (level 5)

1) _____   1) _____ ☐ See attached dictation

2) _____   2) _____

3) _____   3) _____

4) _____   4) _____

5) _____   5) _____

DATA ORDERED (c'):   1. Minimal or none (level 2) 2. Limited (level 3) 3. Moderate (level 4) 4. Extensive (level 5)
☐   ☐   ☐   ☐   ☐

                                             ☐ See attached dictation

Information Sheets Given:

COMPLEXITY OF DATA REVIEWED OR ORDERED (c")

	1. Minimal (level 2)	2. Limited (level 3)	3. Moderate (level 4)	4. Extensive (level 5)
	1. min	2. limited	3. mod	4. extensive

RISK OF COMPLICATIONS &/OR MORBIDITY OR MORTALITY (see examples in Table of Risk)

	1. Minimal (level 2)	2. Low (level 3)	3. Moderate (level 4)	4. High (level 5)
risk of presenting problem(s) (b):	1. min	2. low	3. mod	4. high
risk of diagnostic procedure(s) ordered (b'):	1. min	2. low	3. mod	4. high
risk of management option(s) selected (b"):	1. min	2. low	3. mod	4. high

NATURE OF PRESENTING PROBLEM(S)

1. minor	(level 2)	Problem runs definite and prescribed course, is transient in nature, and is not likely to permanently alter health status; OR, has a good prognosis with management and compliance.
2. low	(level 2)	Problem in which the risk of morbidity without treatment is low; there is little to no risk of mortality without treatment; full recovery without functional impairment is expected.
3. low - mod	(level 3)	Problem in which the risk of morbidity without treatment is low to moderate; there is low to moderate risk of mortality without treatment; full recovery without functional impairment is expected in most cases, with low probability of prolonged functional impairment
4. moderate	(level 3)	Problem in which the risk of morbidity without treatment is moderate; there is moderate risk of mortality without treatment; prognosis is uncertain, or there is an increased probability of prolonged functional impairment.
5. mod - high	(levels 4, 5)	Problem in which the risk of morbidity without treatment is moderate to high; there is moderate risk of mortality without treatment; uncertain prognosis or increased probability of prolonged functional impairment
6. high	(level 5)	Problem in which the risk of morbidity without treatment is high to extreme; there is moderate to high risk of mortality without treatment, or high probability of severe prolonged functional impairment.

Complete this section only if documented below > 50% of visit time involved counseling and/or coordinating care.

TIME: _____ minutes   ☐ > 50% of visit time involved counseling and/or coordination of care

Clinician's signature:

Date ____/____/_____

Patient Name:_____   Account No._____   DOB:____/____/____

Outpatient Established Visit Form (Supplement):

PHYSICAL EXAMINATION:			General Multisystem Exam (continued)				

General Multisystem Exam (continued)

			Normal/AB					Normal/AB
GU	SCROTAL CONTENTS	Appearance, palpation	☐ ☐	MSKEL	HEAD & NECK	Inspec., palp., percussion	☐ ☐
MALE	PENIS	Appearance, palpation	☐ ☐			Range of motion	☐ ☐
	PROSTATE	Palpation	☐ ☐			Stability or laxity	☐ ☐
GU	EXT GENITALIA	Appearance, palpation	☐ ☐			Muscle strength & tone	☐ ☐
FEMALE	URETHRA	Inspection	☐ ☐		SPINE, RIBS, PELVIS	Inspec., palp., percussion	☐ ☐
(PELVIC)	BLADDER	Palpation	☐ ☐			Range of motion	☐ ☐
	CERVIS	Palpation	☐ ☐			Stability or laxity	☐ ☐
	UTERUS	Palpation	☐ ☐			Muscle strength & tone	☐ ☐
	ADNEXA/PARAMET	Palpation	☐ ☐		RT UPPER EXTREMITY	Inspec., palp., percussion	☐ ☐
SKIN/	INSPECTION	Head, trunk, RUE	☐ ☐			Range of motion	☐ ☐
SUBCU		LUE, RLE, LLE	☐ ☐			Stability or laxity	☐ ☐
	PALPATION	Head, trunk, RUE	☐ ☐			Muscle strength & tone	☐ ☐
		LUE, RLE, LLE	☐ ☐		LT UPPER EXTREMITY	Inspec., palp., percussion	☐ ☐
NEURO	CRANIAL NERVES	II & XII	☐ ☐			Range of motion	☐ ☐
	DEEP TENDON REFLEXES	Knee, ankle, Babinski	☐ ☐			Stability or laxity	☐ ☐
	SENSATION	Light touch	☐ ☐			Muscle strength & tone	☐ ☐
PSYCH	JUDGEMENT & INSIGHT	Subjectively	☐ ☐		RT LOWER EXTREMITY	Inspec., palp., percussion	☐ ☐
	ORIENTATION	Person, place, time	☐ ☐			Range of motion	☐ ☐
	MEMORY	Recent & remote	☐ ☐			Stability or laxity	☐ ☐
	MOOD & AFFECT	Comments	☐ ☐			Muscle strength & tone	☐ ☐
MSKEL	GAIT & STATION	Stability & smoothness	☐ ☐		LT LOWER EXTREMITY	Inspec., palp., percussion	☐ ☐
	DIGITS & NAILS	Color & appearance	☐ ☐			Range of motion	☐ ☐
						Stability or laxity	☐ ☐
		☐ See attached dictation				Muscle strength & tone	☐ ☐

_____
_____
_____
_____
_____
_____
_____
_____

1. Problem focused = 1-5 elements (level 2) 2. Expanded = 6-11 elements (level 3) 3. Detailed = 12 or more elements (level 4)
4. Comprehensive = document two (or more) elements in each of nine (or more) systems (level 5)   *Optional

_____
_____
_____
_____
_____
_____
_____
_____
_____
_____
_____
_____

Importance of Adhering to Practical E/M Principles With Medical Records

As discussed throughout this book, an effective medical record is critically important for compliance, for productivity, for confirming the extent of care performed if a physician is under review for potential professional liability, and, most important, for assisting physicians in providing quality patient care.

Regardless of whether a physician is using a medical record as basic as a blank sheet of paper, or one as sophisticated as an intelligent medical record (IMR), there is a potential to encounter problems related to the information documented (or not documented) by the physician. These problems can occur either when the medical record being used lacks one or more features needed for optimal functioning, or when a physician does not correctly use the features available in his or her medical record.

The IMR is designed to include all the features essential to help physicians achieve maximal quality, efficiency, and compliance. Each physician must use these tools correctly to achieve the intended results. The purpose of this section is to review the importance of correctly following Practical Evaluation and Management (E/M) principles when working with an IMR (or any other medical record) to prevent potential negative consequences for care, compliance, and medical liability.

Precaution Regarding Partial Use of IMR Forms or Use of Partial IMR Forms

The IMR form design results from a completely integrated and interdependent relationship among the four mandatory elements of E/M documentation and coding: medical history, physical examination, medical decision making, and nature of the presenting problem (the E/M system's measure of "medical necessity"). Proper utilization of these forms, to ensure compliance in the context of quality medical care, *requires* completion of all sections of these forms and use of the Practical E/M methodology, as summarized below.

Partial utilization of the forms, or insertion of portion(s) of an IMR form into another medical record form, violates both the intent and the integrity of the Practical E/M approach. Such improper utilization carries with it significant risk of noncompliant documentation and coding. In the event of an external audit, this could result in substantial financial penalties and/or the designation of "false claims," which could result in even greater financial loss.

Although the examples in this section directly address using the IMR correctly, they are also applicable to other medical records, regardless of whether they are written records, dictated records, or electronic records.

Table E.1 looks at possible ways that improper use of an IMR could potentially lead to less than ideal results for compliance, for quality care, and for medical liability protection. Each of these examples illustrates one or more possible consequences of not following Practical E/M methodology while using an IMR. This table is included to emphasize that, regardless of how many benefits and protections we design into the IMR, physicians must use it correctly to realize these benefits.

TABLE E.1

Possible Consequences of Not Following Practical E/M Methodology While Using an IMR

Section of Medical Record	Category of Improper Use	Possible Worst Case Scenario(s)
PFSH (1) Initial visit	Clinician reviews PFSH but does not sign (or initial) that he (she) has reviewed all the information in this section	• **Compliance:** Audit of initial visit record concludes there is lack of documentation of PFSH. No credit given for PFSH (if not documented, it wasn't done). Causes downcode to level 2 • **Compliance:** Audits showing repeated downcoding for lack of documentation of review of PFSH could lead to investigation for fraud, with severe financial penalties

PFSH (2) Initial visit	Clinician does not review PFSH section and does not sign (or initial) that he (she) has reviewed all the information in this section	• **Compliance:** Same as above.
		• **Quality of Care:** Clinician overlooks information critical to patient care; for example:
		  – Overlook past history of cancer, delaying diagnosis of metastatic disease
		  – Overlook past history of hypothyroidism, resulting in unnecessary testing and delayed diagnosis
		  – Overlook family history of anesthesia problems, resulting in life-threatening (or life-ending) episode of malignant hyperthermia during a surgical procedure
		• **Malpractice:** Litigation due to consequences of not addressing issues such as those listed above

PFSH (3) Initial visit	Clinician does not review PFSH section but does sign (or initial) that he (she) has reviewed all the information in this section	• **Compliance:** Same as both issues cited in PFSH (1), *with significantly higher risk of penalties for fraud. Little or no defense against a claim of fraud* (the medical record claims care was provided, and it was not) • **Quality of Care:** Same as all issues cited in PFSH (2) • **Malpractice:** Litigation due to consequences of not addressing issues such as those listed above. *Little or no defense if accused of practice that is inconsistent with the standard of care; the medical record clearly documents that physician did not follow the standard of care* (eg, the patient reported positive family history of anesthesia problems, and MD failed to follow standard precautions to avoid potential problems)

PFSH (4) Established visit	Clinician does not update status of PFSH since previous visit	• **Compliance:** Audit of established visit record concludes there is lack of documentation of PFSH. Causes downcode to level 3 if medical history is one of two required E/M components considered for coding
		• **Quality of Care:** Clinician overlooks information critical to patient care; for example:
		  – Patient has suffered a myocardial infarction since previous visit
		  – Patient has started on new medication with side effects that might account for presenting symptoms

PFSH (5) Established visit	Clinician updates status of PFSH, but previous (or initial) visits did not document a complete PFSH	• **Compliance:** Audit of established visit record must determine level of PFSH to be at same level as documented during previous (or initial) visits

continued

TABLE E.1

Possible Consequences of Not Following Practical E/M Methodology While Using an IMR, cont'd

Section of Medical Record	Category of Improper Use	Possible Worst Case Scenario(s)
ROS (1) Initial visit	Clinician reviews ROS but does not sign (or initial) that he (she) has reviewed all the information in this section	• **Compliance:** Audit of initial visit record concludes there is lack of documentation of ROS. No credit given for ROS (if not documented, it wasn't done). Results in downcode to level 1 • **Compliance:** Audits showing repeated downcoding for lack of documentation of review of ROS could lead to investigation for fraud, with severe financial penalties
ROS (2) Initial visit	Clinician does not review ROS section and does not sign (or initial) that he (she) has reviewed all the information in this section	• **Compliance:** Same as both issues cited in ROS (1) • **Quality of Care:** Clinician overlooks information critical to patient care; for example: – Overlook positive history of headache. Patient suffers ruptured intracranial aneurysm – Overlook positive history of chest pain. Patient suffers myocardial infarction – Overlook positive history of weight loss. Results in significant delay of diagnosis of cancer • **Malpractice:** Litigation due to consequences of not addressing issues such as those listed above ROS (3)
ROS (3) Initial visit	Clinician does not review ROS section but does sign (or initial) that he (she) has reviewed all the information in this section	• **Compliance:** Same as both issues cited in ROS (1), *with significantly higher risk of penalties for fraud. Little or no defense against a claim of fraud* (the medical record claims care was provided, and it was not) • **Quality of Care:** Same as all issues cited in ROS (2) • **Malpractice:** Litigation due to consequences of not addressing issues such as those listed above. *Little or no defense if accused of practice that is inconsistent with the standard of care; the medical record clearly documents that physician did not follow the standard of care* (eg, patient reported chest pain and physician did not evaluate or refer for this potentially life-threatening medical problem)
ROS (4) Established visit	Clinician does not update status of PFSH since previous visit	• **Compliance:** Audit of established visit record concludes there is lack of documentation of ROS. Causes downcode to level 2 if medical history is one of two required E/M components considered for coding • **Quality of Care:** Clinician overlooks information critical to patient care; for example: – Since the previous visit, patient has experienced chest pain or other significant symptoms unrelated to the presenting problem(s)
ROS (5) Established visit	Clinician updates status of PFSH, but previous (or initial) visits did not document a complete PFSH	• **Compliance:** Audit of established visit record must determine level of ROS to be at same level as documented during previous (or initial) visits
HPI (1)	Clinician reviews and documents fewer than four elements of HPI, resulting in documentation of a "brief" present illness rather than an "extended" present illness	• **Compliance:** Results in downcode to level 2 for initial visit; downcode to level 3 for established visit • **Compliance:** Audits showing repeated downcoding for lack of documentation of extended HPI could lead to investigation for fraud, with severe financial penalties • **Quality of Care:** Delayed and/or incomplete diagnoses due to insufficient information to help identify an effective differential diagnosis • **Malpractice:** Litigation due to consequences of delayed diagnosis

continued

TABLE E.1

Possible Consequences of Not Following Practical E/M Methodology While Using an IMR, cont'd

Section of Medical Record	Category of Improper Use	Possible Worst Case Scenario(s)
Physical Examination (1)	Clinician does not provide narrative detail of *all* exam elements documented as abnormal	• **Compliance:** A reviewer will likely judge that these exam elements have not been (adequately) performed, as required by the *Documentation Guidelines*.[1] This may result in E/M downcoding • **Quality of Care:** Lack of detailed description of exam may result in significant difficulty following patient's response to treatment and clinical progress • **Malpractice:** Reduced ability to defend medical decisions made and/or justify reasons for not making other decisions
Physical Examination (2)	Clinician does not provide narrative detail for normal findings of exam elements essential to the patient's HPI	• **Compliance:** Though unlikely, due to the brief descriptors designed into the IMR's check box section, a reviewer might judge that these exam elements have not been (adequately) documented, as required by the *Documentation Guidelines*. This could possibly result in E/M downcoding • **Quality of Care:** Lack of detailed description of these exam elements might result in difficulty following a patient's clinical progress if the patient did not respond to treatment and the medical problems became more severe • **Malpractice:** Reduced ability to defend medical decisions made and/or justify reasons for not making other decisions
MDM (1)–number of diagnoses and/or treatment options	• Clinician documents only the most probable diagnosis, not indicating reasonable differential diagnoses and/or symptomatic secondary illnesses • Clinician *also* documents only the single treatment provided, not indicating other possible treatments	• **Compliance:** Documentation of only one element of diagnosis and treatment option often results in problem-focused MDM. This results in downcode to level 2 for initial visit. It may result in downcode to level 2 for established visit • **Compliance:** Audits showing repeated downcoding because of documentation of only one diagnosis and only one treatment option could lead to investigation for fraud, with severe financial penalties • **Quality of Care:** Documentation of only one diagnosis may reflect active consideration of only one possible disease process at a time (rather than evaluation of several likely diagnoses). This could delay identifying correct diagnosis • **Malpractice:** Documentation of only one treatment option could significantly reduce ability to defend a claim based on lack of informed consent (which legally requires physicians to discuss all treatment options with the patient)
MDM (1) – risks	Clinician fails to document one or more of the three risks defined by CPT codebook[2] (risk of presenting problem, risk of diagnostic procedures, and risk of management options)	• Lack of documentation of the elements of risk leaves the interpretation of the risk of the patient's illnesses, evaluations, and treatments to the sole discretion of a reviewer. In some cases this could result in inappropriate downcoding
Nature of Presenting Problem	Clinician fails to document the NPP	• Lack of documentation of the NPP leaves the interpretation of the severity of the patient's illnesses to the sole discretion of a reviewer. In some cases this could result in inappropriate downcoding

Abbreviations: CPT®, Current Procedural Terminology; HPI, history of present illness; MDM, medical decision making; NPP, nature of presenting problem; PFSH, past, family, and social history; ROS, review of systems.

References

1.   Health Care Financing Administration. *Documentation Guidelines for Evaluation and Management Services*. Chicago, IL: American Medical Association; 1997.

2.   American Medical Association. *Current Procedural Terminology CPT® 2008*. Chicago, IL: American Medical Association; 2007.

Appearance Options for the H&P Record

Chapters 22 and 23 considered two options for the final appearance of the history and physical (H&P) record that physicians retain in their paper or electronic medical charts: (1) a hybrid record that contains both graphic and narrative components with the same appearance of the forms used to document the H&P (ie, the appearance of an intelligent medical record [IMR] form), and (2) a pure narrative recompilation that presents the appearance of a completely dictated medical record, such as those stored in traditional paper records. As discussed in Chapter 22, these options arise in the paper format for physicians who prefer to dictate the narrative elements of the H&P. Using a hybrid record with writing for the graphic components and dictation reserved solely for the free-text sections not only saves physician time and transcription costs for the practice, but also proves to be a superior model for most physicians and coders who read these H&P records. It includes all of the evaluation and management (E/M) elements needed for compliance, and it is easier and faster to read. It is also easier to use when searching for and identifying specific normal and abnormal findings.

These choices become universal in most electronic records, applying to records with data entry being performed by keyboard, dictation, or writing. Even though most electronic health records (EHRs) collect clinical information by means of a combination of graphic and free-text components, they almost all recompile this data into an H&P record that is indistinguishable from a dictated paper record from the 1970s. In addition to being more cumbersome to review, this appearance format is missing a significant amount of compliance documentation that is included on the hybrid IMR form.

This appendix provides a side-by-side comparison of these two appearance options, showing each of the four pages of an initial outpatient visit form. The clinical information used is from an actual record of a patient whose initial-visit comprehensive history revealed a severe illness that warranted level 5 care. In addition to illustrating the increased readability and usability of the hybrid appearance for paper records, these images should provide software designers and physicians with a model for developing more sophisticated screens than the outdated transcription form for the final appearance of the electronic H&P. Since the IMR form appearance also fulfills E/M compliance requirements, designers of EHRs are encouraged to include this configuration at least as an optional appearance that physicians can choose.

In addition, the last section of this appendix provides an example of the original consultation letter that an EHR could compile by transferring information from the IMR form into sections of Template B.2, which was shown in Appendix B.

APPEARANCE OPTIONS FOR THE *ELECTRONIC* H&P RECORD

The most effective EHR systems will likely present electronic screens for data entry that employ a sophisticated combination of graphic and narrative interfaces. The graphic components, commonly using check boxes or allowing entry of data from selection lists, provide enhanced usability and efficiency for physicians documenting select portions of the H&P:

- The screening information captured for the past, family, and social history (PFSH) of an initial visit
- The screening information captured for the review of systems (ROS) of an initial visit
- The physical examination elements examined, with an indication of whether the findings were normal or abnormal
- Frequently ordered treatments for the treatment options section of medical decision making (MDM) (to supplement the primary narrative section)
- Frequently ordered diagnostic tests for the data ordered section of MDM (to supplement the primary narrative section)
- Complexity of data in the MDM
- The three elements of risk in the MDM
- The nature of the presenting problem (NPP)

The narrative portions of the record include explanations of positive responses in the PFSH and ROS sections of initial visit forms, the history of present illness, descriptions of abnormal physical examination findings, and listing of diagnoses and management options.

All the clinical information recorded during a visit is then stored in an H&P record of the encounter. Under most circumstances, physicians need to reference only selected portions of previous records. Whether during subsequent visits, telephone calls, or documentation of laboratory results, they generally review only the listings of diagnoses, management options, and data ordered, which are all found in the MDM section of previous records. Although physicians do not frequently revisit the remaining portions of a previous visit, there is a distinct benefit to having the appearance of that record be easy to use and allow rapid identification of data being sought. In addition, records that are sent for outside review should present both structure and content that ensure E/M compliance and present the quality of care provided in an easily comprehensible fashion.

Most current EHRs recompile the clinical data that was captured by means of sophisticated EHR interface designs during an encounter into a traditional transcription presentation that is indistinguishable from the narrative-only records physicians dictated when creating paper-based records. While having the advantage of creating a record with an appearance familiar to most physicians, this architecture for the H&P record predates EHRs, and it predates the documentation requirements of E/M compliance. Such records are particularly cumbersome to use if they are well documented, accurately reflecting the extent of care and decision making performed. Their structure makes it challenging for a reader to identify important abnormal responses and findings or the *pertinent* normal responses and findings within sections containing long narrative descriptions that include both positive and negative responses.

Instead, physicians and software companies should consider the benefits of saving a final H&P record that is comparable to the appearance of the screens provided for physicians to enter their H&P data. In addition to the appearance being familiar to physicians, who use the same screens during every visit for data entry, most physicians should find them easier to use when searching for specific details of previous encounters. When based on the Practical E/M (or Practical EHR) design principles, such records should also prove to more effectively demonstrate compliant care and documentation when submitted in response to request for audit by payers.

FIGURE F.1

PFSH, Initial Outpatient Visit: Hybrid Model, Paper Form or EHR Screen (note: for paper forms, the transcribed narrative sections may appear on a separate page)

Patient Name: Account No.   DOB: ___/___/___

Patient Medical History Form (p. 1): Please provide the following medical information to the best of your ability:

Date: January 10, 2002	Age: 47	List any ALLERGIES TO MEDICATIONS:
What problems are you here for today? Ears clogged		Codeine - causes nausea

Past Medical History:
  1) Please check the "Yes" or "No" box to indicate if you have any of the following illnesses; for "Yes" answers, please explain

	Yes	No			Yes	No	
Diabetes	☐	☒		Stomach or intestinal problems	☐	☒	
Hypertension (high blood press)	☐	☒		Allergy problems/therapy	☒	☐	seasonal, in Spring
Thyroid problems	☐	☒		Kidney problems	☐	☒	
Heart Disease/cholesterol probs	☒	☐	elevated cholesterol	Neurological problems	☐	☒	
Respiratory problems	☒	☐	occasional asthma	Cancer	☐	☒	
Bleeding Disorder	☐	☒		Other Medical Diagnosis	☐	☒	

Mild seasonal allergy symptoms in the spring, with frequent sneezing and watery eyes

  2) Please list any operations (and dates) you have ever had *(including tonsils & adenoids)*:

Right knee surgery 1999 - repair lateral cruciate ligament

  3) Please list any current medications (and amounts, times per day);
      (include aspirin, antacids, vitamins, hormone replacement, birth control, herbal supplements, OTC nasal sprays/cold/sinus/allergy meds):

Ibuprofen, 400 mg as needed for pain; deongestant X prn allergy Sx, atorvastating 10 mg. per day

Social History:

	Yes	No		Please list details below:		
Do you use tobacco?	☐	☒	List type and how much:			
If no, did you use it previously?	☒	☐	List type and how much:	1/2 pack per day for 1 year	When did you quit?	age 19
Do you drink alcohol?	☒	☐	List type and how much:	4 - 5 beers per week		
Do you drink caffeine?	☒	☐	List type and how much:	2 - 3 cups coffee per day		
What is your occupation?			Electrician			

Family History:
    Please check the "Yes" or "No" box to indicate whether any relatives have any of the following illnesses:
    If yes, please indicate which relative(s) have the problem

	Yes	No	
Hearing problems	☐	☒	
Heart problems / murmurs	☒	☐	Father died of heart attack, had high cholesterol
Allergy	☒	☐	Mother has spring and fall allergies
Diabetes	☐	☒	
Cancer	☒	☐	Mother had breast cancer - cured with surgery and radiation
Bleeding disorder	☐	☒	
Anesthesia problems	☒	☐	Mother has nausea following general anesthesia

Reviewed by: XXX

Figure F.2

PFSH, Initial Outpatient Visit: Transcription Model

Patient is a 47-year-old male who presents with

Chief Complaint: Clogged ears

Past Medical History:

Medical Illnesses: Patient reports a past history of elevated cholesterol and occasional asthma and mild seasonal allergy symptoms in the spring. There is no history of diagnoses of diabetes, hypertension, thyroid problems, heart disease, cholesterol problems, respiratory problems, bleeding disorders, stomach or intestinal problems, kidney problems, neurological problems, cancer, or other medical diagnoses

Operations: Right knee surgery 1999 – repair lateral cruciate ligament

Medications: Ibuprofen, 400 mg as needed for pain; decongestant X prn allergy; atorvastatin 10 mg daily

Social History: The patient does not smoke. He previously smoked $\frac{1}{2}$ pack per day for one year, stopping at age 19. He drinks 4-5 beers per week. He drinks 2-3 cups of coffee per day. He is an electrician.

Family History: There is no family history of hearing loss, diabetes, or bleeding disorders. His father had high cholesterol and died of a heart attack. His mother has spring and fall allergies. His mother had breast cancer, cured with surgery and radiation. His mother reports nausea following general anesthesia.

Figure F.3

ROS, Initial Outpatient Visit: Hybrid Model, Paper Form or EHR Screen (note: for paper forms, the transcribed narrative sections may appear on a separate page)

Date____/____/____

Patient Name:　　　　　　　　　　　　　　　　　　　Account No.　　　　　　　　DOB: ____/____/____

Patient Medical History Form (p. 2):　Please provide the following medical information to the best of your ability:

Review of Systems:

1) Please check the "Yes" or "No" box to indicate whether you presently have any of the following symptoms:

2) For any "yes" responses, please check the "current" box if this symptom relates to the reason for your visit today

Category	Symptom	Yes	No	Current	Symptom	Yes	No	Current
GENERAL	chills	☐	☒	☐	weight loss or gain	☒	☐	☐
	fatigue	☒	☐	☐	daytime sleepiness	☒	☐	☐
ALLERGY	environmental allergy	☒	☐	☐	sneezing fits	☒	☐	☐
	post-nasal drip	☒	☐	☐				
NEURO	headache	☐	☒	☐	weakness	☐	☒	☐
	passing out	☐	☒	☐	numbness, tingling	☐	☒	☐
EYES	eye pain / pressure	☐	☒	☐	vision changes	☐	☒	☐
	watery or itchy eyes	☒	☐	☐				
ENT	ear pain or itch	☒	☐	☐	ear drainage	☒	☐	☒
	hearing loss	☒	☐	☒	ear noises	☐	☒	☐
	dizziness	☐	☒	☐	lightheadedness	☐	☒	☐
	nasal congestion	☒	☐	☐	sinus pressure or pain	☒	☐	☐
	sense of smell problem	☐	☒	☐	problem snoring, apnea	☒	☐	☐
	hoarseness	☐	☒	☐	throat pain	☐	☒	☐
	throat clearing	☒	☐	☐	throat dryness/itching	☒	☐	☐
RESPIR.	cough	☒	☐	☐	coughing blood	☐	☒	☐
	wheezing	☒	☐	☐	shortness of breath	☒	☐	☐
CARDIAC	chest pain	☐	☒	☐	palpitations	☐	☒	☐
	wake short of breath	☒	☐	☐	ankle swelling	☐	☒	☐
GI	difficulty swallowing	☐	☒	☐	heartburn	☒	☐	☐
	abdominal pain	☐	☒	☐	nausea/vomiting	☐	☒	☐
	bowel irregularity	☐	☒	☐	rectal bleeding	☐	☒	☐
GU	frequent urination	☐	☒	☐	painful urination	☐	☒	☐
	blood in urine	☐	☒	☐	prostate problems	☐	☒	☐
HEME/LYM	swollen glands	☐	☒	☐	sweating at night	☐	☒	☐
	bleeding problems	☐	☒	☐	easy bruising	☐	☒	☐
ENDO	feel warmer than others	☐	☒	☐	feel cooler than others	☐	☒	☐
MSK	joint aches	☒	☐	☐	muscle aches	☐	☒	☐
SKIN	rash	☐	☒	☐	hives	☐	☒	☐
	itching	☐	☒	☐	skin or hair changes	☐	☒	☐
PSYCH	depression	☐	☒	☐	anxiety or panic	☐	☒	☐

Allergy: History of allergy testing and treatment, both as a child and as an adult. He does not report significant sneezing or ocular symptoms. He does use QQQ nasal spray prn. The patient reports A.M. nasal congestion; he also has forced air heat in his bedroom (note: I have advised use of a bedroom humidifier from October thru April). He has occasional mild left frontal pain

GI: Moderate heartburn over the last six months. He also reports occasional throat clearing and post nasal drip sensation.

Resp: Patient reports a long-term history of episodic wheezing, which was significant , approximately six months ago. Pulmonary function testing in the past has indicated presence of asthma

Snoring: Patient reports loud snoring at night, plus occasional episodes of waking up gasping for breath. He commonly wakes feeling tired and also has frequent daytime fatigue, despite getting approximately seven hours sleep per night (the patient denies nocturnal medications or alcohol ingestion). Has not fallen asleep while driving

Weight gain: Patient reports gaining thirty pounds over the last several years.

Reviewed by: XXX

Figure F.4

ROS, Initial Outpatient Visit: Transcription Model

Review of Systems:

General: Patient reports gaining 30 pounds over the last several years. He commonly wakes feeling tired and also has frequent daytime fatigue, despite getting approximately seven hours of sleep per night (the patient denies nocturnal medications or alcohol ingestion). Has not fallen asleep while driving. He has no chills.

Allergy: Patient complains of sneezing fits and postnasal drip when symptomatic. History of allergy testing and treatment, both as a child and as an adult. He does not report significant sneezing or ocular symptoms. He does use QQQ nasal spray prn. He reports AM nasal congestion; he also has forced-air heat in his bedroom (note: I have advised use of a bedroom humidifier from October through April). He has occasional mild left frontal pain.

Neuro: There is no history of headache, passing out, weakness, numbness, or tingling sensations.

Eyes: Patient has itchy eyes seasonally in the spring. He denies vision changes or eye pain/pressure.

ENT: The patient notes that his ears itch at times and have small amounts of waxy drainage. There is no history of tinnitus, dizziness, or lightheadedness. He reports AM nasal congestion; he also has forced-air heat in his bedroom (note: I have advised use of a bedroom humidifier from October through April). There is occasional mild left frontal pain. There is no difficulty with the sense of smell. The patient reports loud snoring at night, plus occasional episodes of waking up gasping for breath. Patient denies hoarseness or throat pain, but does complain of occasional throat clearing, postnasal drip sensation, and throat dryness or itching.

Respiratory: Patient reports a long-term history of episodic wheezing, which was significant approximately six months ago. Pulmonary function testing in the past has indicated presence of asthma. He has episodes of coughing and shortness of breath, but no history of coughing blood.

Cardiovascular: There is no history of chest pain, palpitations, or ankle swelling.

GI: Moderate heartburn over the last six months. There is no history of difficulty swallowing, abdominal pain, nausea or vomiting, bowel irregularity, or rectal bleeding.

GU: There is no history of frequent urination, painful urination, blood in the urine, or prostate problems.

Heme/Lymph: There is no history of swollen glands, sweating at night, bleeding problems, or easy bruising.

Endo: There is no history of feeling warmer than others or feeling cooler than others.

Musculoskeletal: The patient has joint aches in his knees. There is no history of muscle aches.

Skin: There is no history of rash, hives, itching, or skin or hair changes.

Psych: There is no history of depression or panic/anxiety symptoms.

Figure F.5

History of Present Illness and Physical Examination, Initial Outpatient Visit: Hybrid Model, Paper Form or EHR Screen (note: for paper forms, the transcribed narrative sections may appear on a separate page)

Date____/____/____   Patient States Consultation Requested By_____

Patient Name: Account No.   DOB:____/____/____

PRESENT ILLNESS   Chronology with: 1. one to three elements (level 2)   2. four to eight elements; OR status of 3 chronic or inactive conditions (level 3, 4, or 5)

      (1) duration   (2) timing   (3) severity;   (4) location   (5) quality   (6) context   (7) modifying factors   (8) assoc. signs & symptoms

The patient reports both ears feeling intermittently clogged for approximately two weeks; the clogged sensation seems to have increased in the last several

days, with diminished hearing bilaterally and a sense of pressure in the left ear. There is no history of drainage from the ears. Of note, the patient

reports a history of problems with wax, and he cleans his ears with cotton swabs on a daily basis.

The patient also reports ear pressure problems in airplanes during landing. He is also concerned that he may have hearing loss related to noise

exposure, since he plays drums in a rock band.

PHYSICAL EXAMINATION: Ear Nose & Throat

GENERAL   (at least 3 measurements of vital signs)   HT _5_ ft _7_ in   WT __205__ lbs

      BP sitting-standing _124_ / _78_ mm Hg   BP supine ____/____mm Hg

      PULSE _68_ /min   regular - irregular   RESP _16_ /min   TEMP _____ o (F-C)

			Normal/AB					Normal/AB
	GENERAL APPEARANCE	Stature, nutrition	☒	☐	**NECK**	MASSES & TRACHEA	Symmetry, masses	☒	☐
	COMMUNICATION & VOICE	Pitch, clarity	☒	☐		THYROID	Size, nodules	☒	☐
HEAD/	INSPECTION	Lesions, masses	☒	☐	**EYES**	OCULAR MOTILITY & GAZE	EOMs, nystagmus	☒	☐
FACE	PALPATION / PERCUSSION	Skeleton, sinuses	☒	☐	**RESP.**	RESPIRATORY EFFORT	Inspiratory-expiratory	☐	☐
	SALIVARY GLANDS	Masses, tenderness	☒	☐		AUSCULTATION	Lung sounds	☐	☐
	FACIAL STRENGTH	Symmetry	☒	☐	**CVS**	HEART AUSCULTATION	rhythm, heart sounds	☐	☐
ENT	PNEUMO-OTOSCOPY	EACs; TMs mobile	☐	☒		PERIPH VASC SYSTEM	Edema, color	☒	☐
	HEARING ASSESSMENT	Gross; Weber/Rinne	☒	☐	**LYMPH.**	NECK/AXILLAE/GROIN/ETC.	Adenopathy	☒	☐
	EXTERNAL EAR & NOSE	Appearance	☒	☐	**NEURO/**	CRANIAL NERVES	II - XII	☒	☐
	INTERNAL NOSE	Mucosa, turbinates	☐	☒	**PSYCH.**	ORIENTATION	Person, place, time	☐	☐
	*AFTER DECONGESTANT	Septum, OMCs	☐	☒		MOOD & AFFECT	Comments	☒	☐
	LIPS,TEETH & GUMS	Mucosa, dentition	☒	☐		*ROMBERG		☐	☐
	ORAL CAVITY, OROPHARYNX	Mucosa, tonsils, palate	☒	☐		*TANDEM ROMBERG		☐	☐
	HYPOPHARYNX	Mucosa, pyriforms	☐NV ☐			*PAST POINTING		☐	☐
	LARYNX (mirror: adults)	Anatomy, vocal cord mobility	☐NV ☐			☐ See attached dictation			
	NASOPHAR. (mirror: adults)	Mucosa, choanae	☐NV ☐						

Hypopharynx, larynx, and nasopharynx not visualized due to 4+ hyperactive gag reflex

Ears: Impacted cerumen was cleaned from the left external auditory canal, revealing mild thickening of the posterior portion of the TM and mild positive

pressure on pneumo-otoscopy (note: the patient was performing Valsalva maneuvers prior to the examination). The right tympanic membrane has normal

appearance and mobility. Weber is midline; air conduction is greater than bone conduction bilaterally.

Nose: Mild inferior turbinate congestion bilaterally. Following spray, there is a mild septal deviation high to the right, and there is a large

middle meatal polyp visible on the left.

Mouth: Enlarged soft palate and uvula

1. problem focused = 1-5 elements [level 1]   **2. Expanded = 6-11 elements [level 2]**   **3. detailed = 12 or more elements [level 3]**

4. comprehensive = document every element in basic areas AND at least 1 element in each optional area [level 4 or 5]   ***optional**

Figure F.6

History of Present Illness and Physical Examination, Initial Outpatient Visit: Transcription Model

---

History of Present Illness: The patient reports both ears feeling intermittently clogged for approximately two weeks; the clogged sensation seems to have increased in the last several days, with diminished hearing bilaterally and a sense of pressure in the left ear. There is no history of drainage from the ears. Of note, the patient reports a history of problems with wax, and he cleans his ears with cotton swabs daily. The patient also reports ear pressure problems in airplanes during landing. He is also concerned that he may have hearing loss related to noise exposure, since he plays drums in a rock band.

Physical Examination:

General:

  Vital signs: Height 5 foot 7 inches; weight 205 pounds; pulse 68; blood pressure 124/78

  General appearance: normal stature and appearance

  Communication and voice: normal pitch and clarity

Head/face:

  Inspection: no lesions or masses

  Palpation/percussion: normal skeleton and sinus palpation

  Salivary glands: normal without masses or tenderness

  Facial strength: normal symmetry

ENT:

  Pneumo-otoscopy: Impacted cerumen was cleaned from the left external auditory canal, revealing mild thickening of the posterior portion of the tympanic membrane and mild positive pressure on pneumo-otoscopy (note: The patient was performing Valsalva maneuvers prior to the examination). The right tympanic membrane has normal appearance and mobility.

  Hearing assessment: Grossly normal; Weber is midline; air conduction is greater than bone conduction bilaterally

  External ear and nose: Normal appearance

  Internal nose: Mild inferior turbinate congestion bilaterally. Following spray, there is a mild septal deviation high to the right, and there is a large middle meatal polyp visible on the left

Lips, teeth, and gums: Normal mucosa and dentition

Oral cavity, oropharynx: Enlarged soft palate and uvula

Hypopharynx (mirror exam): Not visualized due to 4+ hyperactive gag reflex

Larynx (mirror exam): Not visualized due to 4+ hyperactive gag reflex

Nasopharynx (mirror exam): Not visualized due to 4+ hyperactive gag reflex

Neck:

  Masses and trachea: Normal symmetry and absence of masses

  Thyroid: Normal size and absence of nodules

Eyes:

  Ocular motility and gaze: Normal extraocular movements, no nystagmus

Respiratory:

  Respiratory effort: Normal inspiratory and expiratory effort

Cardiovascular:

  Peripheral vascular system: No edema, normal color

Lymphatic:

  Neck: No adenopathy

Neuro/psych:

  Cranial nerves: Normal nerves 2–12

  Mood and affect: Normal comments

Figure F.7

Medical Decision Making and NPP, Initial Outpatient Visit: Hybrid Model, Paper Form or EHR Screen (note: for paper forms, the transcribed narrative sections may appear on a separate page)

Date____/____/____

Patient Name: Account No.   DOB: ____/____/____

MEDICAL DECISION MAKING
DATA REVIEWED (a):   2 of the 3 sections (a vs a' vs a", b vs b', c vs c') must meet or exceed indicated level of care
1. Minimal (level 2)   2. Limited (level 3)   3. Moderate (level 4)   4. Extensive (level 5)

Audio   Bilateral symmetrical sloping sensori-neural hearing loss (compatible with history of noise exposure)

Tympanometry   Type A bilaterally

IMPRESSIONS / DIFFERENTIAL DIAGNOSES (b):   **PLANS / MANAGEMENT OPTIONS (b')**
1. Minimal (level 2)   2. Limited (level 3)   3. Moderate (level 4)   4. Extensive (level 5)

Impressions / Differential Diagnoses	Plans / Management Options
1) Cerumen impaction left ear	Cerumen cleaned; D/C use of cotton ear swabs
2) High frequency sensori-neural hearing loss, likely secondary to noise exp.	Consider hearing aid evaluation
3) History of barotrauma with flights	Use ventilating ear plus with flights
4) Obstructive sleep apnea with snoring, nocturnal waking, daytime fatigue	
5) Laryngo-pharyngeal reflux	Proton pump inhibitor, elevate HOB, diet modification
6) Chronic polypoid rhinosinusitis with left middle meatal polyp	Steroid nasal spray
7) History of allergic rhinitis	
8) History of asthma	

DATA ORDERED (a'):   1. Minimal (level 2)   2. Limited (level 3)   3. Moderate (level 4)   4. Extensive (level 5)

☐ Audiological   ☐ ENG   ☐ ABR   ☐ Allergy evaluation   ☐ MRI / CT

1) Overnight sleep study

2) Return 2 weeks for fiberoptic examination of larynx and pharynx

3) Future evaluation for extent of sinus pathology

Information Sheets Given: ☒ Ear Care   ☐ Balance   ☐ Hearing   ☐ Vestib Exercises   ☐ Throat eval   ☐ Gerd F/U   ☐ Voice
                   ☐ Nose&Sinus   ☐ Nose Care   ☐ URI info   ☐ Childhood Airway Obstrct   ☒ GERD   ☒ APNEA

COMPLEXITY OF DATA REVIEWED OR ORDERED (a")
1. Minimal (level 2)   2. Limited (level 3)   3. Moderate (level 4)   4. Extensive (level 5)
                            ☐ min   ☐ limited   ☒ mod   ☐ extensive

RISK OF COMPLICATIONS &/OR MORBIDITY OR MORTALITY (see examples in Table of Risk)
1. Minimal (level 2)   2. Limited (level 3)   3. Moderate (level 4)   4. Extensive (level 5)

	min	low	mod	high
risk of presenting problem(s) (c):	☐	☐	☐	☒
risk of diagnostic procedure(s) ordered or reviewed (c'):	☒	☐	☐	☐
risk of management option(s) selected (c'):	☐	☐	☒	☐

NATURE OF PRESENTING PROBLEM(S)

☐ 1. minor   (level 1)   Problem runs definite and prescribed course, is transient in nature, and is not likely to permanently alter health status; OR, has a good prognosis with management and compliance.

☐ 2. low   (level 1)   Problem where the risk of morbidity without treatment is low; there is little to no risk of mortality without treatment; full recovery without functional impairment is expected.

☐ 3. low - mod   (level 2)   Problem where the risk of morbidity without treatment is low to moderate; there is low to moderate risk of mortality without treatment; full recovery without functional impairment is expected in most cases, with low probability of prolonged functional impairment.

☐ 4. moderate   (level 3)   Problem where the risk of morbidity without treatment is moderate; there is moderate risk of mortality without treatment; prognosis is uncertain, or there is an increased probability of prolonged functional impairment.

☐ 5. mod - high   (level 4,5)   Problem where the risk of morbidity without treatment is moderate to high; there is moderate risk of mortality without treatment; uncertain prognosis or increased probability of prolonged functional impairment

☒ 6. high   (level 4,5)   Problem where the risk of morbidity without treatment is high to extreme; there is moderate to high risk of mortality without treatment, or high probability of severe prolonged functional impairment.

Complete this section only if documented below >50% of visit time involved counseling and/or coordinating care.

TIME: _____ minutes   ☐ > 50% of visit time involved counseling and/or coordination of care

Clinician's signature: XXX

Figure F.8

Medical Decision Making and NPP, Initial Outpatient Visit: Transcription Model

---

Data reviewed:

> Audiometry: Bilateral symmetrical sloping sensorineural hearing loss (compatible with history of noise exposure)

> Tympanometry: Type A bilaterally

Impressions:

1) Cerumen impaction left ear

2) High-frequency sensorineural hearing loss, likely secondary to noise exposure

3) History of barotraumas with flights

4) Obstructive sleep apnea with snoring, nocturnal waking, daytime fatigue

5) Laryngopharyngeal reflux

6) Chronic polypoid rhinosinusitis with left middle meatal polyp

7) History of allergic rhinitis

8) History of asthma

Plans/Management Options/Data Ordered:

1) Cerumen cleaned; D/C use of cotton ear swabs

2) Consider hearing aid evaluation

3) Use ventilating ear plugs with flights

4) Proton pump inhibitor, elevate head of bed, diet modification

5) Steroid nasal spray

6) Overnight sleep study

7) Return in two weeks for fiberoptic examination of larynx and pharynx

8) Future evaluation for extent of sinus pathology

[Note: this portion of a traditional transcription presentation fails to provide documentation of complexity of data reviewed and ordered, the risk of the presenting problems, the risk of diagnostic procedures ordered, the risk of management options selected, and the nature of the presenting problem(s).]

APPEARANCE OPTION FOR CONSULTATION REPORTS

Chapter 9 and Appendix B presented an option for recompiling the pertinent findings of a patient encounter into a true consultation report. It provides the framework for a report that incorporates the relevant information from the H&P record of a consultation visit to create a meaningful clinical document that meets CPT compliance guidelines for consultation and provides well-organized and pertinent details to a requesting physician or other appropriate professional.

The following pages show a consultation letter compiled from the clinical information illustrated in the H&P record (Figures F.1, F.3, F.5, and F.7) in this appendix.

Figure F.9

Sample Consultation report associated with IMR paper forms or electronic screens

---

Letterhead Containing Practice Demographic Information

Date: January 10, 2008

XYZ, MD
1234 Blank Road
City, State 00000

Re: A. B. Person

Diagnoses:

1) Cerumen impaction left ear

2) High-frequency sensorineural hearing loss, likely secondary to noise exposure

3) History of barotraumas with flights

4) Obstructive sleep apnea with snoring, nocturnal waking, daytime fatigue

5) Laryngopharyngeal reflux

6) Chronic polypoid rhinosinusitis with left middle meatal polyp

7) History of allergic rhinitis

8) History of asthma

Recommendations:

1) Cerumen cleaned; D/C use of cotton ear swabs

2) Consider hearing aid evaluation

3) Use ventilating ear plugs with flights

4) Proton pump inhibitor, elevate head of bed, diet modification

5) Steroid nasal spray

6) Overnight sleep study

7) Return in two weeks for fiberoptic examination of larynx and pharynx

8) Future evaluation for extent of sinus pathology

Dear Dr. XYZ:

At your request, today I had the opportunity to evaluate A. B. Person, a 47-year-old patient who arrived with the following primary concern(s): The patient reports both ears feeling intermittently clogged for approximately two weeks; the clogged sensation seems to have increased in the last several days, with diminished hearing bilaterally and a sense of pressure in the left ear. There is no history of drainage from the ears. Of note, the patient reports a history of problems with wax, and he cleans his ears with cotton swabs daily. The patient also reports ear pressure problems in airplanes during landing. He is also concerned that he may have hearing loss related to noise exposure, since he plays drums in a rock band.

Assessment of the patient's past medical history and review of symptoms indicates the following additional significant concerns: History of allergy testing and treatment, both as a child and as an adult. He does not report significant sneezing or ocular symptoms. He does use QQQ nasal spray prn. The patient reports AM nasal congestion; he also has forced-air heat in his bedroom (note: I have advised use of a bedroom humidifier from October through April). Moderate heartburn over the last six months. He also reports occasional throat clearing and postnasal drip sensation. Patient reports a long-term history of episodic wheezing, which was significant approximately six months ago. Pulmonary function testing in the past has indicated presence of asthma. Patient reports loud snoring at night, plus occasional episodes of waking up gasping for breath. He commonly wakes feeling tired and also has frequent daytime fatigue, despite getting approximately seven hours of sleep per night (the patient denies nocturnal medications or alcohol ingestion). Has not fallen asleep while driving. Patient reports gaining 30 pounds over the last several years.

continued

Relevant physical examination findings include:

EARS: Impacted cerumen was cleaned from the left external auditory canal, revealing mild thickening of the posterior portion of the TM and mild positive pressure on pneumo-otoscopy (note: the patient was performing Valsalva maneuvers prior to the examination). The right tympanic membrane has normal appearance and mobility. Weber is midline; air conduction is greater than bone conduction bilaterally. NOSE: Mild inferior turbinate congestion bilaterally. Following spray, there is a mild septal deviation high to the right, and there is a large middle meatal polyp visible on the left. MOUTH: Enlarged soft palate and uvula. LARYNX AND PHARYNX: Not visible secondary to 4+ hyperactive gag reflex.

I have reviewed my impressions with the patient. The symptoms and findings are compatible with the diagnoses listed above. Appropriate recommendations at this time are also listed above. Thank you for requesting my evaluation of this patient.

Sincerely,

Name of consultant, MD

Center for Medicare & Medicaid Services (CMS). The government agency that administers Medicare.

Clinical Examples. Representative brief clinical summaries of patient illnesses, correlated with medically indicated levels of care for many of the common E/M types of service. These appear in Appendix C of the current edition of the CPT code book.

Consultation. A type of medical service provided by a physician whose opinion regarding evaluation and/or management of a specific problem is requested by another physician or other appropriate source. The consultant's responsibilities for a consultation include (1) documenting the written or verbal request in the medical record, (2) documenting his or her opinion and any services that were ordered or performed in the patient's medical record, and (3) sending a written report of his or her opinion and any services that were ordered or performed to the requesting physician or other appropriate source.

Data Entry. The process of recording clinical information in the medical record.

Data Entry Personnel (DEP). Individual(s) who enter information into the medical record.

Documentation Guidelines for Evaluation and Management Services. A collection of principles developed jointly by the American Medical Association and the Health Care Financing Administration to provide physicians and reviewers with advice for creating, or reviewing, documentation for Evaluation and Management services.

Efficiency. Description of ability to perform a task with optimal speed without sacrificing quality, compliance, or data integrity and reliability.

Electronic Health Record (EHR). An electronic medical record system with the ability to provide interconnectivity and interoperability with external medical systems, such as pharmacy, laboratory, radiology facilities, and hospitals. This type of system also supports services for collecting information and importing medical information for clinical decision support.

Electronic Medical Record (EMR). A computerized software system for entry, storage, and retrieval of digital medical records.

Established Patient Visit. Any subsequent medical encounter within three years of a visit with a specific physician or any of his or her associates in the same specialty and in the same medical group.

Evaluation and Management (E/M) Coding System. The portion of the CPT coding system, involving codes 99201 – 99499, that addresses cognitive medical services. These types of service generally involve investigation of medical problems and/or consideration of diagnostic evaluation and treatment. These services are distinct from procedure services.

Extenders. Individuals who assist physician with obtaining and/or entering medical information into the medical record.

External Audit. Review of medical records by an outside entity, such as a Medicare or private insurance company, for purpose of evaluating compliance.

Format. The medium for entering data into the medical record or for storing and retrieving medical record data.

Health Care Financing Administration (HCFA). Now known as the Centers for Medicare & Medicaid Services (CMS).

Health Insurance Portability and Accountability Act of 1996 (HIPAA). Legislation addressing elements of health care system reform. The components of the act deal with (1) health insurance access and portability; (2) preventing health care fraud and abuse (including standardization of rules for electronic transmission of health care administrative and financial transactions, privacy standards, provider identifiers, employer identifiers, and security); (3) medical savings accounts and health insurance deductibility; (4) group health plan provisions; and (5) revenue offset provisions.

History and Physical (H&P). The process of evaluating a medical patient. The term also refers to the medical record that documents this process.

History of Present Illness (HPI). A chronological description of the development and characteristics of the patient's presenting medical problem, from its onset until the time of the medical visit. It includes a description of one or more of the eight elements of the HPI.

Initial Visit. The first medical encounter, within a period of greater than three years, of a patient with a specific physician or any of his or her associates in the same specialty and in the same medical group.

Intelligent Medical Record (IMR). This is the term applied to customized medical record tools that incorporate all the criteria of E/M coding and the Documentation Guidelines for Evaluation and Management Services as well as functionality for assisting the physician in performing quality care while achieving compliant E/M coding and documentation. Different IMR templates may be appropriate for different types of services, since each type of service has its own documentation and coding parameters.

Interface. Structural appearance of a medical record, designed to facilitate various options for data entry.

Internal Audit. Review of medical records by a medical practice itself. These reviews may be performed by trained audit staff or contracted consultants. The purpose is to evaluate all aspects of the medical record, including compliance, extent of medical history, and appropriateness of E/M code selection.

Medical Decision Making (MDM). One of the key components of E/M care. It examines the degree of complexity involved in establishing a diagnosis and determining management options. This component includes (1) the number of diagnoses and/or treatment options; (2) the amount and complexity of data ordered and reviewed; and (3) the levels of risk of the illness, the diagnostic procedures ordered, and the possible management options.

Medical Necessity. Health care services that a physician, who is exercising prudent clinical judgment, performs for the purposes of evaluating, diagnosing, treating, and/or preventing an illness, injury, or symptoms. These services should be clinically appropriate, provided in accordance with generally accepted health care standards, and not primarily for the convenience of the physician or the patient.

Nature of Presenting Problem (NPP). The presenting problem is the disease, condition, injury, symptom, sign, finding, complaint, or other reason for a medical encounter. The various types of nature of the presenting problem refer to the natural history of the medical problem; ie, the risk of morbidity without treatment, the risk of risk of mortality without treatment, the certainty of prognosis, and/or the probability of prolonged functional impairment.

Past Medical History (PMH). Review of the patient's past experiences with illnesses, injuries, and treatments. This includes operations, medical illnesses, allergies, current medications, etc.

Physicians at Teaching Hospitals (PATH) Audits. Audits of coding and documentation by physicians working at hospitals associated with medical teaching programs. These were conducted by the Office of the Inspector General of the Department of Health and Human Services.

Practical E/M. The methodology presented in this book, comprising consideration of quality, compliance, efficiency, and usability in medical records. This approach focuses on providing effective medical record tools (ie, IMR) that integrate documentation coding and coding compliance principles into physicians' recognized process for providing optimal medical care.

Quality of Care. In this text we described this concept as calling for physicians to (1) make the optimal effort to determine correct diagnoses, (2) in the most timely manner possible, and (3) institute the optimal therapies to address patient problems, with (4) a minimum number of complications. Quality care also involves identifying patients' risk factors, providing preventative counseling and interventions, and maintaining a good patient-physician relationship. Finally, consideration of cost-effectiveness has become an additional and important component of quality in today's environment.

Resource-based Relative Value Scale (RBRVS). Basis for the Medicare and Medicaid reimbursement systems, which was adopted in the 1989 Omnibus Budget Act. It applies relative values to the physicians' work, practice expense, and professional liability expense.

Review of Systems (ROS). Inventory of body systems obtained through a series of questions designed to identify signs and/or symptoms the patient may have experienced.

SOAP Note. A medical record structure presented by Dr Lawrence Weed in 1969, many years prior to the introduction of the E/M coding system. This acronym presents only four general components: (1) subjective, (2) objective, (3) assessment, and (4) plan. Significantly, this documentation system was originally described as appropriate for only subsequent care visits. Even though its original description also considered inclusion of detailed or comprehensive care, documentation using this structure most commonly demonstrates only "problem-focused" care.

Table of Risk. Table published in the Documentation Guidelines for Evaluation and Management Services that provides common clinical examples of levels of risk for the presenting problem(s), diagnostic procedure(s) ordered, and management options selected.

Type of Service (TOS). Sub-classifications of evaluation and management services. These are based on the location and circumstances of the specific medical encounter.

Usability. The ability to accomplish a required task effectively and efficiently.

CD-ROM Installation Instructions

NOTE: the content of this CD-ROM will not be installed on your computer. Always have the CD available each time you want to use the forms.

The *Practical E/M* CD-ROM is only for Windows-based PCs.

To run the CD-ROM, follow these steps:

1. Insert the CD-ROM into your CD-ROM drive.
2. If autorun is enabled, the CD-ROM will autorun and begin the installation process. *Please read the End-User License Agreement (EULA) before choosing to either **Accept** or **Not Accept** the terms of the EULA.*
3. Once the installation is complete, the **hyperlinked** Table of Contents will automatically open. (Note: all the linked pages and forms have a hyperlinked <u>Back to TOC</u>)

NOTE: To navigate between the **hyperlinked** Table of Contents and the linked forms and documents without closing the **hyperlinked** Table of Contents <u>each time</u>, follow these steps in Adobe® Acrobat Reader 8.0 and higher. You can download Adobe®Acrobat Reader free at <u>www.adobe.com</u>.

    a. Go to View > Toolbars > Select More Tools

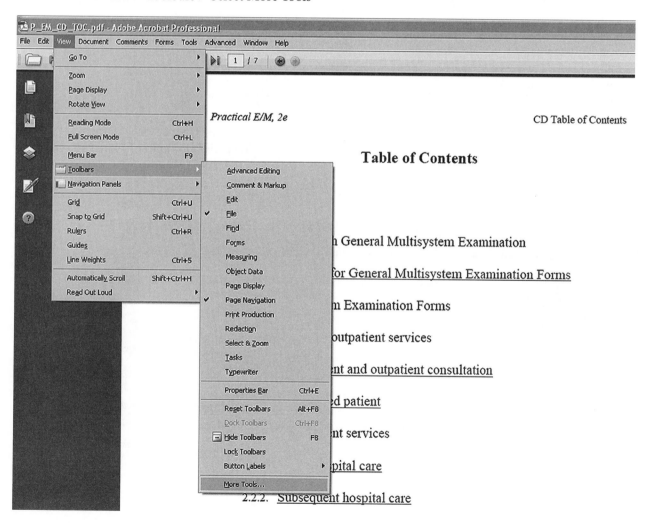

b. In the **More Tools**-dialog box, check the **Page Navigation Toolbar** option and all the sub-navigation options such as **First Page, Previous Page,** etc and click the **OK** button.

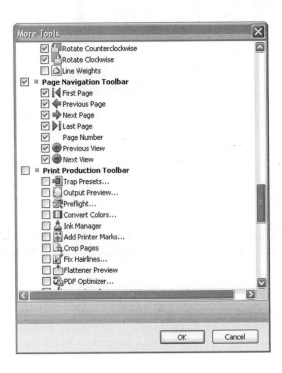

c. You should see two sets of navigation arrows on the toolbar: **page navigation and page view navigation.**
  • Use the **page navigation** arrow to navigate between pages of the linked forms or documents.
  • Use the **page view navigation** arrow to navigate back to the **hyperlinked-Table-of-Contents**-view after viewing the linked forms or documents. NOTE: Although the Adobe® Acrobat Reader 9.0's page navigation arrows are vertical (points up and down) instead of horizontal, the functions are the same.

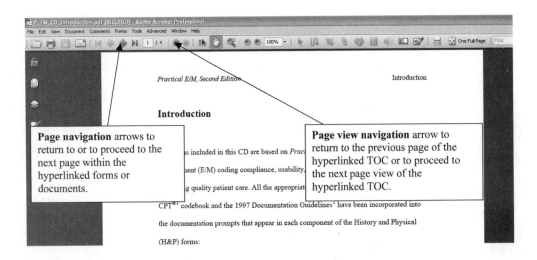

Minimum System Requirements
Windows
CD-ROM drive
Microsoft® Windows® NT, 2000, XP, Vista
64 MB RAM